Pittenweem
Sojourn

Best wishes to Lyn

from Nancie McLeod

Also by
Nanzie McLeod

TALES
of the
ARLINGTON

TALES
of the
EAST NEUK

Pittenweem
Sojourn

Nanzie McLeod

First published in the United Kingdom by
Nanzie McLeod, Glasgow

The author has asserted her moral rights.

British Library Cataloguing in Publication Data.
A catalogue record for this book is available from
the British Library.

ISBN 0 9529527 2 6

Origination by Robographics, Glasgow
Printed by Bell & Bain Limited, Glasgow

Contents

Part One

Contents continued

Part Two

Thanks to
Jean Reid and Jak Edwards
for their valuable assistance.

Thanks also to my four daughters
Kate, Esther, Sarah and Alice
for their support and encouragement.

This book
is dedicated to
my mother

Ann Cumming
1902-1980.

A creative and courageous woman.

Prologue

The wedding was a splendid affair conducted by the Moderator of the Kirk of Scotland. The well-dressed guests arrived in luxurious black motors at the marble-clad doors of the opulent function rooms of the mystically named 'Rhul Tea Rooms' in Sauchiehall street.

Three mounted policemen astride enormous, well-polished beasts controlled the crowds.

It was a typical September day in Glasgow, with periods of bright sunshine occasionally blotted out by swiftly moving clouds which, apart from one brief shower, had fortunately not fulfilled their threat. The sprinkled populace had remained stoically in place, for this was a free entertainment not to be missed.

After each shiny top hat and morning suit negotiated its exit from the taxi and each silk clad leg below an elaborate gown stepped down uncertainly to the pavement, most couples stood there for a moment as if unsure where to go next, then with brief self-conscious smiles to the crowd, mounted the four shallow stairs and disappeared into the warm, perfumed depths of the building.

The comments from the crowd were continuous, clear and mostly complimentary. The extended and exaggerated vowels and the complete absence of any plosives in the sing-song Glasgow accent made these comments sound melodious and yet strangely melancholy.

"Och, look a' that dress noo. Is tha' jist no' luvily."

"Aw, aye, it's jist luvily. Luvily colour, so i' is."

"Thon colour's ca'ed majinta."

"Izzat majinta? Awfy rich lookin', intit."

"Ah've niver heard o' majinta."

"Ur ye shair tha's majinta?"

"Aye, that's majinta."

"Mair like helio tae me."

"Naw, it's majinta."

"Kinda purply like."

"Aye. But ye ca' it majinta."

There was little colour amongst the crowd. Most of the

onlookers were small pale women with straight lank hair, bobbed, parted at the side and held back with a metal grip. One or two had a middle parting, with two grips and a small tight bun at the back of their heads. Some wore heavy woollen shawls to help support a small pale uninterested baby.

"Here an auld yin, wi' a white mouser."

"He's a hansum big bloke, a' the same, an' he's no' tha' auld."

"Here 'is wife, noo. She luks a loat yunger than him an' my, *she's* no missed her denner oafen."

"Aye, she's a big yin righ' enuff. Big bust an' a'. But ma Goad, itza beeyootiful dress she's wearin' though, intit. That fancy bit doon the side, it's jist luvily. An' a' they furs an' the long beads swishin' aboot. That's the best yin yit, Ah'm thinkin'."

"She's goat awfy thin ankles."

"It's the peerie heels mak thim luk thin."

"Ah don't know how she kin walk in thim."

"She's awfy tall fur a wumman."

"Aye, she's no' needin' high heels, is she."

"Didya see her diyamond rings, big whoppers, so they wur."

"She's smilin' nice though, i'nt she. S'a luvily smile she's goat."

"An' big broon eyes."

After that couple had climbed the stairs and disappeared, there was a lull in the arriving guests and the conversation became louder.

"Here, Sadie Donnelly's sayin' that they big tall folk that's jist went in, ur the bride's Maw and Paw."

"Sadie aye huz tae know everythin'. Hoo duz she ken that?"

"Aw, Ah wisht Ah'd seen thim better."

"Sadie's sayin' he's an artist an ' he lives in a big swell flat at Charin' Cross."

"Rubbish!"

"She says her freend Maggie scrubs thur close and the sterrs ur a' thon marble an' bloody cauld fur kneelin' oan."

"Oh aye, that'll be right."

"Mebbe he is."

"Mebbe he is whit?"

"An artist!"

"Naw! Yur no' tellin' me an artist cud pey fur a weddin' like this. Thur canny be ony money in pentin' picturs."

"Weel Sadie says thur is."

"Ach! Sadie!"

Next two young men arrived and a little shiver went through the crowd.

Here was the groom.

The lamb for the slaughter.

The sacrifice at the nuptial altar.

But which one was it? The tall one or the shorter one with the very black moustache?

"Ah think it's the wee yin. He's a hansum wee bloke."

"S'awfy skinny-lukkin'. His cheeks is a' caved in an' his coat's hingin' oan'm."

"S'cheeks is awfy rid'n shiny a' the same."

"Is it no' the tall yin, the groom?"

"Naw, he dizny luk worrit enough."

"Ah'm thinkin' it's the tall yin."

"Naw! It's the wee yin. He's trim'lin' all ower."

"He is nut trim'lin'."

"Aye he is. Jist luk at'm. Trim'lin' Tam."

She and her friends laughed quietly, but the groom, who was indeed the smaller of the two, did not notice.

The bright colour of his high cheek bones and his thin lips, which were unusually red for a man, contrasted strongly with the dark rectangle of his short moustache and the whiteness of the skin where it was stretched taut across the bridge of his large bony nose. Although it was less than two hours since he had shaved, dark growth was already starting to shadow his hollow cheeks. He looked unreal and dramatic, like an actor in makeup seen unexpectedly offstage. Bruce Corning was not a calm man at the best of times. Today, the strength and energy, which were his main characteristics, surged through his body and he felt every nerve alive and shouting. Although Bruce was not absolutely trembling, his skin seemed to sizzle, and every minute or two his shoulders shrugged involuntarily inside his morning coat and his deep-set eyes darted back and forth, as if unwilling or unable to focus. He would have liked to run fast down the street, leaping over anything that came in his way.

He was not a happy man.

"It must be the wee wan, look hoo he's jumpin' aboot. Pair wee sowl, he canny staund still!"

"Aye, Ah think ye're right enuff."

"He looks gey shifty tae me."

"Aw, Ah think he's awfy hansum, like a wee film star."

"Charlie Chaplin, d'ye mean?"

There was more laughter.

The two young men still stood there on the pavement. They appeared unable to make any decision about their next move.

Suddenly a tall sandy-haired man galloped down the stairs and shook hands warmly with each one. He was the best man and obviously confident and organised.

Another tall and very handsome young man joined them, his long legs taking the four steps at a leap and causing the crowd to back away. He was William, brother of the bride and well aware of being the best-looking fellow around that day. Few would notice the nervous glance which he cast at the outer edges of the crowd, before he smiled charmingly at his future brother-in-law and patted him kindly on the shoulder. Bruce smiled for the first time, his wide grin showing large extraordinarily white teeth.

The four young men hurried into the halls with Bruce smiling, nodding and shrugging continuously until he disappeared from sight. His brother Stewart, the taller of the two, smiled less enthusiastically, without showing his teeth. Then, rather wearily, he followed the others into the brightly-lit cave from which faint music now echoed.

"Oh, whit luvly, luvly teeth, did ye see them?"

"Aye, jist like an adver*tis*ement."

"Or a filmstar."

"That last yin that come oot wiz mair like a filmstar."

"Aye, so he wuz."

"Aye, he wuz a stunner."

"Straight from Hollywood, so he wuz."

"Och you an' yur filmstars."

"But the wee yin hud luvly white teeth."

"An' he wiznae a' that wee, wuz he!"

"Weel, Ah thocht he wiz a bit glaikit, staunin' therr oan the pavement like a nosy-wax."

"Och, he wisnae glaikit."

"Aye he wiz. He wiz a wee nyaff an' his cheeks wiz affy rid."

"Ach ye're aye that critical, Biddy."

"Here's mair fowk arrivin' an' thur gey late."

There were more critical comments now, for the crowd was becoming weary.

However when the tall slender bride in pink silk chiffon finally arrived, she was greeted with smiles of approval and gasps and sighs of admiration from the onlookers. Her nun-like head dress and golden-edged veil provided a glimpse into another world for the crowd and they surged forward.

"Aw she's jist luvly!"

"Aw the sowl! She's goat it a' tae learn."

"It's a' aheed o' her."

"Isn't she jist beeyutiful."

"Thin as a bloody rake."

"An' the flooers! Did ye see thim?"

"Ah cud smell thim."

The elderly artist, if it were the case that he was an artist, had returned and now offered his arm to the bride who took it gratefully and hurried inside, smiling in a friendly way to either side as she went.

"Whit a nice gurl she seems."

"Hoo kin ye know that, jist by lookin' at her?"

"No, she seemed a reelly nice gurl. Ah liked her. She hud a kindly sort of face and she hud luvly eyes."

"Ah wunner how good she is at scrubbin' flairs or washin' semmits."

"She'll soon be getting' plenty o' that."

"Ach away, she'll hiv a maid."

"Maids is dearer nor whit they used tae be."

"Well she'll hiv a char then."

"She hud reelly luvly eyes."

"Ah thocht she hud a bit o' a cast in wan o' thim. An she didnae look much happier than the wee man did."

"Och, Biddy!"

The plump, somewhat downcast bridesmaid who left the taxi after the bride, might as well have been invisible as she was allowed to pass inside without comment from the crowd. The twelve-year-old flower girl, with the oversized ribbon in her hair, elicited a few smiles and nods as she skipped across the pavement after the rest of the party.

It was 1929 and not the most propitious year for a young couple to start out in life. Three years earlier, at the period of civic unrest, that same crowd would have shown a different spirit. There would have been screams and shouts and spitting from those pale faces. At that unhappy time, the bride's father had enrolled as a special constable and patrolled the unruly streets of Glasgow with a wooden baton which, as a gentle and scholarly artist, he sincerely hoped never to use. The bride's brother had also done his civic duty, though duty was hardly a favourite word in his vocabulary. He had driven a tram and his dark Mediterranean good looks and well-formed nose had earned him shrieks of, "Bloody Jew boy!" and "Gerroot o' the caur, ya fuckin' blackleg" as well as various noisome missiles, which he threw right back.

Unemployed numbers in Glasgow:
38,000 men, 2,000 boys, 8,200 women, 4,000 girls.

Glasgow Herald, 13th September 1929

Now the bride's father and brother were dressed in impeccable morning suits and carrying shining top hats and the fickle public, in spite of the dissatisfactions and aggressions which still seethed beneath the surface of an unjust society, was prepared to adore the trappings and luxury of wealth again for a short time.

There was a certain amount of seething in the breasts of most of the wedding party too.

It was not a marriage made in heaven. Both the bride and the groom would have been happy to call the whole thing off in the last few weeks before the event. As the day drew near and the disagreements and squabbles worsened, it became apparent that their aims and ambitions were diametrically opposed. They might never agree about anything ever again! They could not even agree upon the destination for the honeymoon.

Nor was either set of parents enthusiastic about their child's choice of a future spouse.

And yet the complex and expensive arrangements which would unite the couple for life, trundled relentlessly forward. Perhaps young people expected less from matrimony or were more fatalistic in that early part of the century. Perhaps, by that time, everything had gone too far to think of stopping it. The presents from the two sets of parents the leather three piece suite, the limed oak refectory table with the six leather seated chairs, the very special bedroom suite, also limed oak, with just a hint of Art Deco, nothing extreme had been delivered to the brand-new, though modest flat, rented in the suburbs. The generous presents from friends and acquaintances were on display at the home of the bride's parents. There were several silver entree dishes, a vast amount of crystal, a fine china dinner service for eight, with three vegetable dishes, five damask linen tablecloths all with matching napkins, two creamy cellular blankets, an eiderdown quilt and matching bedspread of heavenly blue silk, a hideous vase with jagged geometric pattern in orange and black, a few pieces of glass, (the coloured jug and six tumblers were probably the least expensive present of the whole show), pots and pans of the best aluminium, a rolling pin, enamelled bread bin (large enough for a growing family), the latest Ewbank carpet sweeper, sufficient cutlery (complete with fish-eaters and servers), an exquisite cloisonné vase and an exuberantly agile, dancing lady in porcelain, to join the mahogany clock on the mantelpiece, a Jacobean standard lamp with a red silk shade, even a mock-antique model of a full-rigged ship and, of course, several thick deckle envelopes containing very welcome cheques.

There was certainly no chance of backing out for either Annie or Bruce.

Parents

Annie had been discouraged by her parents from considering any sort of employment. After three years at Glasgow School of Art, where her energies had been directed towards social rather than artistic achievement, she was asked to leave. There was no chance that she would gain a diploma. The family attitude was that ladies did not need to work. That did not mean that she did not work in the house. Her help was very useful when domestic staff started to charge more realistic prices for their labour. Annie took over when the live-in maid left. She was twenty one then and loathed the futile round of endlessly scrubbing and polishing in her parent's large flat. Her mother had very high standards.

It seemed that a domestic future stretched uninvitingly ahead, although one or two opportunities to escape did present themselves.

There was the chance to train as a draughtswoman in an architectural firm, but her parents vetoed that as 'quite unsuitable'. Then a friend of the family, who owned a knitwear factory, was intrigued by the complicated Fair Isle patterns which Annie designed and knitted. His suggestion that she should design for his firm and train the knitters seemed like a dream come true for Annie, but it meant that she must leave home and her parents were certainly against that.

Marriage seemed as good an escape as any. It was the only escape. At least it would be her own home that she would be cleaning. And Bruce was a decent fellow, a trained marine engineer, always on the go, great fun and mad about her. He had been helpful too with little jobs around her parent's holiday house in Fife last year, when he visited. She had been impressed. They had a great time together in that lovely summer and it was scarcely his fault about the tap. He had not the right tools for the job and it was never easy with her mother watching every move, expecting mistakes. Annie could not help laughing when she thought of how much water there had been flooding down the stairs and the look on her mother's face. The wash-hand basin did look rather lop-sided now, with only one tap but as there was no hot water system in the house anyway, one tap was sufficient. As Annie always said, holidays in Pittenweem were a case of "stink or swim."

What was a tap here or there? Annie prided herself on being philosophical and making folk laugh whenever possible. It helped her to deal with her mother. And Bruce was terrific at laughing off his own mistakes. She admired that in him. Another fellow might look shamefaced but Bruce seemed quite amused and delighted when he had made a gaffe. He would always say he was sorry, of course, but his eyes twinkled and she could not quite believe that he meant it.

Bruce had the typical male attitude that a man was trapped into marriage sooner or later. That was how his peers viewed it and he also took it for granted. He knew he would be caught eventually and it might as well be Annie, who was fun and a very good-looking girl. Although there was not that magical, obssessive love between them that literature and popular songs teach us to expect from life, they had a lot of laughs together. She had a wonderful figure, so terribly slim and yet with breasts. So few girls seemed to have breasts. It was a puzzle to a bloke with no sisters. Both of them were healthy, lithe and attractive and they danced, golfed, swam and played an excellent game of tennis together. They were young and energetic and that might be sufficient for the happiness that those corny songs mentioned.

Especially when they could go to bed together every night as a matter of course.

Most importantly, marriage meant that they would finally escape from their parents.

Without quite facing the fact, Bruce suffered from a domineering and old-fashioned father, while there was no doubt that Annie's mother liked to be boss at all times.

Both sets of parents had been incredibly difficult.

It is almost impossible to read a young person's character without first investigating their background and observing the lives of their parents. Unfortunately young people in love only wish to observe their dearest one and have no time for the study of parents. If more prospective brides and grooms were to spend time considering their future in-laws, there might be fewer disappointments in marriage. Then again with such study, there might be fewer marriages in the first place.

Let us turn our attention to those parents whose characters and lives seemed unimportant to the young couple, for they form a major part in the large picture, which I hope to paint for you.

◊

John Mackay was a successful artist. From a rural background, he had shown artistic talent and determination from early childhood. This dismayed his father, a deeply religious and fervently teetotal grocer who feared that a life of Bohemian sin would be the natural outcome of such a career. John persevered in his ambition, and after studying in Glasgow, he won a scholarship to London, where many of his teachers belonged to the Pre-Raphaelite group. He fell under the spell of the fascinating John Everett Millais and would always consider him a genius. Later John studied in Paris and Venice. He was a quiet intelligent man, a very competent and successful portrait-painter (the most remunerative branch of his calling) and a fine painter of his real love, the sea. Sea pictures sold well, but were more moderately priced than elaborate presentation portraits. His charming etchings were much in demand at the annual exhibition of the Glasgow Institute.

Like many Glasgow artists in the previous thirty years, he had made a lucrative career for himself in the wealthy art-conscious city. If the end of that golden time was looming, neither John Mackay nor his fellow artists were aware of it.

Shortly before his daughter's wedding, he had finished a dashing full-length portrayal of the Moderator of the Kirk, who graciously agreed to officiate.

Each summer John Mackay moved to the east coast to pursue the favourite aspect of his art, his paintings of the sea and fisherfolk. His successful career had allowed him to buy a roomy cottage in Pittenweem, one of the picturesque little fishing villages of the East Neuk. This house had two benefits, a splendid view of the sea and a separate bright studio.

When John was thirty, before he had quite established himself, he had met and fallen in love with a beautiful seventeen-year-old girl, Mary. She was tall and slender and had the thick massy hair, the large spiritual eyes and the strong well-formed features of the typical Pre-Raphaelite beauty. She was the second oldest in the large family of a rootless and unsuccessful man, a wanderer over the earth. Mary had been born in India when her father was a private in the army. After his return to Britain, he had dragged his ever-growing family from place to place, finally settling in Glasgow as an undertaker's apprentice. She had no education, but she had style and wit and a dramatic presence. Time would show that she had much more than that. She was exceptionally intelligent and had a good business head. Unfortunately she was wilful and domineering and because John considered himself so incredibly lucky to have been accepted by such a wonderful girl, he became her willing slave and spoiled her. The result of John's adoration was that as the years passed, Mary became ever more manipulative and something of a monster. Though the world saw her as an attractive woman of great energy and ability, she was difficult to live with. She ruled the house with selfish determination and though a charming companion while she was in control and the centre of attention, she would rage or sulk if things were not to her liking. To those outside the family she appeared infinitely amusing and fascinating, but Annie had grown up learning to do as she was told and to tip-toe around her temperamental mother if she were in one of her 'moods'. Annie was prepared to go to a lot of trouble to avoid the confrontations that Mary sometimes seemed to seek out. Mary was brave and her husband and daughter were timid. It was a perfect complementary combination and Annie bore a great deal of the burden of her mother's unpredictable temper.

As he got older, though still an adoring husband, John spent more and more time in his studio, working or reading. In the evenings he would often escape to the Art club to play snooker.

William, Annie's handsome and dissolute younger brother had another solution to the problem. He did as he liked and walked out when things got too hot. Like many another mother, Mary adored him and forgave her son a great deal, not knowing, nor wanting to know the full extent of his sins. William was charming and plausible and hard to pin down. He knew exactly how to manipulate his mother and, just often enough to keep Mary in thrall, he would invite her to the afternoon 'the-dansant' at the Plaza ballroom. They were often mistaken for brother and sister, as they performed foxtrots and tangos with almost professional skill. What mother could resist that heady experience and Mary was a very young mother with a son of six feet high, while still in her thirties. William knew well how to smile and flatter and another fiver from the housekeeping would slip discreetly into his pocket.

Five pounds would provide a lot of sinful experience for a determined young man in the decadent twenties.

Mary was not tender to Annie, two years older than William and born when her mother was only twenty. Mary's self-image was based on being 'the artist's beautiful wife' and in her mid-thirties, a well-grown and attractive teenage daughter may have been an unwelcome encumbrance. Perhaps there was jealousy. There was a lack of sympathy certainly. Where Mary loved flamboyant hats, exotic clothes, jewels and elaborate hairstyles, Annie preferred an austere and tailored image. Where Mary was effusive and dramatic, Annie was reserved and sometimes supremely sarcastic. Much of the time Annie did try to please her mother, but she was hardly ever successful.

William and Annie were not close either. They had been good friends as children, but because of their mother's unequal treatment of them they had grown apart. Annie knew all about those regular fivers that entered her brother's wallet. It seemed to her that financially she was very unfairly treated, for her heavy share of housework was unpaid. She was expected to make sure that William had his lunch on time, and also to tip-toe around the house when he had that post-prandial nap, so necessary to those who keep late hours. He must be provided with freshly ironed shirts daily, and was altogether the Prince of the establishment, while Annie felt more like the servant. Worst of all was that no matter how many floors Annie scrubbed or how hard she polished the brasses, nothing she did was ever quite right in her mother's critical eyes. There was no praise and there was certainly no payment. She was a non-earning member of the household and cleaning was seen as her duty. William did earn modest wages at a series of jobs, though truthfully little of that went towards the household. Most hurtful was that each small thoughtful present that Annie gave her mother was discovered to have some flaw or deficiency, while William, not much of a present giver, could make his mother deliriously happy with a kind look.

Although Annie realised that she could never compete with William for her mother's affections, she kept trying.

◊

Bruce Corning's father, Bob was also a grocer's son from a rural background and also considerably older than his wife. Nevertheless, Bruce's parents were perhaps as different as they could possibly be from the Mackays. Bob had no special skills except those of carefully correct book-keeping, exquisite copper-plate hand-writing, talking dogmatically on most subjects and the ability to write the Lord's Prayer on a sixpence. He would always earn his living by working as a clerk in an unimportant little office, but there was no doubt about who wore the pants in the Corning house. His wife Jane would defer to Bob on every subject with a sweet femininity. There may have been times when by wheedling or other manipulations, she gained her own ends, but there were no confrontations, no shouting matches. Jane was happy to leave all initiative to her husband. It meant fewer problems and less responsibility and she could not be blamed if things went wrong.

Jane had grown up in a comparatively wealthy family in Lancashire where there were servants, good clothes and unexciting holidays on the Cumbrian coast. No demands were made on her other than to dress well and behave nicely and at these she was successful. Her appearance was unremarkable, with round deep-set eyes and high cheek bones. She was small and pretty in a way that would quickly fade. Sadly none of the eligible young men of Lancashire seemed to notice her smallness or prettiness sufficiently to seek her in marriage.

The family was of Scottish origin and still spoke with a markedly Scottish accent. When the new clerk from Glasgow joined the office in Bolton, it may have been the familiar vowels which attracted Jane, for Bob's appearance was unprepossessing. He was small, dour and fourteen years her senior. It may have been that his arrogance and dominating personality appealed to Jane. Or perhaps she was fascinated by his effulgent walrus moustache. Possibly he represented the only chance of achieving her one aim in life, marriage. At any rate she accepted him. Although her parents cannot have considered Bob Corning to be a great match, Jane was now twenty-eight and they gave her a lavish wedding and a handsome dowry.

She had always known that Bob could not provide her with the comfortable background that she had known in Lancashire. Those extravagant days were behind her and she willingly learned to cut her coat according to her cloth. She had taken nothing to do with the ample provisioning of her family while she remained at home. She knew nothing of household shopping and when her new husband trained her in the careful penny-pinching methods which were his second nature, she accepted his tenets eagerly. Bob showed her how to watch for bargains and how to buy less than seemed necessary, rather than more. Her dinners might still be the accepted three courses, but by clever management she could cut down on the amount of meat and vegetables required. So long as she watched the accounts carefully, she had freedom to run the house. She was a highly conventional woman, with few ambitions and not many skills. Marriage had been her aim in life, she had achieved it and she would not count the cost.

Bob and Jane returned to Glasgow and rented a small flat in the Woodlands area, just west of the city centre. It was quiet, convenient and pleasant enough, but somehow it was always a little dreary and dull. Jane did not have the knack of creating an interesting background to her life. They lived in this flat for the next twenty-seven years until just before this story begins with the wedding of their older son, Bruce. He was born in 1902, in the same year as his future bride. Coincidentally, each had a brother born two years later in 1904. Bruce's brother was called Stewart

Stewart Corning was as different from William Mackay as it is possible to imagine. He knew nothing of dance halls, nightclubs or gambling dens. Almost miserly with his money, unsociable and uncomfortable with the female sex, Stewart was a puzzle to his mother, although his father saw in him the perfect son. Stewart was certainly dutiful and well-behaved at all times, unlike his wilder, older brother who, almost hyperactive, delighted in practical jokes, mischief and loud laughter. While Bruce would gallop off each night to join his friends in pursuit of one sport or another, Stewart was pleased to stay at home and read and have discussions with his father, or rather listen while his father spoke endlessly on the issues of the day or on various ethical problems. It would be wrong to say that Bob Corning disliked his older son, but he did not quite trust him. He felt that Bruce had a superficial attitude to life and needed a firm hand at all times.

Somerset Maugham has observed that few misfortunes can befall a boy which bring worse consequences than to have a really affectionate mother. To offset Maugham's cynicism, Freud has suggested that a boy with a really loving mother, remains a hero to himself all his life. Take your choice of these opinions. What is certain is that Jane adored Bruce and spoiled him terribly.

Though more intelligent and more energetic than his father or brother, Bruce was idolised by his mother and his maternal grandmother in a way that is dangerous for an unthinking boy. Jane was his absolute and devoted servant. No task was too great or too small for her to perform for her darling. Though Jane's health was not of the most robust, she would not hesitate to leap from her sick bed if Bruce needed any small service. She adored him on a servile daily basis, while his grandmother in Bolton, now a wealthy widow, also made a little god of the clever, energetic first-born grandchild. Throughout Bruce's childhood and adolescence his grandmother lavished money on him, dressing him in expensive clothes, taking him to fashionable hotels and enrolling him in a boarding school in the Lake district when he was twelve. Her aim was to create a 'little gentleman'. Truthfully some of it was an ordeal for the hyperactive boy, especially the clothes, but he acquired some degree of polish and gentility, as well as a very strong sense that he was a most special and delightful person.

His grandmother's favourite comment on Bruce was that he was 'like a little ray of sunshine when he came into the room'. Bruce, too spoiled to add the necessary seasoning to this fond adulation, believed her implicitly and fully accepted this description of his own persona.

His less-favoured brother, dressed in hand-me-downs and inexperienced in expensive holidays, may be forgiven for failing to feel the sunny warmth of Bruce's presence.

◊

For the first ten years of their married life, the Mackays had lived in a large flat near Blythswood Square. It was an elegant building and for Mary, who had been fascinated by murder trials throughout her life, the flat had the added attraction of overlooking the basement window through which the notorious Madeleine Smith had passed the cup of cocoa to her unhappy lover; cocoa which was said, though never proven, to be laced with arsenic.

The sitting-room was large enough to accommodate a concert grand piano, which the young Annie loved dearly. When not practising her scales or Mozart, she would crawl underneath the enormous instrument with Sconny-Jonny, her beloved, flat-faced doll and create a secret life which excluded her demanding mother and her teasing brother.

Unfortunately there was no north facing room in the flat suitable for a studio and John had to rent one nearby. This was inconvenient and necessitated the waving of a dish towel from the kitchen window to attract his attention when a meal was ready or if he were wanted on the telephone. They always knew that this flat would be a temporary home.

In 1911, Glasgow Corporation bought a large painting of Pittenweem harbour by John Mackay. It set the seal on his success. He had already painted several portraits of wealthy Glasgow citizens, and he was becoming known as an artist who could 'get a good likeness' as well as make a fine imposing life-size painting. His fascinating and stylish wife, with her entertaining anecdotes and witty conversation, was also well-known in social circles.

It was Mary who heard of the splendid flat to rent at Charing Cross, a flat specially designed for a successful artist. Burnett, the architect had, some twenty years before, been advised to incorporate studio accommodation into the luxurious Albany Mansions. The 'artist's flat' was a two storey flat and made use of the roof space in a way that was unusual. The entrance hall was the normal size for a Glasgow apartment, but two swing doors led into the imposing main studio or gallery which was two storeys high. As well as three conventional windows facing north, forty percent of the north slope of the roof was glazed and this immense room was filled with the clear and unchanging light required by a painter. On the west wall a flight of stairs of fashionable Japanese simplicity, led to a long cantilevered landing above one of the two fireplaces. The design of each fireplace, with flat undecorated brass canopy, unadorned marble surround and plain uncarved wooden mantel, showed admirable restraint and was in marked contrast to the outrageous flights of architectural fancy that were the focal point of many Glasgow living rooms, at the turn of the century. A second flight led to the upstairs studio or atelier, which was single storey and L-shaped, with an attic roof and again a north light. Part of this room projected over the flat next door, adding more space to the impressive concept. The staircase balustrade extended back along the south wall of the lower studio, creating the effect of a balcony eleven feet above floor level and separating the upper room from the lower. Downstairs a second fireplace graced the east wall. The mantels, like the sturdy square-cut bannisters, were stained black The elegance and space were breath-taking..

"John, it's so modern! What a wonderful place it is! I think it's just *marvellous*, I've quite fallen in love with it already. Don't make that face now. This is our chance. What an elegant room! Imagine inviting a sitter to come here! I can just see the Lord Provost or, or ... anybody ... I don't even need to see the rest of the house."

John jingled his keys in his pocket and took off his hat, smoothed his thinning hair, coughed a small dry cough and replaced his hat.

"Don't let's hesitate, John. We'd be mad to let this place go. You could have an exhibition here and right away we'd save all that commission that the gallery takes. And people would come just to see the flat, you know. Curiosity would bring them ... quite apart from your pictures. And once they were here, they would buy, I'm absolutely sure. They couldn't resist the atmosphere of this place!"

"It's certainly quite a studio, amazing really. I never met old whatisname that lived here before but I heard he had a marvellous studio."

"Pity his paintings didn't live up to the studio."

"No, he didn't have much success."

"No wonder, with those awful daubs. Let's go upstairs."

Mary ran upstairs and John followed more slowly, pausing on the landing and gazing up into the high ceiling.

"Oh, what a view from up here!" Mary laughed from the top of the stairs, "It makes me feel quite dizzy. And wait till you see what is up here! You will love it!"

John did love the Dutch stove with the tiles decorated with sepia views of Holland. He had painted in the Netherlands for some months and felt a great affection for that flat land.

Mary stood at the balcony and looked down into the main gallery.

"What an environment to paint an important sitter! And to entertain! We could have a whist drive or a dance here easily."

Mary was president of the Glasgow branch of a ladies' charity.
"It won't be easy to heat such a great big place."
"No, that's true, John."
Then with one of her instinctive lightning decisions, Mary added,
"I think it would be best to partition off this upper studio. You need to have somewhere private that's workable and untidy. You know how much clutter you collect. A joiner could do that quite quickly and then it would be easier to heat and I could keep downstairs nice and tidy for unexpected visitors. And buyers especially! And we'll put hessian on the walls rather than paper. Hessian will be a good background to show off the paintings. Let's look at the rest of the house now, though I don't care what it's like. We should grab this place, it's such an opportunity! Come on John, cheer up. This is just the best move we've made yet."

And it certainly was an excellent business move. The Mackays would eventually buy the 'artist's flat' and live in it for the next forty years.

Significant Visits

Ten months before the wedding it was arranged that the Cornings should visit the Mackays. Although they lived less than a mile apart, their social circles were very different and they had never met. The Cornings' acquaintances practically all came from their local church, and bazaars, teas and soirees were their main social events. The Mackays, though members of Glasgow Cathedral, were not much involved with religious matters. Through John's work and the Art Club and Hilton Park Golf Club, they were friendly with a wide variety of successful tradesmen, merchants, architects, lawyers and doctors, as well as other artists. They entertained and were entertained in return. They visited the theatre each week, golfed, played bridge and regularly ate in restaurants. Making contacts was part of the business of selling paintings and although John was a shy man and would have preferred to spend more hours in his studio, he knew it was necessary to meet people. Mary, through her charity work, had met and chatted with politicians, aristocrats and famous actors. She enjoyed the social life and was adept at every aspect of what would now be called public relations.

Mr and Mrs Corning had met Annie only twice since the engagement was announced. She had found their house dismal and suffocating. She had also blotted her copybook badly that first night, when Jane Corning asked her dear son to sing 'Lovely as a Tree'. Annie had laughed out loud, positive that it was a joke. She was not overfond of the human voice at any time and she gave her fiancé no credit for possessing musical ability. However Bruce did sing, while Annie sat squirming and Jane looked daggers at the unappreciative female who would steal her precious boy away. It was an embarrassing evening and the second visit was even less successful.

A Difficult Position

I know that to be a mother-in-law is not easy. Jim has been our spoilt boy at home. Whether he came home early or late, a meal was always waiting for him. His clothes were brushed and kept in order and when he wanted to talk, we all listened attentively.

In spite of this he remained a dear lovable fellow ... I find it so irritating when a pert little minx orders him about and insists that she is the one to be waited upon ...

Woman's page, Glasgow Herald 11th September 1929

Jane was sure that her imperial son had made a dreadful mistake in allying himself with this insensitive, unmusical, common girl, daughter of an artist, part of a coarse Bohemian family. She wept each night, as she thought of all the lurid tales that she had heard of the immoral behaviour of artists in general. What sort of wife had Bruce chosen for himself? She dreaded to see the home-life in which this young woman had been dragged up. When she tried to discuss her worries with Bob, he was strangely reluctant to talk. Was he, too, worried about his elder son's future? Or perhaps he was relieved at the possibility of this rambunctious son leaving home in the near future.

◊

The Saturday afternoon arrived for the visit to the Mackays' house. Jane was neat and unexciting in a brown tailored costume with a small gold and diamond brooch pinned to the centre of her modesty vest. She was very pale and her heart beat alarmingly as they climbed the marble stairs to the top flat of Albany Mansions. There were six flights of stairs, two to each floor and the marble was sparkling white and obviously well-scrubbed. The stairs certainly surprised the Cornings, but not as much as the soaring two-storey sitting room with its flight of stairs, the boudoir grand piano, the antique furniture and the fresh flowers. On all the walls hung large impressive, gold-framed paintings of blue sea, brown-sailed fishing boats, pretty fisher girls mending nets and children playing in the sand.

Annie looked ethereal and virginal in cream linen and amber beads. Mrs Mackay, a perfect hostess, was resplendent in a frock of pale grey silk, worn with a black chiffon 'bridge coat', which was edged with fine lace and covered with tiny embroidered flowers. Though Jane might have left her wealthy days behind her, she still recognised an expensive garment, almost certainly from Paris, when she saw one. The coat was a garment such as she had never possessed.

When Annie brought in the tea tray with home-made pancakes and raspberry jam, poor Jane Corning was forced to revise all her preconceived ideas about artists. She asked in a stifled voice if Mrs Mackay had been baking.

"Oh yes," Mary answered with a light laugh, "I just got home in time from the golf course to throw them together, but I always think they seem better when you make them in a rush, don't you? I think these are extra good today, John, don't you?"

John agreed enthusiastically, while Jane nodded uncertainly. Baking was quite an ordeal for her, something for which she left herself ample time and pancakes were never her most successful productions, and in her experience, golf was an occupation reserved for men. Suddenly she felt a great and unusual anger welling up inside her breast. She did not recognise it, but it was the fury of jealousy. Mary Mackay, golfer, baker of supreme pancakes and dressed in an exquisite coat, was the epitome of self-confidence as she sat there in her beautiful home, telling some amusing story of the golf course. As she spoke, her eyes moved to each member of her audience in turn, lingering just long enough to show that she needed and enjoyed their complete attention. Her delicate hands gesticulated as she talked and the two large diamonds of her ring sparkled entrancingly. She smiled a little as she remembered the incident she was describing and Bob Corning smiled too. The story was short and to the point and had a sharp and unexpected ending at which everyone, except Jane, laughed uproariously.

Almost immediately Mary launched into another story, this time a poignant tale told quietly, but with dramatic pauses and flashing eyes, but Jane was not listening. She refused to be caught in the net of this woman's fascination. Jane was observing the very fine objects around the room, the crystal, the Persian rugs, the silk lampshades and the banded linen curtains. Would Jane have felt better if she had known how comparatively little all these luxuries had cost? Apart from the embroidered bridge coat, which had been very expensive, Mary was a great bargain hunter and had an eagle eye at bazaars and auctions for very good things at throwaway prices. Not one of the Persian rugs had cost more than a few pounds. Mary had made the curtains from cheap sheeting and used chintz at sixpence-a-yard, for the profession-ally piped and frilled loose covers on the three-piece suite. The room itself, with the great windows in the ceiling and the elegant staircase, was unlike anything Jane had ever seen. There was such a feeling of space and light. Jane tried to convince herself that it was not at all comfortable or homey. Nevertheless, there they sat around the fire in a cosy little group, taking afternoon tea and Bob was laughing in a more animated way than she had ever seen him laugh before.

Jane suddenly stood up at twenty past four and announced that they must be leaving now.

Bob looked surprised and disappointed, for he had been enjoying himself, but he followed his wife dutifully.

In twenty-eight years of marriage, Bob had never found Jane so determined, so intractable, as she was after that visit to the Mackays. In vain he pleaded that it was financially impossible for them to move house just at that time, but she was adamant. Before the Mackays made the conventional return visit, it was *imperative* that the Cornings were established in a bigger and better house.

Within six weeks the Cornings had moved to a large flat in Doune Terrace, which overlooked the River Kelvin and part of the Botanic Gardens. It was an expensive move, as new furniture must be bought and some decoration was required. Unfortunately the new flat retained the dreariness and dullness of the former one and Jane never forgave the Mackays for their magnificent home.

Such were the parents and families of the young couple. Annie and Bruce might have learned a lot about their future problems, had they studied the psychological profiles of their respective families in the eight months of engagement preceding the wedding.

But in those months, they were too busy kissing or quarrelling

An Incident in Garnethill

Five weeks before the wedding, Annie and her mother had gone shopping. Mary had taken control of buying the trousseau and as Annie had no allowance and no money of her own, she was completely dependent on what her mother was prepared to spend and to choose. Annie felt like a schoolgirl again and could generate little interest in the long days of trailing around department stores and small boutiques. While Mary believed in inspecting every aspect of her purchases, Annie's thoughts wandered off to the latest disagreement with Bruce and whether the marriage had any hope of succeeding. Mary was the customer that every saleswoman dreads. Interminable relays of goods would be brought to the counter and displayed before she would make a decision. After information was demanded on size and price, country of manufacture, the authenticity of the fabric and its washing capabilities, garments would be turned over, rubbed, smoothed, crushed in a fist, held up to the light and generally viewed with a lack of enthusiasm. The actual trying on of clothes was a nightmare for Annie as her mother looked her up and down, shaking her head dubiously and telling her to turn around just once more. When Mary made the final decision to buy, it was not only a relief to everyone, but a great surprise. For Annie the worst part was yet to come. It was when Mary would inquire, as she invariably did, about discount for cash payment, or suggest that if the price were in guineas, the shillings be knocked off. Then her daughter longed to sink into the floor. The whole process was embarrassing and exhausting for Annie, who did not have her mother's stamina for serious shopping and who would rather have played a couple of games of tennis. The neatly wrapped parcels which they carried home at the end of each long day seemed to have nothing to do with the bride-to-be.

Strangely, today Mary had been easier to please. And very generous. The small, pale blue parcels were particularly light and contained gossamer silk underwear, which Annie had to admit was gorgeous.

The next item required was a hat to match the rose-pink

going-away suit. Mary headed for a tiny and exclusive boutique in Cambridge Street and Annie followed, as usual one and a half steps behind her brisk mother.

Suddenly Mary stopped and Annie almost collided with her.

"We cross over here, I think."

Annie followed dutifully. She had not visited Chapeaux Regine before and would have preferred to go to the department store where she usually bought hats.

After circumnavigating a tramcar and reaching the other pavement, Mary uncharacteristically paused and looked from side to side as though lost.

"Have you forgotten where it is?"

"No, no, I haven't forgotten but..."she turned back towards Sauchiehall street then stopped again.

"I think we'll just go to Coplands for the hat after all. They have a good selection and I'm ready for a coffee soon, I think."

Annie was astonished. Her mother could shop for six hours at a stretch without a break, but she said nothing.

That night in her mother's bedroom, Annie tried on the beige velour cloche which had been chosen from the department store and admired herself in the mirror. The hat suited her very well indeed. It was decorated with stylised flower shapes in felt, of exactly the same pink as her suit.

"I love this appliqué. I'd like to try making something like that. A jacket, perhaps? It's so effective and it wouldn't be too difficult."

Her mother was not listening. She sat on the bed with her right hand caressing the left side of her neck and gazed across the room with a faraway expression. Brodie was a family name and this day-dreaming state had become known to her children as the 'Brodie stare'.

"What's the Brodie stare for, Maw?"

"Oh, it was just something that happened today. I wasn't going to mention it to you. Really, it doesn't matter."

"You'll have to tell me now. What was it? Nice or nasty? Go on, tell me!"

Her mother's face changed suddenly. Annie wondered if she were going to weep. Then her voice burst out loud and harsh.

"It was horrible, really horrible. I didn't want you to know about it, just when you're so happy about the wedding and everything."

"Tell me! You can't not tell me now. I'll just imagine something even worse than it was."

"I don't think that there is anything much worse to imagine."

Chills ran up and down Annie's spine.

Two or three interminable minutes passed before Mary started to speak in a monotone. She had changed again and used none of her accustomed dramatic arts or flourishes. It was as though she were speaking to herself.

"It was when we were in Cambridge Street today...that road that goes off up the hill, I don't know what you call it. I heard a funny noise ... a strange high-pitched sound ... it's a wonder you didn't hear it too ... it made me think of an animal ... screaming"

Her lips were quivering like an old woman's and she stopped and clasped her hands in front of her mouth for a moment, then lowered her hands and pressed them underneath her chin, as though praying. Very quietly, she started to speak again.

"There was a steam road roller coming down the hill and the driver must have lost control of it and a woman was caught underneath ... and slowly ... she was being ..."

She stopped once more and looked at her daughter. Both women were breathing with short shallow gasps and their large eyes were wide and unblinking.

"You mean that enormous weight was rolling over the woman?"

"Yes."

"Over her legs?"

"I suppose so."

"You saw this happening today?"

"Yes."

"You must have glimpsed it all very quickly."

"I just saw it momentarily, in a sort of flash."

"How did I not see this?"

"I don't know. I saw it all happen and ... well ... I ... got us back to Sauchiehall Street as quickly as possible."

"But why did I not hear anything? This ... screaming that you're talking about. Why didn't I notice it?"

"Well, the traffic was noisy, I suppose and you go around with your head in the clouds at the best of times. Why do you ask me all these questions?"

Mary, always quick to anger, had changed her tone of voice.

"Are you doubting my word? Don't you believe I saw it happening? Because *I can assure you ...*"

"Of course I believe you saw it happening, Maw. It's just so strange that I heard nothing at all and saw nothing"

Annie did not in fact completely believe in the terrible accident. In the first place it seemed almost impossible that it could happen at all. Why would anyone be near enough to such a fearsome vehicle to become entangled in it? And how could she have missed hearing the sounds of distress?

"You saw nothing because I hurried you away as fast as I could." Mary's voice was loud and sharp.

"And this screaming woman, what about ...?"

"I didn't say the woman was screaming." Mary interrupted irritably. She was more normal now and spoke very loudly, emphasising each word in an ominous way.

"Well, who was screaming then, Maw?"

"It was the driver who was screaming. The woman was making a very different sort of noise."

And her mother stood and walked quickly from the room, the expression of horror on her face replaced by the more familiar one of displeasure.

Annie was never sure of the truth. Could it have been a hallucination? It seemed as though her mother certainly believed the accident to have happened, but nothing was reported in the newspapers. Annie combed through them for several days and there was no mention of any trouble with a steam road roller in any of them. However, she could not put the incident real or imaginary from her mind. It haunted her and the fact that she had seen nothing made her more dependent on her mother's horrific description and obvious anguish. She could not imagine how the woman could have been trapped. Various possibilities continuously passed through her mind until she felt sick and exhausted.

Mary never again spoke of the woman and the steam road roller, but as the weeks before the wedding passed with increasing speed, the story assumed a mythic symbolism for Annie, for she herself seemed to be the woman who was caught beneath the inexorable, rolling wheel of the marriage machine.

After the Wedding

L et us return to that those nuptial celebrations which started our story, dear reader. Of course there were set-backs and disappointments throughout the day. What wedding was ever perfect?

The weather was typical of a September day in Glasgow with quick changes from brilliant sunshine to short heavy downpours of rain, but no one expected better. There was a little problem with a piece of jewellery which Mary was determined that the bride should wear for 'good luck'. Annie was unenthusiastic about the old brooch, but as it could not be found at the last minute that problem was solved.

Vida, the chief bridesmaid, a lumpy girl who had been jilted the previous year, arrived with a very long face. She apologised, but felt sure that she could not go through the ceremony with all the sad memories that it would conjure up. She had thought it would be possible, now she found it was not possible. Then she burst into tears. Fortunately the charm and subtle flattery which Mary could always produce at a moment's notice was able to sway the poor girl's determination. Vida washed her face, applied a little papier poudre, drank a thimbleful of sherry and bravely reassumed her responsibilities for the day, although it might have been noted that she did not carry them out with the bright gladness expected of a chief bridesmaid.

One of the younger bridesmaids was a pretty girl of twelve with the most glorious, golden, waist-length hair. When she arrived at the Mackays, Annie was terribly disappointed to see that the mother had chosen to take the girl to a hairdresser for the big event, a hairdresser lacking the aesthetic sense to appreciate the natural beauty of this fine attribute. The hair had been cut and frizzed and an outsize bow of pink ribbon attached precariously to the side of her head, making it necessary for the poor girl to carry her head a-tilt throughout the long day. It did not occur to Annie to change the ribbon. She felt passive and powerless and was quite beyond any decisive action.

She lived that day in a dream, helplessly allowing life to wash over her.

As expected, Mr McLean-Watt, the Moderator of the Kirk Assembly in 1929, officiated splendidly at the ceremony but he realised his full potential at the reception. His after-lunch speech was a masterpiece. Well-known as a wit and raconteur, he had a great fund of stories, each of which appeared to be heading towards a highly improper ending, but an unexpected last-minute swerve preserved each one as entirely acceptable for a minister of the church to be telling. It was skilfully naughty and dangerous and he held the audience in the hollow of his histrionic hand. Their continuous and helpless laughter, together with the excellent meal provided by the well-trained staff of the Rhul, not to mention a plentiful supply of champagne, made the wedding a truly enjoyable affair.

The couple left after the speeches and were sent on their way with blessings, ribald remarks and thrown rice.

As they climbed into the taxi, the day nearly turned to tragedy, for Bruce choked on a grain of rice. The well-wishers, unaware of the life or death struggles of the groom in the back seat, laughed and waved merrily. The driver pulled away and Annie beat Bruce on the back as hard as she could. It was like a nightmare as the grinning faces receded. The feeling of impending doom that Annie had experienced so often in the last few weeks seemed as through it were about to be realised. As well as the terror of the moment, Annie's mind worked on a different level, as she thought cynically that she need not have worried so much about marrying Bruce, as his death from choking would now resolve everything.

The grain of rice was coughed up, Bruce wiped his red face and they kissed each other with a new fierceness.

"Ur yiz all right in the back therr?"

"Fine thanks."

"Jist newly merrit, ur yiz?"

"Aye, that's right." said Bruce proudly though croakily

"Best o' luck tae yiz both."

"Thanks," Bruce laughed and massaged his throat. "We'll need it, I expect. I was nearly a gonner there."

The couple smiled affectionately at each other and rubbed their noses together.

"We've got hours before the train leaves, Bruce. Let's go to the pictures."

"Good idea, honeybun. Driver, take us to a cinema somewhere."

"Right ye are, surr. Which wan ur ye wantin'?"

"No idea. Annie can you think of one? Or what's on anywhere?"

"Maybe the taxi driver can suggest one."

"Yes, driver, do you know what's on anywhere? A nice, swell cinema for us to go to in our new duds? Don't want any rotten wee fleapit, y'know."

"Thur a new yin oot west. Jist opened a coupla months' ago in the Crow Road. S'called the Tivoally," putting the accent on the second syllable, "S'awfy swell. Black'n white stripes a' acrost the front like a muckle black'n white strippit ba'," the driver chuckled hoarsely, "An' it seems tae be big'n posh inside, forby."

Annie had read about the new cinema, built like an Italian palazzo and called the Tivoli and she nodded her agreement to Bruce.

"Sounds fine. D'ye know what's on?"

"Nae idea."

"As long as it's not that 'Mammy' chap. Couldn't stand that again." Annie had hated Al Jolson in the 'Jazz Singer', "I hope it's Chaplin or Buster Keaton and I won't care if I've seen it before." Annie thought they were both geniuses.

"Anyway it'll be cosy and we can have an ice-cream and relax after all that bloody rigmarole."

"Bruce! Ice-cream! You're an awful man for your stomach. I'll never be able to feed you enough. Mind you, when I think of it, I believe I would like an ice-cream too."

They giggled helplessly, their heads close together. For the first time in months they were in complete agreement. Though it was unlikely to last, it was very pleasant and comforting.

Nerves had stopped either of them from doing justice to the wedding breakfast and after the cinema they realised they were absolutely starving. Bruce whistled up another taxi and directed the driver to the Malmaison, the prestigious restaurant belonging to the Central Station Hotel. There they ate sole a la bonne femme and a stupendous mixed grill, before dashing to collect their luggage and catch the London train by the skin of their teeth.

"My, we're living like real toffs, aren't we!" Bruce laughed as they were shown to their overnight sleeping compartment.

"Not half." Annie smiled lovingly"

The next two weeks were much like those of all honeymooners, with some pleasurable surprises and many disappointments. Equal time was devoted to: A, establishing a balance of power B, making love and C, outright squabbling.

Generally speaking, they were both pretty well satisfied with the vows which they had pledged to each other in the Rhul.

◊

And what of the wedding guests? Their jollifications continued unabated for the rest of the day, with dinner at the Art Club, followed by a visit to the King's theatre, then dancing at a private club.

In spite of Mary's entreaties, the Cornings had not attended the theatre performance, not even waitied for coffee at the Art Club. Bob made their excuses,

"We never take stimulants in the evening and I think Jane is very tired. Thank you so much for your kindness in providing such a ... a ...". he paused, for he had been appalled at what the day must have cost, "*generous* send-off for the young people."

After they left, Mary muttered to John,

"What funny people those are!"

The Cornings were silent in the taxi, for not only had it been a sad and emotional day for Jane, but she had felt unhappy with her hat. It was a dowdy hat compared to all the others at the wedding. This hat had not been her first choice. The one that she had really liked was twice the price, but Bob had dissuaded her and now she knew that had been a terrible mistake. A small bubble of resentment sat like a stone in her chest. They had little to say about the wedding, though Jane did comment on the morose chief bridesmaid.

"That plump bridesmaid was miserable and she wasn't hiding it well. I wonder if she had a hankering for Bruce?"

When Bob snorted contemptuously at this suggestion, Jane's eyes filled with tears and her heart swelled with a very un-wifely fury.

◊

By two a.m. what was left of the wedding party had returned to the Mackays flat.

There, Mary, who did not normally drink but rather enjoyed champagne, decided to entertain her friends with a favourite trick.

"Ladies and Gentlemen! Can I have your attention *please!*"

The wedding gifts were still on display in the main studio and Mary, with a quick and decisive flick, removed the tablecloth from a small table without first removing the crystal articles which sat upon it. Everyone gasped and hands flew out as the three vases and two bowls rose imperceptibly into the air, then settled safely once more on the bare mahogany. Before anyone could move, she displayed her prowess with a clock and some ornaments on another table. When Mary, with the exaggerated flourish of a magician, folded that cloth, bowed to right and left and headed towards a third table loaded with fine china, John hurried across the room. However Sonia, a close friend, reached Mary first and linking arms with her, managed to distract her from performing her trick a third, and possibly less lucky, time.

When everyone had finally gone and John and Mary were alone, she tried another skill from her repertoire, which she had fortunately repressed previously. She started to high-kick over the various displays. She was an agile woman, with long legs and she went around the room laughing and kicking with alternate legs over chairs and couches as well as the laden tables. Only once did she misjudge her kick and an aluminium saucepan, possibly of inferior quality, lost its handle, but there were plenty of saucepans and she was not deterred.

John, who never ceased to be amazed at his high-spirited wife, just stood quietly watching her. It had been a long day and he felt terribly tired.

The first approach to 'seeing by wireless' becoming as commonplace as hearing by wireless, was made at the Radio Exhibition at Olympia today, when wireless traders were given a foretaste of the first television broadcast that is to be sent through the London studio of the BBC on Monday.

Glasgow Herald 26th September 1929

Married

For Annie, it was wonderful to have her own home. She had a pleasant and unaccustomed sense of possession as she arranged and rearranged the new furniture, the china, the crystal, the rugs and the ornaments. For the first time in her life she was cleaning things that belonged to her. Many of the articles she had chosen herself and it certainly made housework more enjoyable.

Perched on the top of a hill on the south side, where a fresh breeze always blew, the small flat was newly built, compact and convenient. It was so very different from her parents' big flat in the city centre, where the constant struggle with the sooty filth of downtown Glasgow was a battle which would never be won.

Most important was the feeling of freedom she experienced, without the constant and critical eye of her mother watching every action. Mary was unable to let anyone else make decisions or pursue a project in their own way. She always 'knew best' and was relentless in her demands that this knowledge be recognised and acted upon. Annie sometimes wondered if her mother realised the extent of her domination over those around her and how unlovable it made her. Who could like a dictator? Given the choice, Annie would prefer to be popular rather than powerful. Confrontation was something she would always avoid if possible, while Mary seemed to thrive on it.

Now, in her own little flat, Annie felt like a princess in a fairy story who, after many years, has been released from a spell. She felt guilty and disloyal to her mother for these thoughts, but never the less they were enjoyable. Now she could experiment with cooking and work out her own domestic schedule. She intended trying the different ways of tackling chores that she had read about in magazines.

She decided that she was incredibly happy, though there were regular disagreements with Bruce, who seemed to have as quick a temper as her mother. He also shouted a lot and occasionally sulked. But their arguments were altogether more equal and Annie often had a pleasant feeling of having won.

Her quiet sarcasm could vanquish Bruce's raised voice. Quite often, when Annie pointed out some really daft remark that he had made, the row finished with laughter and kisses.

After a while, Annie noticed that Bruce was generally ready to pick a fight when he was hungry so she determined to have food always ready for him. He was very thin and he worked and played hard. "A hungry man's an angry man" had been a favourite family saying, though her own father had seldom proved this adage true.

Life with her father had not prepared Annie for life with Bruce. John Mackay was a quiet unassuming man with a wry sense of humour and an addiction to reading. Most of his time was spent in his studio and if he were not painting or sketching, he would be reading. He was certainly capable of anger, but it was seldom expressed in his home. In a house filled with the dramatic personality of Mary Mackay, there was little room for the emotional statements of others. John had lived a bachelor life for many years before his marriage. If he felt hungry, he would quietly make himself a piece of toasted cheese or finish off a slab of cold milk pudding, of which he was inordinately fond. He was likely to wash up a few dishes in the kitchen as he fed himself.

Bruce, on the other hand had been reared to consider the kitchen entirely a female domain.

After dinner, on the very first night in their new house, he had peered around the door of the tiny kitchen which opened directly from the living room.

"Do you expect me to give you a hand?" he asked with an engaging smile, but no real enthusiasm.

"Well you don't have to, but it would be nice. We could 'chat companionably', as it suggests in the book." They had been given a slim paperback called 'Sensible Advice to Young Married Couples'.

"But no dirty stories, Bruce! Or we'll start to laugh and maybe break something."

"Righty-ho then, but I warn you this is strange territory for me. No earthly idea where to start ... what do I ..."

"Just grab a dish towel and start drying. It couldn't be easier."

Bruce wound the towel around a cup, then unwound it awk-wardly, nearly dropping the cup, but cleverly catching it before it

hit the floor. Then he took a soup plate and polished it continuously, first one side then the other, for several minutes. As he polished, he gazed at her with the intense and unblinking stare
which he had developed during the honeymoon.

Annie had supposed at first that it was a fond and admiring
stare and she knew that she should be flattered by it, but truthfully it was never-ending. It had become embarrassing in the
Devon hotel. She found it unsettling to be so gazed upon. When
she had remonstrated that folk were looking at them, he had
replied that he was just so proud that she belonged to him and
to him alone. Of course she smiled lovingly and said no more,
but a small alarm bell had rung in the back of her mind. Did she
want to *belong* to him? Or belong to anyone, except herself?

While Bruce worked on his second soup plate, which like the
cup, was saved from destruction by his speedy reaction, Annie
finished washing up and also dried the rest of the china.

"That was fun, Annie. I never knew that it was such good
fun in the kitchen. I've been missing out all these years."

He put his arm around her and drew her back to the warmth
of the sitting room.

"This is really what married life is all about, Honeybun."

Bruce never picked up a dish towel again and Annie was
quite relieved.

The new couple had chosen an upper flat in a block of four
houses. This style of two-up and two-down was popular in the
speculative building boom of the suburbs to the south and west
of Glasgow. The houses were slight and not so well insulated
against temperature or noise as the old solid tenements, but
they had modern kitchens and bathrooms and were inexpensive
to rent. With the steep south-facing garden, the fresh air and the
lack of traffic, it seemed idyllic and country-like to the couple.
The house was brand-new and although the rooms were small,
they were square and to Annie's delight they all required to be
decorated. She started immediately after the honeymoon and
used ingenuity and hard work to avoid disruption as much as
possible. Her ambition was that Bruce would hardly be aware
of the on-going decoration. Everything that his mother had
done for him would still be done and the food would be better!

What a sense of power she had in choosing the colours for
each room, and although Mary was anxious to have some say in

the choice, it was possible for Annie, for perhaps the first time in her life, to side-step her mother's opinions. Annie tried hard to find out what sort of wallpapers or colours appealed to Bruce, but he was not at all interested.

"No, no, I've no idea about anything like that. You just choose exactly what you want. I'm not interested. I know nothing about colours. You're the artist, aren't you? That stuff's all for women to deal with, isn't it? Or maybe pansy men with long hair and limp wrists and big black bow ties. Ha, ha! No, no I couldn't help you there, Honeybun. You could paint it all brown for me. I wouldn't care. Just as long as you're here waiting for me, with a nice big tasty meal on the table. Anyway, Saturday morning, I'm playing in the medal at the club. Much rather be out on the course, y'know."

"Well as long as you like it fine when I've done it, Bruce and you don't complain about it."

"No, no I'll trust your taste. It'll be great. Just don't spend too much, cash is pretty tight at the moment. Now, if you'll excuse me I must rush off, I'm meeting a bloke in town. Cheerio, sweetheart."

He seemed to know a tremendous number of people, though he seldom spoke of more than the few cronies that Annie knew through the baths club.

Annie felt the usual ambivalence about his lack of interest in the decoration. She would have been pleased if decisions about their home had taken precedence over Bruce's golf, but at the same time she was delighted that she would have peace to make her own choice in the paint shop. From previous experience she knew that shopping with Bruce was fraught with irrelevant remarks, juvenile jokes, flirting with the salesgirl and general disruption of the job in hand. She expected it was because he saw shopping as demeaning to his masculinity, or some other daft notion. He certainly made it difficult to concentrate and in fact unnecessarily extended the time spent on a job that she did not particularly enjoy herself. Perhaps it meant that she was not a good wife? But yes, she was *glad* not to contend with Bruce in the paint shop.

Annie threw herself into transforming the house with tremendous enthusiasm. She chose vivid colours. Chinese red for the hall, soft grassy green for the kitchen, a daring orange and blue for the bathroom and a sunny yellow with white touches for the bedroom. The sitting room was more restrained, with coffee and tan as a background for her dark leather suite. She chose simple textured papers for the sitting room and hall and a pretty sprigged one for the bedroom. The kitchen and bathroom had shiny oiled papers with small geometric patterns. Covering the plain wood with the delicious colours was charming and fascinating. She had never hung wallpaper before, but with help from a copy of 'Household Skills' and a large kitchen table, she soon became proficient. The element of danger between the pasting table and the wall particularly appealed to her and she often laughed and encouraged herself, saying, with memories of her school cricket:

"Well held, sir!"

"Well caught, there!"

"Not bad at all, Annie"

"Attagirl!" when another piece was successfully plastered neatly to the wall with no wrinkles and the patterns matching.

Each day, as soon as Bruce left for business, Annie brought everything out and worked until three thirty, when she stopped and cleared up, washed brushes, put away the step ladder and paint pots. It was a wonderful project and she felt much more positive than she ever had in her life before. She felt useful and productive and decided that the satisfaction came from doing it in her own way, for herself and for Bruce too, of course. All that cleaning and cooking for her mother and father, all the music exams and the art exams, all the knitting of Fair Isle pullovers and lacy dresses, all those embroidered tablecloths, she now realised that it had all been done to please other people. She hated embroidered tablecloths! There was a wedding present of a yellow damask linen cloth that was so much smarter than cross stitch and lazy daisy, so chic. She loved painting and decorating! Sometimes she day-dreamed about starting a little business. She had never heard of female painters and decorators, but she was good at it and she enjoyed it. How terribly nice, how incredibly wonderful it would be to earn her own money. She imagined herself in smart white dungarees and, for some reason, a bright blue beret and red neckerchief, pushing a green barrow loaded with ladder and paint pots, through the streets to another little house just like this one. There were streets and streets of houses in the area, all needing to be brightened up. What fun to think up a different set of colour schemes for exactly the same layout. It was a charming and satisfying picture and she always smiled at this point of the daydream. Of course it would cause a scandal if the daughter of the famous artist started papering and painting for a living. Her mother would be furious. And the Cornings would be heart-broken that their son's wife had turned out so badly. But then it would be no worse than they had expected, she was sure. They were doubtless disappointed in Bruce's choice of bride. Jane Corning had looked at her with down-turned mouth and mournful eyes too often for Annie to feel like a successful daughter-in-law.

Sadly, Annie realised her potential had become apparent just too late. *She already had a job.* She was a wife now, with a wife's duties. It was a pleasant daydream though.

After the decorating materials were cleared away Annie changed from her paint-streaked clothes, made herself a coffee and sat down for twenty minutes with a cigarette and a magazine.

Then, at four thirty sharp, she started the meal, washed dishes and did any necessary housework. She was determined that he should not be able to complain of neglect in any way because of her decorating. He should be unaware of it! She worked very, very hard, and each Saturday morning while Bruce golfed, she bought more supplies of paper and paint. She did no painting at the weekend while he was at home. She had a silly and secret wish to make the house beautiful as if by magic and she did not want to share the work with Bruce. Not that he seemed remotely likely to offer a hand.

It was almost a relief that Bruce hardly noticed the results of what she was doing. In her usual confusion about what it was that she wanted exactly, she was a little hurt, but not particularly surprised. He was not an observant man, though he had a wonderful memory, a prodigious memory for any events which had touched his life in any way. And though not a great reader, he seemed to remember every detail and nuance of the books which he had read. It was impressive. Annie had always read a lot, but much of it immediately faded from her mind. Perhaps the answer lay in the fact that Bruce read little. But then she wondered if she were being unfair to him yet *again*.

He did make some remarks about the house as it became transformed, but they were few and they were always jokey or slightly derogatory. Annie decided that they were kindly meant and laughed politely when he quipped,

"This hall's like the inside of a furnace. S'like walking into Dixon's blazes."

He commented on the bathroom

"Thought I'd fallen into a fruit salad.

"Is that the glue coming through or is the paper supposed to be shiny like that?"

That was the kitchen.

"It's like the Botanic Gardens on a sunny day."

That was the bedroom.

He always laughed heartily and nodded his head vigorously when he made these remarks, to show that he was in a terribly good mood and only joking

Annie would just smile. Inside her head was a little phrase which echoed constantly and helped her.

"Just let it pass, let it pass."

In those first months of their marriage, while she worked so hard on the house, she also discovered how terribly untidy Bruce was. Because she was fulfilled with her interior decoration, she said little about it and meekly tidied up after him. He left dirty clothes strewn in the bedroom, wet towels dripping in the bathroom and newspapers scattered across the sitting-room. He seemed unable to aim properly at ashtrays and cigarette ash powdered Annie's new rugs and furnishings. Eventually she could stand it no longer and tried to point out the extra work it caused, in as polite a way as possible. Bruce kept his eyes fixed on his newspaper as though she had not spoken.

She tried again.

"Doesn't your mother ever complain about your messiness, Bruce?"

"No, she certainly does not."

Immediately his face darkened with fury and within ten minutes he had grabbed his coat and hat and left the house. She could hear the motorbike revving loudly and then he was gone. She was dumbfounded. Had her timid suggestions really been so offensive? Where had he gone?

He did not return until nearly midnight and when she asked

where he had been, he informed her sulkily that he had gone to see his mother. This became the pattern, whenever there was any hint of reproach or criticism in Annie's remarks or if they disagreed on any subject. It meant that Annie was left alone with her anger and frustration and none of their problems was ever resolved. And although he would always return that same night there would be a cool uneasiness between them for a few days.

After each disagreement, Bruce would return wearing a clean shirt, freshly laundered by his mother. Annie found that particularly insulting, but feigned ignorance of the fact.

◊

There were lots of good times too. They saw some excellent films together and went dancing once or twice but they seemed to be the only married couple at these dances and only danced together.

When the orchestra played "Good little, bad little you!", the tune which had been so popular in the tense months before the wedding, they gazed at each other and smiled meaningfully. Bruce, like most men of moderate stature, prided himself on his strength and he crushed Annie to him in a bear hug. It was painful, but somehow it made her feel happy and protected.

Then, one night, he said with a laugh,

"I expect our dancing days are just about over, now we're an old married couple."

"Oh, don't say that, Bruce. I love dancing and you're my favourite partner."

"Am I, honey dear. Well I was never all that keen on dancing anyway. I think it's just a way for young folk to get to know each other, don't you?"

"I suppose so, but I'd go dancing with you every week if I could. I really enjoy it. Don't you?"

He grunted and they never did go dancing again.

However, they could always make each other laugh. They were both good at telling risqué stories and acquired a fund from their different friends.

One Friday night, after too much coffee, they had stayed awake telling each other story after story until two in the morning, chortling and guffawing as they lay comfortably in bed.

Suddenly Bruce exclaimed,

"D'ye know Annie, I'm absolutely starving."

"Well, now you say it, I'm pretty peckish myself. It's all that laughing!"

"What have you got in the house to eat? Anything?"

"I've got the pies for tomorrow's lunch."

"Tae hell with tomorrow's lunch. Let's have them now."

"With baked beans?"

"You bet!"

They had more coffee with their pie and beans but they slept soundly until ten and Bruce missed his golf that Saturday.

And their flavour! Well! What else could you expect with such delicious little pea-beans, richly flavoured right through with wonderful Tomato Sauce made from full-ripened tomatoes freshly gathered from the vine?

That's the kind of dish that makes you happy and keeps you joyous and fit for work and play.

The joy of living for a few pence a day.

Heinz Advertisement, Good Housekeeping 1930

Throughout that first winter together there were occasional times when Bruce dropped his superficial jokey style of talking, his endless laughing references to what Sandy, Bobby, Bill or Johnny had said in the pub or in the Turkish, or at the fourth green. It made Annie very happy to learn of a more serious side, a more real aspect of this man with whom she had linked her life. When he was in the mood to talk, he would rattle on for the entire evening and she was pleased to listen.

He spoke of his childhood. When he was twelve, his maternal grandmother had paid for him to go to a boarding school in the Lake District. At first he had been extremely conscientious but lonely and miserable. Later, he had discovered the pleasures of breaking rules and kicking over the traces. He had gained popularity with the other boys in this way, although not with the staff. Annie realised, as he spoke, that a lot of the stories he normally told of his life now, echoed this theme of being 'naughty' and 'putting one over' on others, especially those in authority. Nothing illegal, just slightly rackety. Bruce had a more elastic attitude to truth than Annie, who had always held it sacred. Bruce told these stories with a certain smugness and obviously enjoyed and admired this mischievous aspect of his own persona.

"Right enough, I pulled the wool over his eyes" was one of his favourite expressions.

Outright lying was something which Annie abhorred and she wondered how often he had 'pulled the wool' over her eyes. Did he enjoy practising small deceptions on her, as much as he obviously enjoyed misleading other people? She hoped not.

After boarding school (and Bruce was vague about why or when he left the Lake District school) he returned to Glasgow and went to Hillhead High School, which was a semi-private school similar to Glasgow High School for Girls, where Annie had been educated. These were both schools for the children of middle-class professionals and aspired to produce future professionals who would speak and behave decorously. Subsidised by the Corporation of Glasgow, the fees for these schools were moderate, but parents were responsible for the smart uniform and for the provision of books and other educational accoutrements.

Bruce said little about Hillhead High, but spoke long and vehemently about his life when he left school and started to train as a marine engineer in a Clydeside shipyard.

"God! That was a hell on earth for me at the start. Those other blokes, the apprentices, could have been speaking Serbo-Croat for all I understood. And it was 'fuckin' this' and 'fuckin' that' and I didn't know what this word was. I'd never even heard it! And there were other words that I won't mention. Luckily, I wasn't the only nice young West End boy. Dick Ballater had gone to High School. I think he knew your brother. We were greenhorns right enough, with our terribly correct accents and our pleases and thankyous."

Bruce stopped and laughed heartily till he almost choked. "We thought, ha ha, we thought, ha ha, damn and hell and bloody were the worst things you could say. We soon learned though. We soon learned the way to do it, and got roughened up a bit, I expect."

Annie was fascinated by the stories of the unsafe working conditions of the shipyards. The thought of the red hot rivets thrown through the air and dexterously caught in a bucket made the palms of her hands sweat. Her imagination was touched by the unprotected freezing cold life that they led in the winter with the one small luxury of 'pieces' heated up in a

shovel over a brazier. She could almost taste the metallic gritti-
ness of those crisped and ashy sandwiches.

No doubt Bruce had experienced a life that was hard and
dangerous and she felt very much closer to him and impressed
by his ability to deal with such a life.

On another talkative evening he spoke of Stewart Turnbull
and Company, the name of the small chemical works in the
Gallowgate where he and his father and brother worked. It was
an ancient and rather broken down business, which had been
producing charcoal, wood alcohol and acetic acid for a very,
very long time. According to Bruce it was a historic works, built
on the banks of the Molendinar Burn. Vinegar Hill was named
after the acid, which had been used as a cheap vinegar substitute for pickling and in fish and chip shops, until it was deemed
illegal for human consumption. Bruce suspected it was still in
use.

The men employed in the works were labourers, mainly illit-
erate and living in profound poverty and squalor. Bruce talked
of them with a degree of compassion that Annie had not
realised he possessed. He described the overcrowded tenements
and the filthy wynds and closes of Glasgow's East End and the
long dirty hours that these men worked for a paltry wage.
When he had first joined the firm in 1928, they had no toilet
facilities other than a pail and there was no shelter provided for
them to eat their 'piece'.

"I put in a cludgie in a wee lean-to outside the office. The
plumbing was all there and it didn't cost much, in spite of what
my father said. Then I picked up an old broken-down bus for a
fiver, so now they can come in out the wind and rain to eat. Aye,
it's great to see them lounging in the fancy seats. They think
they're real swells now. Of course my father thought it was a
bad idea. He watches every penny, the old fellow. He thought
they would get too comfortable in the bus and shirk. But I think
they work better, myself."

Annie enjoyed those evenings. She learned of an unknown
Glasgow and was ashamed of her ignorance. Her relationship
with Bruce took on new meaning as he revealed this more sympathetic side.

While she had been involved in her decorating, Annie had
dropped her previous social life almost completely. She had

been too focussed and involved with her new life to find time or energy to attend the Arlington Baths club for a swim, or the Wednesday night sewing-bee that she and her friends had held for so many years. She felt that she had enough exercise running up and down the ladder. Those nights of frantic embroidery or knitting, with endless cups of tea and cigarettes and rude jokes, which had been such an important part of her girlhood, now seemed superficial and unreal. Nevertheless she missed her friends, for none of them lived in the King's Park area and it was quite a long journey into town. She expected that she would start seeing folk again at some future date.

◊

By the end of January, the flat was completely decorated and Annie felt aimless and without energy. She was physically tired and the day was long before Bruce returned home at six.

For a few weeks she spent her day reading and knitting, but she felt sluggish and seemed to want to do less and less. The thought struck her that she might be expecting a baby.

That was quite a thought! She was not sure if she liked the idea or not, so was not disappointed to find that she was not.

She saw an advertisement for a Readicut rug. She had never heard of these before and it sounded intriguing. It was a complete kit with the exact amount of each different colour of wool, cut to the correct length and ready to hook into the canvas which had the pattern printed on it. A diagram indicated the colours to use. It was quite expensive, but she still had a few pounds of her wedding money in the bank and she sent off for a half-moon shaped rug in a smart Art Deco design. She knew that she would have to listen to endless wisecracks from Bruce about the abstract pattern and what the hell it was supposed to be, with various vulgar suggestions thrown in, but she was getting used to that by now. She would just smile at his wit and admire the autumn colours in the rug which would look perfect in the sitting room.

She really enjoyed hooking the rug and she started to think of making another for her mother's birthday. Readicut produced traditional Persian-type patterns which would appeal to Mary.

In the spring of 1930, after seven months of a marriage in which Annie had created a comfortable and pretty little home to

which Bruce seemed almost oblivious, Annie happened to mention that the steep hillside of their garden would need some sort
of terracing if they wanted to cultivate it. It was an idle remark
on her part, but to her astonishment, Bruce, who with his work,
his meetings with various acquaintances and his golf and swimming clubs, spent hardly any time at home, seemed to be enthusiastic about the garden. To Annie's astonishment, he borrowed
some garden tools from a neighbour and started that very afternoon, which happened to be a Saturday.

As with everything that he did, he threw himself into it with
tremendous energy, some of which might have been saved by a
little more forethought.

It was very stony ground and he dug out large stones and
riddled out small ones. He hacked and picked and trenched and
grappled with the difficult terrain until he panted and his shirt
was soaked in sweat. Several times he lost his footing and slith-
ered down towards the fencing at the foot of the hill, dropping
to his knees or sitting down on his backside. Under his breath
he kept up a continuous discussion with himself about what he
should or shouldn't, could or couldn't do, what he must buy in
the future and what he should have bought if he had known he
was going to do this bloody job. Occasionally he whistled
through his teeth when things went well, more often swearing
loudly when they did not.

Annie watched him from the window. Did he always work
with such superhuman speed and energy, she wondered? And
was he or was he not enjoying himself? He could not possibly
finish the job today, but he looked as though he intended to try.
He was absolutely *filthy*. How did he have the stamina to work
like that all week and still have enough strength to golf and
swim several times, too? To say nothing of his enthusiasm in
bed. This husband of hers was really quite an exceptional fellow, although so infuriating. She was touched that he should
have started to work immediately on something which she had
mentioned so lightly.

She made happy plans of the plants and cuttings that she
would fetch from the garden in Fife.

She would certainly have some of the dark red carnations
with the strong scent of cloves.

She would always remember the day that she and Bruce had

returned from their honeymoon, they had found the house romantically perfumed by masses of those carnations. Mary Mackay, with one of the gracious gestures so well–known to her friends though less familiar to her family, had arranged to have a boxful sent through from Fife and had filled every vase with the rich aromatic blooms to welcome the young couple home.

When the flowers had finally faded and Annie emptied the vases, she was startled. The strong carmine dye had seeped into the water and she had the impression of watching blood drain away in her kitchen sink.

Crazy Paving

Beauty alone will lure few men to the altar. The sterner sex is interested in the physically fit woman rather than the pretty-pretty girl. Nice features must always be accompanied by vivaciousness, vitality and personality. The greatest of these is the vitality born of rich red blood coursing through the veins, which is the real giver of the bloom of youth. By taking Bile Beans at bedtime, you can acquire a clear, soft complexion, sweet breath and sparkling health.

Advertisement in Good Housekeeping 1930

In June of 1930, Annie was looking pale and seemed less energetic than usual. She laughed less often at her husband's jokes and, while she had made the garden very colourful, she complained of feeling tired after working in it. She often chose to go to bed early and read a book.

The possibility that she was avoiding his company did not for a moment strike Bruce. The "little ray of sunshine" was too firmly imbedded in his self-image to consider such a possibility, but in fact Annie was worn down by her life with him. They seldom went out, except to the cinema or to visit their parents. Bruce's wisecracks and loud laughter were relentless and it was hard for Annie always to react as he expected. His sudden changes of mood puzzled and almost frightened her. He could become so angry in an instant and often the reason for his anger was inexplicable to Annie. Though she was lonely without him, his presence was overpowering and irksome. She found him upsetting and it sapped her confidence in dealing with other people. Her own mother had often suggested to her that she was 'difficult'. Now she found that she angered her husband as well. Obviously she must be a pretty awkward sort of person, yet she got on fine with her friends. She missed them very much. There was no telephone in the house and a letter or telegram was required to arrange visits or meetings. Perhaps the truth was that Annie felt so despondent about her married state that she could not face her unmarried friends and their breezy questions about marital bliss.

All her life, Annie had spent the three summer months in the fresh sea air of Pittenweem and she found the dusty humidity of the city enervating. She longed for the sea.. Her parents were in Fife as usual and she missed them and had occasionally thought of joining them for a week or two, but felt that her duty lay in Glasgow with her husband. It would be unfair to leave him alone and working hard, though in fact she saw little of him. He ate his evening meal then rushed off to golf in the long summer evenings and she did not grudge him this pleasure. Unfortunately, he had made friends with a man who, if not a drunkard, certainly drank too much. Bruce had always frequented pubs, for he enjoyed the male company, but his drinking had seldom exceeded a couple of pints of beer. With this man Bobby Forrester, there was more drinking and most of it was whisky. Bruce had never returned home drunk exactly, but he was certainly more foolish after a night with Bobby and often belligerent. Annie would be glad to have Bruce away from Bobby's bad influence for a short time. Perhaps Bobby's drinking habits and other shortcomings would be more apparent to Bruce after a break.

With difficulty, and not without misgivings, Annie persuaded Bruce to go to Pittenweem that summer when the works closed for the Glasgow Fair. He did not relish the idea of spending his holiday under the eagle eye of his mother-in-law, but there was no cash for any other destination and he finally agreed.

"I was thinking I'd better take a present to your mother."

"Well that would be nice, Bruce, but it needn't be much, you know. Just a small gift. I'm sure she'd appreciate the gesture, but she knows we're hard up."

"I'm not all that hard up, you know! She'll be feeding us for a fortnight. That'll cost money."

"I'm sure my mother will be pleased to have us and not consider the cost."

"I'll get her something nice anyway, just leave it to me. I know a bloke that can help me."

"It's got to go through with us on the back of the bike, remember. It can't be too bulky."

Annie did not know what made her say that. Perhaps it was a look in her husband's eyes.

The day before leaving, Bruce brought home a gramophone

and three records. Annie said nothing but wondered why, when she had so little money to run the house, Bruce felt able to give such an expensive present. But she had watched the delight on his face when he presented a gift and she knew that he prided himself on his generosity. As this was for her own parents, she said nothing.

Taking the gramophone on the motor bike made the journey to Pittenweemt incredibly difficult, but Mary was as thrilled as a child with her present.

For once in his life, Bruce had really pleased his mother-in-law.

The gramophone was a brilliant success and Mary Mackay took a quick trip to St Andrews to buy more records.

Annie was surprised to see her mother taking trouble to be very charming to her son-in-law and producing spectacular meals, which Bruce fully appreciated. The sea air sharpened his always excellent appetite and his mother-in-law cooked and baked as if she were trying to overpower him with food. Bruce was always ready to eat and exclaim over how delicious every-thing was.

It was a challenge for both of them, Annie decided, with her mother striving to produce more food than any normal man might be expected to consume and Bruce generally succeeding in leaving every plate and serving dish empty.

"Have some more roast beef, Bruce. Plenty potatoes and Yorkshire pudding too. Pass the gravy to Bruce, Annie."

"Wonderful beef, Mrs Mackay! Did you buy that in Pittenweem? At the local butcher's? Would that beef be reared in Fife? And would it be slaughtered locally? Wonderful flavour and so tender. And yes, I'll have a few more of the new potatoes."

Bruce's questions were asked with no thought of receiving an answer, nor did Mary reply to them.

"I always put a few sprigs of fresh mint with the potatoes, it makes all the difference, I think."

"Yes, indeed it does, Mrs Mackay. I couldn't agree more and that is a wonderful Yorkshire pudding. I believe it's even lighter than my mother's."

"Possibly she does not use as many eggs. The secret is in using new-laid eggs and plenty of hard beating too, of course."

"Is that the case, Mrs Mackay? I never heard that before."

"In the fresh air, if possible. That's how they do it in Yorkshire."

"Fancy! I never knew that, Mrs Mackay."

Annie raised one eyebrow, for the areas of cookery about which Bruce was ignorant would have filled several volumes.

"Here's a bit of that nice cabbage left, might as well finish that off, Bruce."

Annie watched them with a secret delight. Who would win the contest? She was sure that they viewed each other with deep dislike, but they were behaving with such sweetness and charm. It was hilarious. She was well aware that her mother was likely to comment later.

"What a guts that man has, there's no filling him ... I don't know how you manage ... he's just a bottomless pit! The Glesca Glutton right enough ... 'Rab Ha's no' deed' while Bruce is about. And yet he's so thin, almost skeletal!"

While Bruce would complain petulantly,

"That mother of yours thinks of nothing but food. I'm sure I've put on pounds since I came here. No wonder she's so hefty herself. And her cooking is nothing so very special, I don't think. Not as good as my mother's! Or yours either, Annie. She's got a great idea of herself, though, hasn't she!"

But two hours after the substantial lunch, there would be afternoon tea in the garden with freshly baked, thickly buttered soda scones and pancakes with home-made jam. Bruce would eat several of each and after overwhelming his mother-in-law with praise, would chat to her and listen to her stories as if he were her most devoted admirer. Ensconced in a low deck chair, he would gaze up at Mary, who sat at one end of the white wooden bench, her beautiful, long-sighted brown eyes fixed on the horizon and her graceful hands gesticulating and adding drama to the simplest of stories. The sunlight made golden glints in Mary's thick dark hair and Annie thought, not for the first time, what a pity it was that her mother had not made a career on the stage.

Annie, her long legs crossed, smoked a cigarette at the other end of the bench, silently listening to their one-sided conversation and expressing her disdain by blowing perfect smoke rings into the sultry air.

By seven thirty there would be records playing on the new gramophone and cold roast beef sandwiches or perhaps crisply fried, fresh Pittenweem fish for supper. Even Annie put on a little weight.

Fortunately Bruce had a supreme metabolism, which instantly turned everything he ate into manic action. He soon found a project on which to expend his phenomenal energy and work off any excess pounds which he might have gained.

Three days after Annie and Bruce arrived in Pittenweem, there was a spectacular fire in the town one night.

A four-storeyed shop called the 'Emporium' stood in the High Street. It sold a wide variety of goods and was almost a department store. The building was large and ugly and entirely out of keeping with the historic and picturesque little town, where many of the buildings dated back to the seventeenth century.

Whether there had been a careless cigarette thrown down, or whether it was a desperate act when profits were too low for any hope of recovery, the building burned completely to the ground that breezy summer night.

The following night, as Annie and Bruce lay in bed, the silence of the town was suddenly broken by the sound of a squeaking wheel-barrow rolling past their house. Quite soon it returned, more slowly. They heard it again and once more it returned. Then the rattle of a cart passed over the cobbles, then once more the squeaking barrow. Then both returned. Then another sound of different wheels passed back and forth and there were a few quiet words spoken in the street below. Annie giggled.

"D'ye think there is smuggling going on or something?"

Bruce jumped out of bed and peered out the window.

"Their barrows are full of stones!"

"It's the Emporium! They're gathering up what's left of it!"

"By jove, you're right! We'll need to get some of this!"

And Bruce crammed trousers and shirt over his pyjamas in his usual speedy way.

"Bruce! You're not going to go along there at this time of night are you? Is that not stealing? Or grave robbing or something. And what do you want them for? Have we got a barrow? What on earth will you do with stones?"

"It's salvage. Perfectly acceptable. Your mother said she would like a crazy-paving path and those stones are just what we're needing."

And Bruce hurried out the door.

Annie lay there smiling to herself. No one could deny that her husband was a man of action. Too much so sometimes, but it was endearing in a way, just like an enthusiastic little boy. She went back to sleep.

Bruce worked for the rest of the holiday laying the curving path which would delineate two sides of the small lawn. It was like a gigantic jigsaw with the stones varied in colour, shape and size. Although he sometimes asked advice from Annie or her mother about the arrangement, Bruce never followed it. He found pleasure and satisfaction in solving the puzzle himself.

Although the holiday was not as she had envisaged, for they did not swim or play tennis, Annie was proud of the way that Bruce worked and stuck at the back-breaking task and made a very artistic job of it. Of course he would have vigorously and indignantly denied any artistry, for he was adamant, insultingly so, that such a word could not apply to him. With Mary so involved in culinary matters, there were floors and windows for Annie to wash, cupboards to clean and jam to make. Her mother always found plenty for her to do. When Annie papered a bedroom, Mary seemed almost impressed with her daughter's new-found expertise.

In the evening dusk, the young couple would escape from their labours and from Mary's entertaining, but relentless anecdotes, and take long walks by the seashore. It was romantic, with the quiet lap of the waves on the shore and the full moon reflected in the sea reminding them of their honeymoon.

On their return, Bruce would have a light snack of cold roast beef or home-made potted meat on a soda scone.

Altogether it was a successful holiday and they both returned to Glasgow looking tanned and healthy.

Tribulations

Annie felt wonderfully fit after her holiday, determined to make their marriage happy and complete, if she possibly could. She realised sadly that Bruce needed a life with his male friends which she could not share and she must create her own social life. She started to attend the baths regularly again and meet up with friends for coffee. Amongst her friends, she found she was able to brush aside the inadequacies of her marriage with humorous comments.

As she grew happier, she wondered guiltily if she had been rather unwell during the previous year, without quite realising it. Perhaps the problems were her fault? Perhaps such an energetic husband had found her lazy. Her Mother had described her as lazy, more than once. What was the necessary amount of work to accomplish in one day, in order to avoid being designated lazy? She comforted herself with the thought that surely no lazy person could have done all that papering and painting.

For their first wedding anniversary in September, they entertained neighbours very successfully and were later entertained in return. Annie enjoyed those evenings and felt that the marriage was starting to 'jell'. The couple promised themselves that they would go to the pictures together every week and to the theatre once a month. Annie pointed out that her folk had gone to the music hall every Saturday, in the early years of their marriage.

"Well, we could do that too, Honey. Would you like that?"

She was not sure that variety would be her favourite entertainment, but she nodded enthusiastically, for she felt that, as a married couple they should spend more time together.

They saw a few films together, but they never did get to the theatre. Bruce always had other things to do or they were too hard up.

Annie finished the Readicut rug for her mother's birthday in October and Mary was moderately pleased with it, though her first reaction was disappointing. Her familiar, small, disparaging laugh was somewhere between a grunt and a giggle.

"Is it supposed to be a Persian rug?" she asked with a slightly raised eyebrow.

Mary was a great collector of authentic Persian rugs, if she could buy them cheaply enough, and she had some very beautiful silk rugs and carpets as well as some older, worn ones. Annie felt a fool for having thought that an imitation would have found favour with her mother, no matter how thick and luxurious the pile.

"And it won't be easy to keep clean, a big woolly rug like that." Mary frowned at the rug which Annie had worked at so hard and lovingly.

Nevertheless, Mary must have liked the Readicut copy, for she commissioned Annie to make one for her friend Marion.

"Could you have it finished for Christmas? That would be a nice present for her. I never know what to give her. She gave me really beautiful gloves last year."

"It would certainly be a very nice present. A lot more expensive than gloves!"

"They were French suede, really beautiful. Of course I would pay for the raw materials. How much do those rug kits cost anyway?"

When Annie mentioned the price, she could see that her mother was surprised.

"And you would need a couple of pounds for doing it too, wouldn't you. Oh well, maybe I won't bother."

"You don't need to pay me for making it, Maw. I'll do it for love. I enjoy doing them. It will be a bit of a rush to get it finished for Christmas, but I'll choose one of the simpler ones. That Persian pattern took a lot of counting and concentration."

"Oh, I don't think Marion would like that modern sort of one that you have in your sitting room! It was the Persian style that I thought she would like."

So it was another Persian rug that Annie worked feverishly on for Christmas, staying up until one and two in the morning. At least it stopped her feeling lonely, for she saw little of Bruce and when he did come in he went straight to bed and immediately fell asleep. A faint whiff of whisky seemed to permeate Annie's dreams.

After Christmas they became particularly aggressive towards one and other, with no good times at all.

Annie felt her life had little purpose and her energy level dropped again. She was alone most of the day and cleaning and cooking did not take much effort in the small house. Bruce's return in the evening was the raison d'être of her life and as he often stayed only long enough to eat before going out again. Annie spent an almost reclusive life.

Two or three times, she suggested tentatively that she would like to go out with him and he immediately agreed that it was a good idea. He could be very amiable in the brief period between finishing dinner and leaving the house. Enthusiastically, he would assure her that they certainly would go out. Next week perhaps? But no suitable night ever occurred because his chosen companions and pursuits were entirely masculine, with no place for wives.

Eventually Annie stopped mentioning it.

She was unwilling to visit her mother more than once a week. Mary would ask prying questions, always expecting the worst of the union. Annie would not give her the satisfaction of knowing that she had been right all along and Bruce was poor material for a husband. Besides, Annie was an optimist and hoped that things would improve in the future. It would be idiotic to moan to her mother, who would remember and exaggerate every complaint when things did improve.

Annie was particularly unhappy about the influence that Bobby Forrester exerted on Bruce. There was too much time spent drinking spirits and she felt that Bruce had started to imitate Bobby's callous attitude towards women. He had developed a habit of making belittling generalisations about women, then roaring with laughter. Annie hated it, but felt unable to protest, for his anger was always so near the surface that any hint of criticism meant a flaring quarrel. It was better to keep silent. One day when he had quoted Bobby yet again, she blurted out,

"I don't know what you see in that tubby wee man! You seem besotted by him, but he doesn't strike me as having much fascination."

"Oh, he's a kind, kind fellow. You've no idea how generous! And he's helluva funny." Bruce laughed heartily as if at the memory of some joke. "You'd like him, too, if you got to know him, Annie. You would, I'm sure you would. You could come along, too, any time you wanted and visit. And you'd like Peggy, too. She's a great wee housewife, really, she's just always working away. The house is spotless, absolutely sparkling. I bet she'd give you a tip or two." Bruce saw Annie's face and immediately rephrased his statement, "Yes, I bet the two of you could exchange a good few wrinkles. Yessir. Ha ha. Cooking and cleaning, oh yes, you'd get on well. Have lots to talk about."

"I'm afraid the thought of discussing housework doesn't exactly thrill me, Bruce, and it can't be easy for her to keep the house so very spotless with that fat, smelly, old spaniel shedding its hairs all over the place!"

"Oh, a dog's no trouble around a house. No trouble at all. A well-trained doggie is a great pleasure. Peggy adores that dog."

"I daresay."

The next time that Bruce was going to see the Forresters, Annie suggested that she might come along too. Anything was better than another evening by herself.

"Oh, Annie, that's a great idea. I'm glad you suggested it."

"Well, it was you that suggested it, remember?"

"Eh, yes, yes. I'm just thinking though that tonight wouldn't be the best night. You see, Bobby and I will be at the pub till nine and Peggy goes visiting tonight and doesn't get home till later, but the next time I'll take you. That'll be great. I think you would like Peggy. And her friend, Bridie, is often there too. She's hysterical. What a clown that girl is. You would really get on well. You'd like her!"

Annie had not heard Bridie mentioned before and she was quite sure that she would not like Bridie. She could hardly admit to herself how painful it was to hear that Bruce was part of a cosy foursome, rather than just spending time with a male friend whose wife fussed around in the background. She assured herself that she was not jealous of this newly-revealed Bridie and made a secret vow that she would never offer to accompany him to the Forresters again. And Bruce never again suggested it.

Throughout the winter, Bruce continued to spend much of his leisure time with Bobby and spoke about it quite openly to his wife. He described meals and card games where Bridie was present, without any apparent thought that it was unusual for a wife to be so excluded. Eventually Annie started to tease him about Bridie being fond of him. She was quite proud of the cool way that she introduced the subject.

"I expect Bridie is quite attracted to you."

"Oh no, no. Annie no. There's nothing at all like that, Annie."

Bruce looked shocked and uncomprehending.

"Well, she must like your company."

"I suppose she does."

Bruce smiled to himself.

"But ... Oh, no, no. She knows I'm a married man. There's nothing at all like that ... in fact she's a churchgoer, very devout too. Oh I wouldn't like you to think there was anything like that going on. You didn't think anything like that, did you? Oh no, you can trust me completely. Oh, every time Annie, you can trust me."

One night after supper, as Bruce was shrugging himself into his coat and talking about Bobby and what a clever fellow he was, Annie, who was fed up hearing about Bobby, said scathingly,

"If he were really clever, he wouldn't be drinking as much as you tell me he does."

Bruce, undaunted, continued the tale of Bobby's wit and intelligence and of the amusing nicknames that he bestowed on all his friends and acquaintances. Bruce was called 'Wee Cheery', Annie, whom Bobby had only met twice, was called ' The Dragon Lady', while Bobby referred to his own wife as 'my slave' and 'the cleaner'. Bruce thought this was hilarious and could not understand Annie's inability to appreciate the joke.

"And what does Peggy say when he calls her these names? Does she seem pleased?" Annie's tone was dangerously restrained.

"Oh, it's all just fun. I don't think it worries her at all. She's an old-fashioned girl and she likes fussing around and doing things for her man. I think it gives her pleasure to serve him. He's bringing in quite a good salary as a teacher, y'know. She never had much before she married Bobby and she knows she's got a comfortable berth there. She knows she's on Easy Street. She enjoys attending to his little creature comforts. Spoiling him, y'know. Just like you do for me, Honeybunch. You're my little slave, aren't you, darling!"

"Oh no! I most certainly am not your little slave! And do not ever dare to refer to me as a slave, yours or anyone else's!"

And taking a leaf from her husband's book she put on her coat and hat and walked out of the house.

The problem was that she had no motorbike on which to

escape. She could walk the half mile to the tram stop and go into town, perhaps visit her parents, though it was late in the evening for that, or just look in shop windows and then return. But there was a lack of spirit in sitting passively in a trundling tramcar, that could never compare with the noise and fury of revving up the bike and whirling off into the night.

Instead, Annie just walked and walked, very quickly, around the new suburban streets of King's Park, turning right and left indiscriminately and losing all sense of direction. She passed Kingshouse Avenue, Kingswood Drive, Kingsbrae Avenue. She had not realised before that every single street in the area used the word King. There were roads, streets, avenues and drives but all had the royal prefix. She started counting the number of kingly names that she passed, Kingshurst, Kingshill, Kingsbarns, Kingscourt, Kingsbridge, Kingsdyke, Kingslynn, Kingsheath, Kingsknowe, Kingscliffe, Kingsdale, Kingsford, on and on. Annie was appalled at such a lack of imagination, although it could not have been easy to find a suitable geographical location for so many sovereigns. How did postmen find their way around all these similar names?

After an hour and a half of walking, Annie returned home to Kingsacre Road. As it was the longest street and curved along the crest of the hill, it was easily reached by ascending at any point. As she trudged briskly upwards, feeling energised by her walk and enjoying the challenge of the incline, she felt that she had accomplished something that evening, although she was not absolutely sure what it was.

She wondered if Bruce would be in the house or not.

She did not care.

Expecting

In June of 1931 Annie realised that she was expecting a baby. For the rest of her life, she would always suspect that the pregnancy had been suggested to Bruce by his parents. She could just hear old Bob saying,

"Aye, Bruce, I think you should get her in the family way. That would give her something to think about and stop some of her fussings an' nonsense. Aye, the more I think of it, that's the answer, that's the ticket. You just get her in the family way and things will start to settle down better."

Annie imagined his resonant old voice with its pedantic pronunciations saying this so vividly, that she truly believed that he had said it. She even heard her mother-in-law's voice chime in with,

"Yes, Bruce dear, I'm sure that's the best thing that could happen. I'm sure many flighty girls are transformed when they become mothers."

No doubt Bruce would not be keen but, always the dutiful son, he would have carried out his orders swiftly and efficiently. Annie's thoughts were bitter and she was wrong, for Bruce always blamed Annie for the pregnancy. He was pretty sure that it was a cunning way to entrap him forever.

In fact, Helen was an accident. Like most babies at that time, she was a completely unplanned infant.

Throughout her twenties Annie had remained very thin, almost too thin. Perhaps it was a conscious decision, because it was certainly the fashion to be flat as a board. Perhaps it was in rebellion against her mother who was described by those who wished her well as 'statuesque' and by others as 'fat'. Whatever the reason, Annie was stylishly gaunt. Her mother took such slenderness as a personal insult and suggested that perhaps Annie should see a doctor about 'her condition'. As well as remarks about 'lean flanks' and 'lantern jaws' Mrs Mackay constantly urged extra helpings on her daughter at the dinner table.

Bruce carried no excess weight, but he was heavily muscled and not tall. Though proud of his elegant willowy wife, his comments were, as usual, clumsy.

"My, ye're as thin as a wee wumman from Moscow. Ye'd think ye'd been in the Russian Famine. I can nearly get my arm twice round your waist and is that not snow on your hat I can see? The Russian Famine right enough."

Unfortunately, Bruce was of that numerous band who believes that a well-rounded bon mot is worthy of repetition and Annie learned to dread the words "Russian Famine".

However, with the pregnancy, Annie started to gain weight and a glowing beauty and Bruce appreciated both. As the interesting bump grew larger and started to kick, Bruce became fascinated and spent much more time at home. He only saw Bobby at the club and never went drinking with him. The evenings at Bobby's house were as though they had never existed.

"You never seem to see your girlfriend these days."

"Girlfriend! What girlfriend's that? I don't know what you're talking about."

"Bridie. You know."

"Bridie?"

He looked completely blank.

"You know! Peggy Forrester's friend."

"Oh, her! Aw, she was a silly bitch, that girl. Always smirking and screeching with laughter."

His visits to his mother became fewer and more irregular. He even started to grumble about them and he no longer wore a newly laundered shirt when he returned home.

Bruce also found that as an expectant father he had gained importance at the club. Other members asked how his wife was, when the baby was due and if he thought it would be a boy or a girl. He had never asked any questions like this himself and he was surprised and pleased to be treated with so much respect.

As he spent more time with his wife, he rediscovered her wit. Annie could always make him laugh.

He was also tickled by the strange fancies that Annie had developed. Late one Saturday night, he combed the Glasgow fish shops for mussels, returning triumphant with three pounds of shiny dark blue bivalves, feeling boyishly like a knight errant. They enjoyed them together and it seemed like a return to the warmth and intimacy of the early days of their marriage.

Annie also crunched her way through pounds of monkey nuts and the small brown and pink scented sweets called 'aromatics'.

"Is it a wee sweet smelling monkey ye're going to produce?" Bruce would ask each time he brought her more supplies and they would laugh together, remembering their honeymoon when Annie had greatly fancied the marmosets in London Zoo. Bruce had even made enquiries about buying one for his bride, but had been strongly advised against it.

Earlier that year, they had made arrangements to travel to the Isle of Man in August, to watch the Tourist Trophy motorbike races. They planned to travel there on his motor-bike and Bruce had been looking forward to it tremendously. Annie was touched when he spoke of cancelling the trip because of the baby.

"I suppose it would be bad for you to go all that way on the back of a bike in your condition."

"I don't feel I am in any 'condition'! I feel perfectly normal. The baby is just a tiny scrap of nothing just now. Of course you could always just go yourself."

"Oh, I wouldn't do that and leave you alone at a time like this."

"Well, we'll just go together. I'll be fine. But don't tell any of our folk that I'm expecting. They'd probably fuss like hell."

They travelled to the Isle of Man on the motor bike. Annie and the baby were both fine and they had a very enjoyable holiday.

Annie had always been fond of knitting. Fair Isle patterns were her special pleasure but she had dressed many friends in lacy jumpers and even dresses of finest two-ply wool. These were works of art in their own way and the result of many hours labour. For Bruce, knitting was just a 'woman's hobby' and not much of an accomplishment, for he measured every woman against his mother, and she did not knit. Now Annie started to produce an amazing array of tiny white garments, dresses, vests, pilches, jackets, leggings and bonnets. As Bruce was so positive that it would be a boy, some of the jackets had delicate yokes of blue Fair Isle and the mitts and bootees were threaded with blue ribbon. When she completed an exquisite shawl of cobwebby lace, Bruce was too impressed to joke about it. He seemed almost afraid to touch it with his work-roughened hands.

On his next visit to his mother, he told her about it.

"Y'know, mother, ye've never seen anything like that shawl."

"I suppose it's like the ones they knit in the Highland crofts. They're not expensive in the shops."

Bruce paused for a moment, then continued,

"Really, it's just beautiful and she's making another one now a bit thicker ... for everyday and in case the weather is really cold when the wee one arrives. Oh, she can be very sensible y'know and practical too, sometimes. And she made some lovely jam last week, damson jam. She's got a pot laid aside for you, but I forgot to bring it. It's awful tasty jam. I don't think you've ever made damson jam have you? I don't remember, but this stuff is really great and I'll maybe just have a piece and jam just now, if you've plenty bread in the house. Your jam is always delicious I know, and that was a lovely dinner of course. As usual, Mother. I enjoyed it thoroughly, but it's funny, I'm still just a wee bit peckish. Funny that, isn't it?"

Bruce was surprised to find that his mother's conventional three-course meals were not as filling as Annie's, though he was not yet ready to admit to himself that his wife's more adventurous and lavish cooking also looked and tasted better.

"And she's putting a wee blue border around the thick shawl because we're both sure it's going to be a boy."

Mrs. Corning put an extra amount of energy into the knife that she was polishing and then threw it into the cutlery drawer and pronounced in a loud voice.

"I've always thought there were far too many stones in damsons to make really good jam."

As Bruce munched his bread and jam, he was puzzled and disappointed by his mother's reaction to the shawl and all the rest of Annie's preparations for the baby, but Mrs Corning did not relish hearing such extravagant praise of Annie. It had suited her very well when Bruce was full of complaints about his wife's inefficiencies. For once, Bruce did not pay much attention to his mother.

The pregnancy had certainly brought the couple much closer to each other.

Annie was the first of her friends to have a baby and everyone was excited and interested. She visited Elsie, Nancy, Jen and found to her surprise that they envied her. Even Vida, who was still unmarried and getting more and more like an old maid, was anxious to discuss the possible sex and names for the expected arrival. Annie had suspected that no one really ever wanted a baby. She herself had never yearned for motherhood, but with the general enthusiasm, she started to feel pleased and anticipatory. She read childcare articles in magazines and bought a book by Truby King.

At seven and a half months, she still had not been to see a doctor. There was no doubt that she was pregnant and she felt fine. But when the Cornings indicated that they would be willing to pay for a nursing home, she visited Dr Mason who confirmed, unnecessarily, that she was pregnant. At her mother's suggestion she was booked into the newly opened Parkgrove Nursing Home, which was an elegant house on the hill above Kelvingrove Park, recently converted to facilitate the safe arrival of babies whose parents (or grandparents) could afford such luxury.

One night Bruce arrived home an hour late and full of apologies.

"I'm so sorry Annie, the dinner's not wasted is it, I hope? I just popped home to Mother for a wee visit. Dad said she was upset about something and I can always cheer her up."

"The dinner's fine, but I'm sorry about your mother. Is she keeping all right? Were you able to cheer her up?"

"She's fine now, just a wee kefuff with Betty. Nothing that matters."

Betty had been the Corning's cleaning woman for many years and she had once been sent to give Annie a hand, but Annie found her far too familiar and not the best of cleaners, and in fact did not trust her honesty.

"I don't know why your mother didn't get rid of Betty years ago."

"Oh, she's a fine wee woman and a great wee housewife. She just whizzes round the house like a tornado. My mother couldn't do without her. It was just a slight misunderstanding and I gave Betty a couple of quid and everything's right as rain now."

"I hope your mother is satisfied with that solution of the problem."

For once Annie's sympathies were with her mother-in-law.

"Well, Mother doesn't know about the tip and don't you say anything about it."

"I could say that it was a ridiculously large tip for someone on your income to give. It's more than four times my weekly housekeeping."

"Oh now, Annie, don't start that now ... look, my mother sent you a wee present. I'll go and get washed. Is that dinner ready for me yet? I'm a starved man."

Annie decided to say no more about the money. He seemed in a good mood and she would let it stay that way. She looked at the box of dates in her hand. Hardly a wildly extravagant present, but it was nice to be remembered. The thought passed through her mind that perhaps it was not Mrs Corning's gift at all, but a peace offering that Bruce had bought himself. She hastily put that thought away. She really hated lies and it was too unpleasant to suspect your husband.

As they sat with their coffee by the fire, Bruce remembered the dates.

"Will we open up your wee present, Honey bun? That would finish things off nicely, wouldn't it!"

He looked at the box before opening it and started to read the French inscription in a very ignorant schoolboy manner, with no attempt at the correct pronunciation.

"Bruce!"

"What? What's the matter?"

"You studied French at school, didn't you? You know that's not the right way to pronounce it, I'm sure."

"Ye're not expecting me to say it in that pansy way we learned at school with our mouths all screwed up."

"That's not a *pansy* way, it's the way that it's spoken!"

"I always thought it was a pansy way, anyway I don't expect real French men speak like that, real working men I mean. Can't see them pushing their mouths out and rolling their Rs. We must have been taught some fancy arty way of speaking French. I've forgotten it all by now anyway."

He opened the box and popped a date into his mouth then exclaimed loudly,

"This one has a bloody stone in it. They should tell you that on the box."

"Perhaps they do, in French."

"It's very tasty though, you should have one."

He spat the stone into the fireplace and took another, but ate it more carefully, again spitting the stone into the fireplace. Annie was fascinated by his greed and yet he carried not an extra ounce of fat.

When he had eaten seven or eight, almost half the dates in the box, he held it out to Annie,

"D'ye not want one. They're delicious."

"Not just now. I'm not hungry and I don't think eating sticky dates is the wisest thing when you're knitting white wool, but I hope you'll leave me some and I'll have a sandwich tomorrow. I like them in brown bread. Perhaps I should have told you before that it is probably best to open them up and examine them before you eat them."

"Why, what d'ye mean? What would I be looking for?"

"Well, sometimes there is a little grub inside ..."

"A *what*?"

"A grub or a worm, I'm not sure which and eggs, too. I always open them up and look at each date carefully before I eat it."

Bruce had already spat the whole mouthful into the fire.

"And why the hell did you not tell me that before? Letting me eat them like that. That was a rotten thing to do."

Annie could not help laughing as she said,

"Well you were enjoying them so much."

"Bloody hell, I'll never eat any more of those infested buggers ..."

And he threw the box with the remaining dates into the fire.

"Bruce! That was supposed to be my present!"

But Bruce had gone to bed.

The strange thing was that, less than two months later, Bruce again brought home a box of dates and sat and ate them greedily, with no preliminary examination, spitting the stones into the fireplace as before.

Nobody had a better memory for places and events than Bruce, yet the possibility of a hidden grub had completely escaped his mind.

Annie made no comment.

Helen

The German Presidential election is expected to be held on March 13th. The attempt to secure German citizenship for Herr Hitler, the Austrian-born Nazi leader, by appointing him a Commissioner of Gendarmerie in Thuringia has led to much satirical comment.

Many Germans who are by no means enthusiastic supporters of Herr Hitler, have long deplored the obstacles placed in the way of his naturalisation.

The London Times, 5th Feb 1932.

Helen weighed six and a half pounds and was born on Friday, the fifth of February, without too much trouble. Annie had not anticipated the emotions that the baby would inspire. She had thought that probably mother love would flood through her immediately, but that certainly was not the case. As she looked at the small bundle objectively, she decided it was not a pretty baby. It was making noises like a little duck and its uncontrolled struggles made the phrase 'Friday's child is full of grace' seem horribly ironic. It was so very tiny and vulnerable, yet it was a separate and complete human being and would one day turn round and argue with her, no doubt. Where did motherhood begin? And how did it begin? And what did it entail? In spite of her close study of Truby King, she felt terrified. But when she fed the infant for the first time and saw the dark fluffy head laid so trustingly against her strangely large breast, her attitude started to change. Within a day or two, when the little thing showed signs of humanity, even personality, Annie adored her daughter as she would adore nothing else in her life.

Bruce was certainly enthusiastic about Helen, though his behaviour was more reserved than usual and he gazed silently at the baby for minutes at a time. He was glad that everything was over safely. Like most young men, he was ignorant of the whole process of birth and happy to remain so. It seemed to be a messy, mysterious and dangerous business. He had found himself afraid during those hours of labour, in a way that he had not foreseen. The baby had been very safe for all those months in Annie's stomach. Now it was a reality that needed to be looked after and supported financially for years to come. The responsibility weighed him down. Then Annie had experienced something terribly alien to him, she had suffered pain that he could not imagine. Even her life had been in danger, he supposed. He felt reduced in stature, for she had achieved something that he could never achieve.

Not only that, *he must now become a father*, whatever that meant.

What a bloody awful responsibility it was. He broke out in a sweat whenever he thought of that.

He thought of his own father, who was over seventy. An old man. Bruce calculated and felt happier when he realised that this infant would be over forty, when he himself reached seventy. Forty was pretty old. Nevertheless, if she were an old maid, he might still be supporting her. Good God, what a horrible thought. Bruce felt unwillingly transformed into something called a father, and at the same time cut off from those that might have helped him. He felt alone. His parents suddenly seemed remote and elderly, while Annie was obviously completely involved in this infant. Bruce was reminded of the lonely and terribly unhappy time when he first went to boarding school. Things improved later and he supposed that fatherhood might improve with time. Although he could not imagine what sort of things he would be able to share with a daughter. A son would have been different, for he knew fine what all boys liked to do, climbing trees, playing football, getting dirty. Perhaps he could teach her to golf? That thought cheered him immensely.

Of course she was a nice enough wee thing, with all that dark hair. She was small but fat and getting fatter every day. It still seemed strange that it was a girl. He had been so sure that it would be a boy.

For the first time in his life, Bruce was lacking energy. He had no desire to swim or golf and he struggled through his working day.

◊

Annie was kept in bed for a fortnight to recuperate. The life of complete luxury which she lived was something she had never previously experienced. It was wonderful to be waited on hand and foot. There were no other patients in the nursing home and

the baby was hailed as an infantine wonder of beauty and goodness. The nurses and maids were all young, giggly and attentive.
Only the night nurse was older. Much to Annie's amusement, she
hummed the baby to sleep each night with Chopin's Funeral
March.

The food was as delicious as a first class hotel.

Apart from choosing the baby's name, Annie's biggest daily
decision was which one of several pretty bedjackets she should
wear.

The choice of name caused some trouble but Annie, helpless
in bed after the pain of childbirth, held more trump cards than
she usually did. In the hushed atmosphere of the nursing home,
Bruce was deterred from his normal method of winning an argument, that of becoming furiously angry and shouting louder than
anyone else.

Annie's first romantic idea was turned down flat.

"Ye can't call our daughter after a bloody island!"

"Please keep your voice down, Bruce. I think Iona would be a
lovely name. It is a wonderful place and I have such happy memories of that summer that my father was painting there."

"I've never even damned well been there! Oh no, no, I hate
that sort of fancy name. No. What about calling it ..."

"Calling her ..."

"What?"

"Calling *her* ... the baby is a girl, remember."

"Right, right, calling 'her' then, after my mother. Jane is a
lovely old name, I always think."

Bruce had been struck by this brilliant idea quite suddenly in
the middle of the night. His relationship with his mother seemed
less secure than it had ever been, but surely she would be
delighted if the baby were named after her.

"Traditionally it's the maternal grandmother's name that's
used for a first girl." Annie was on unsafe ground here as she disliked her mother's name."

"You're certainly not calling her after your mother and not
mine. I wouldn't have my mother ignored like that."

"We can call her after the two grandmothers then and everybody will be happy."

Annie sat back against her pillows. Anyone who knew her
would have recognised from her expression that this decision

would certainly not make her happy. Bruce saw it but was confused and unable to foresee what problems might arise in the future.

Annie decided there and then, that though the baby might be registered with the two antiquated and ugly names of Mary and Jane, she would never be called by them. Her baby would be known as Helen. It was a name that she had always loved. She imagined the power of exquisite Helen of Troy, whose destructive fascination had led to years of war. If she could not have Iona, she would certainly have Helen.

The baby was registered as Mary Jane and the grandmothers were pleased. There was only a slight start of surprise when Annie referred to 'baby Helen' for the first time. She was the heroine of the hour and at first no one questioned her, they were too astonished. Eventually Bruce grumbled

"What's all this about Helen? I thought we were using our mothers' names."

"She's my baby and I like the name Helen and I hate the names Mary and Jane."

"Aye! But Helen, where did that come from?"

"I like it."

"Righto! That'll be fine then, it's a nice enough old name. Fine."

Bruce was furious and felt that he had been tricked in some inexplicable way, but he had no choice but to accept that women were a species he would never understand.

Mrs Mackay commented in a way that astonished Annie.

"I'm delighted you're not calling the baby Mary. It's an awful name. You'll notice your father never calls me Mary. He once talked some rubbish about my name being too holy to use everyday and I believed him then. I was just a girl. But truthfully, I think he just dislikes it. I know I certainly do. Helen is quite nice, I suppose. We'll get used to it. In time."

The Cornings had plenty to say about the name Helen, but none of it was said to Annie.

The four grandparents were all as enthusiastic about the baby as their personalities would allow.

Annie's father sat close to the cot and shed a few tears. He could not take his eyes from the quietly sleeping bundle. Annie was amused to see him pat the baby at intervals in exactly the same way as he patted Smoky, their grey Persian cat.

Surprisingly, Annie's mother had no fault to find with the baby and she complimented her daughter on looking so well.

Bruce's parents were kindly but reserved. They glanced politely but momentarily at the baby. Mrs Corning smiled and spoke of the mild unseasonal weather, while Mr Corning seemed uncomfortable and kept gazing anxiously around at the well-appointed room. Annie guessed that their generous offer to finance a nursing home had envisaged a more modest establishment.

What most astonished Annie was the delighted praise which the two bachelor uncles lavished on the new addition to the family. They were both charmed, almost hypnotised by the baby and they cooed and gurgled into the cot. Stewart Corning placed a five-pound note at the foot of the crib with a careful flourish.

When Bruce, who always said his brother's middle name was Silas Marner, heard about the fiver he immediately fell to the floor in a mock faint.

William Mackay never had any fivers to produce, but he put down a half crown, on more than one occasion, saying it was 'for sweeties'. He could not stop talking about the baby and how beautiful she was.

Elsie, Vida, Nancy and Jen all came with charming hand-made gifts and assured Annie that no one had ever produced a sweeter or more perfect offspring. She was the first baby to arrive in that group of young women and her sweet vulnerability stimulated their maternal feelings.

For the first time in her life Annie felt she was a complete success.

On the last afternoon before Annie left the nursing home, her mother was sitting with her.

"That really is a most beautiful baby. So calm and composed."

"Not such a big monster as I was of course. I suppose I had a really easy time of it compared to you."

"Yes, you were a very big child, nearly twice the size of that wee soul. It was no joke."

Annie was surprised that her mother had not made more of these facts. All her life Annie had heard what a big baby she had been and what a difficult birth her mother had suffered. A six and a half pounder born in a few hours with no ill effects seemed a bit of a failure, compared with the drama of her own reputed eleven pound entry into the world. She had expected repeated comparisons, but Mrs Mackay had been untypically silent about her own experiences and seemed to have nothing but praise for Helen.

"I was awfully happy when you were born, you know."

Annie was astonished to hear her mother say this. As far as the world was concerned the Mackays had been ideally happy for thirty years. Then she saw tears running down her mother's cheeks.

"What's the matter?"

"Oh, I suppose I'm a bit emotional about it all. Just getting used to being a grandma. It's quite young to become a grandmother at fifty, I suppose, but I'm not complaining. I'm so delighted with your wee baby, she's gorgeous ... just as long as that idiot comes up to scratch ... that's what I worry about."

"Mother! He'll be fine. He's been a lot better these last few months."

"Well he is such a damned fool sometimes."

Annie could not disagree.

"I'm not feeling all that well these days myself, either."

"Aren't you, Maw? What's wrong, d'ye think?"

Annie was immediately anxious as a small cloud of doom appeared on her happy horizon.

"Just tired, I expect. Haven't been eating my usual, but that's all to the good, I suppose. I'm thinner, have you not noticed?"

"I know you haven't been golfing so regularly."

"No. That's how I realised something was wrong ... I was so exhausted after a few holes."

"That's terrible! What is wrong?" Annie's eyes were full of tears and she was half out of the bed.

"Och well, they don't seem to know, really. The doctor just says I'm bloodless and I've to rest and eat good nourishing food, but then I don't seem to fancy anything much these days."

"I'll be round tomorrow and make you some chicken soup and what else would you like, sweetbreads?"

"Oh, no, no, you'll have plenty to do looking after the baby and that overgrown schoolboy ..."

"Mother! But I'll be round as soon as I can and make you something tasty."

It was as well that Annie had enjoyed her fortnight's luxury in the nursing home, because the next eighteen months would be demanding in a way that she had not realised possible.

Not that the baby was any trouble. Helen was a fat and happy baby who behaved just as the book said that babies should behave.

At that time, it was the fashion in child rearing to follow a religiously strict regime of four-hourly feeds for the first eight months and that suited Annie and Helen perfectly. According to the expert, Truby King, if a recalcitrant baby wakened and cried before the proper time, the conscientious mother was advised to leave it crying, until the correct period of four hours had elapsed. Whether Annie could have been as harsh as this to her darling is questionable. Happily, Annie's resolve was never tested, as baby Helen slept deeply and sometimes must be awakened to receive her nourishment, for Annie saw it as a matter of life or death that the feed should be timed exactly.

Annie's problems arose from her husband and her mother.

The first night that she was home with Helen, Bruce had bought a steak and kidney pie from the butcher's and had a tin of baked beans to eat with it. Culinary details were something that he saw as entirely woman's work so, in spite of slight indigestion, Annie was touched that he should have tried so hard. She was pleased to be at home and she complimented him on the meal and how nice the house looked. They seemed very close to each other with their new baby sleeping angelically in the bedroom.

But later in the evening, with the unpredictability that Annie found so difficult to understand, he suddenly remarked petulantly,

"I would have thought your mother would have been here to look after you a bit, just to begin with."

"Perhaps she thought she would give us time to ourselves."

"She usually likes to poke her nose into the middle of things, anyway."

"She's not feeling very well just now. She told me yesterday she's awfully tired. I'm quite worried ..."

"Yes, I thought she looked terrible the other day. She was a guy. Not like herself at all."

Bruce had noticed it and she hadn't. Annie burst into tears.

"Now ssh ssh! don't upset yourself, Honeybun, you'll spoil the milk for the baby or something ..."

Then he was very kind and made Horlicks for her and they seemed to return to the tender relationship of the pregnancy for a few days.

One night when she had been home for a week, Bruce visited his mother and was very quiet when he came home.

"Did you have a nice dinner?"

"Yes, oh yes. The usual, you know. My mother always makes everything *extremely* tasty, y'know."

He sat abstracted and gazed into the fire. The weather had become much colder, more normal for the start of March.

"I've been thinking, y'know."

"Oh, yes?"

If he had looked at her he would have seen her raised eyebrow and faint satirical smile, but he still gazed into the fire.

"Yes, it's a pity in a way ... that the wee one is a girl."

Annie stopped knitting and looked at him steadily, but he continued without meeting her gaze,

"It's a pity in a way. A boy would have been easier, I expect. A girl's such a responsibility ... y'know what I mean"

"What *do* you mean exactly?"

Annie's voice was controlled and very cold.

"Well ... there's always problems with girls, y'know. They're difficult to bring up and they have to be protected and things can go wrong ... and they can lose their reputations. That sort of thing. A girl's always a worry for her parents, more of an expense too, usually ... fancy frocks and hairdressers and suchlike, while a boy is ... well, there are fewer temptations for a boy and he's more likely to be a support and a pleasure to his family ..."

He smiled slightly to himself, obviously thinking of 'the little ray of sunshine'.

Annie knew exactly what he was thinking and it added scorn to her quiet fury.

"What exactly are you talking about? Unmarried pregnancies?

"Well ... that and other things, I suppose."

"It must seem wonderful to you that all my friends and I have managed so cleverly to avoid disgracing our parents with little bastards."

"No, no, it wasn't illegitimate babies only ... exactly ... I wasn't meaning ..."

"Or perhaps you were meaning prostitution? I would point

out that not one of my crowd has fallen into that pit either. Not yet, at any rate."

"You're purposely misunderstanding me. Everyone knows that boys are easier to bring up."

"Oh yes? And what about my brother? He's not been easy to bring up. He's not been much of a 'support and pleasure' to his family. He's been an expense and a bloody nuisance to his family. While I've worked hard for years in that damned big house. An unpaid servant, that's what I've been."

Annie's voice was getting louder and Bruce raised his too.

"Well, you've got it easy now, haven't you? And don't bring your resentment of your brother into our argument. Anyway he's an unusual case."

"I don't think your own brother is any great catch either, what with his miserliness and his ill health and his strange attitude to women. And I don't think that badly behaved men are so very unusual at all. Aren't most criminals men?"

"You're just twisting my words around and changing the subject and trying to confuse me, and I don't want to upset you so soon after the birth of the baby. I'm going to bed. You can make your own Horlicks."

Annie sat up weeping and thinking until Helen's two o'clock feed. While she was certain that Bruce's sentiments were only an echo of his father's, she found it impossible to forgive such stupid old-fashioned prejudice. It was such an unjust attitude. She felt personally attacked. Besides, it was unbearable to think that Bruce would always parrot exactly whatever his father told him to believe.

Those bonds which had started to form between the couple in the previous months were stretched to snapping point that night, and were never to recover the strength and elasticity required for marriage.

Conflicting Demands

After the birth, Annie was less able than she had thought she would be and it was nearly two weeks before she visited her mother. She put the baby in the big black Marmet pram and walked the three and a half miles to Charing Cross, with a pleasant sensation of being pulled along by the smooth-running wheels. She felt slim and strong and active again, almost euphoric, as she peeped at the sleeping infant in the cosy wrappings that she had created herself. She felt that she would like to have a succession of delicious babies like this. Then she remembered her mother and felt guilty.

Even pulling the pram up the stairs to the top flat did not seem like too much effort for Annie.

Mrs Mackay was lying down in a very untidy bedroom. She was in one of her moods and certainly did look unlike the elegant lady that was well-known at Hilton Park golf course or the Art Club dinners. Bruce's cruel description was only too true. Mary looked a guy.

"I was wondering when you would get here. I thought you'd have been here sooner. I feel I could eat a wee bit pudding, sago or rice maybe. I don't know if there's any milk in the house ... and I'd love a proper cup of tea. Your father tries but he's useless. I don't think he lets the kettle come to the boil."

Mary Mackay's thick brown hair was tousled and wild as she heaved herself up to a sitting position. Her face was drawn and sulky, though it changed immediately when she looked into the pram.

"And here's the wee sweetheart? Hullo, my little beauty. What a wonderful darling! You're so cosy, cosy, cosy there! Annie, leave her here with me, will you. Can I take her into bed with me?"

It was against all Truby King's advice, but Annie knew it was a rhetorical question and passed the baby to her mother.

"She likes this just fine, the little jewel. I'll look after her if you have to go out. The purse is in the kitchen drawer and maybe you'd get something for your father's tea while you're out. Come here, my wee darling precious. What a lovely, *gorgeous* baby you are."

While Annie made a pot of tea, her father came into the kitchen with his coat and hat on. She thought he looked old and drawn, too. Surely becoming grandparents did not age folk overnight, but of course John was in his mid-sixties now.

"I'm just away to see McLure about an exhibition in May and I'll probably pop into the club afterwards. How are you feeling now? Fine? that's good. Don't make any food for me, unless are you making pudding? Make plenty, and I'll have some cold. I'll probably be late tonight, so I'll not see you till the next time you come."

He patted her shoulder with his usual shy gesture of affection and smiled.

"You're looking well and the baby is wonderful."

Annie felt a great surge of love and sympathy for her father. She could see his relief at her arrival. He had been longing to get out of the house and away from his wife's demands. Now his daughter had arrived and released him for a few hours. She was glad that she could make him happy, for she doubted that she could do much that her mother would appreciate. Whatever she did or however hard she worked, there would always be alternative suggestions, derogatory remarks and criticisms.

That was what her father was rushing to escape from now. They did not need to discuss it.

It was depressing to know that you would fail before you started. However the baby had cheered her mother up and she would try and tempt her to eat something now. Annie smiled to herself at the thought that, by bringing this wonderful child into the world, she had at last done something right.

That night, she walked home at a slow pace. She had worked hard and was tired and dispirited. The distance seemed interminable. Only a spoonful of the rice pudding had been touched and she realized now how thin her mother had become.

She was really fading away.

She must be seriously ill.

Annie tried to walk faster to dispel her misery. Bruce would be home and looking for his tea. She smiled a little as she thought of her credo, 'a hungry man's an angry man'.

It certainly applied to Bruce, but he worked hard and Annie enjoyed cooking for him. She had a stew with lots of vegetables, all ready to heat up. She would chuck a few doughballs in. She was later than she had meant to be. Now he would have to wait twenty minutes and he wasn't good at waiting. Perhaps he would be a bit later himself tonight, and the food would be ready by the time he was washed and changed. He was always filthy when he got home.

She hauled the pram up the flight of stairs and knew immediately that Bruce was not there. There were no lights.

He had gone to his mother's again.

Just because she was not there to wait on him.

She was half an hour late and he had not waited for her. She felt miserable and furious. What a day. The baby was hardly a month old, and here she was rushing around trying to please these people that she loved and *failing*.

What did they want from her? What impossible goals must she reach to keep them happy and loving?

She felt lonely, exhausted and worst of all, such a *failure*.

She looked around the sitting room that she had painted so lovingly. Bruce had made all sorts of funny remarks about the colour. Did he really dislike it or was he teasing as usual? He certainly spent little time in the house, what with work and all his other pursuits. He did work hard. She appreciated that. Would he change now and spend more time with the baby?

After a cup of Horlicks, she heated some stew for herself. It was delicious and with a small malicious giggle, she comforted herself that Bruce's meal at his mother's would be more frugal and less tasty.

◊

Annie went regularly three times a week to help at Charing Cross, shopping, cleaning and cooking food that was hardly tasted by her querulous mother. It became the rule that Bruce ate at his mother's house on those days. This arrangement seemed practicable, but led to a distancing between the young couple that was never to be lessened. Annie was grateful that she need not rush home to cook for her husband, but she also resented his resumed involvement with his mother. Her own life became increasingly lonely. Perhaps it would have been nice if he had objected to her devotion to her mother and put his foot down. Perhaps some husbands would have said it was too much for a wife to cope with a young baby and the responsibilities of two houses. Bruce, however, accepted the situation, and though friendly enough, showed little interest in Annie's mother's condition. Annie disdained to mention his family.

By April, Mary seemed a little recovered. She was up and about and eating more normally. The doctor had advised minced raw liver on toast each day to help her anaemia.

"I could not eat raw liver to save myself from *death*!" she declared dramatically."

There was no doubt that Mary Mackay had great thespian skills.

As the weather had become so lovely and her mother seemed fairly well, Annie decided to go to Pittenweem for two or three weeks with the baby. She herself was so thin that her clothes were hanging on her. She imagined herself becoming more and more like a paper doll. She had not been sleeping well and had a recurrent dream of having forgotten where she had left the baby. In the dream she watched herself running along strange streets, looking into every pram, large or small, and pleading frantically with expressionless strangers to help her find her little girl. When she awoke from this dream she was filled with relief, but also exhausted. Perhaps some sea air would help her. She could cut the grass and clean up the house ready for summer.

Bruce agreed it was a good idea and he would move back in with his mother while they were away.

"I don't suppose I could take the two of you through on the bike?"

Annie just looked at him.

"Maybe I could borrow Sandy's car."

"Just put us on the train. The pram would never go in a wee car."

"Would you really need the pram?"

"Yes. Just put us on the train and we'll be fine."

Bruce found an empty carriage for Annie and the baby and the three-hour journey was boring, but not difficult. The train did not stop for too long at Thornton Junction and they did not have to change trains. Annie discovered how easy it was to travel with a breast-fed baby, for Helen only wakened once and had her normal midday feed.

Unexpected Visitors

Annie balanced her small suitcase on the pram and the walk from the station was fresh and enjoyable. She was very aware that this was Helen's first introduction to Pittenweem. In only a year or so, her baby would start to enjoy all the things that she herself had enjoyed as a child, playing in the sand, climbing and jumping off rocks and eventually swimming in the sea. It gave her a satisfying feeling of continuity.

The house was dusty and had that faint smell of salty seaside dampness that Annie rather liked. Soon a fire was blazing and she had blankets and pillows draped around to air. Though she was a little tired, the peace was wonderful. She smiled down at her sleeping infant. It was just the two of them. This wee one was her only responsibility and such a delightful, chuckling, easily-pleased, little responsibility. For the next three weeks there would be no demands, no criticisms, no deadlines, no assertions or aggressions. It seemed like heaven. At this very moment she could do exactly what she wanted. She could go for a walk along the shore, or she could visit a friend, or even just go to bed and lie there for a few hours. It seemed incredible and she could not at first, quite take advantage of her freedom.

That night the house became very cold and Annie, disregarding the stringent advice of her guru, took Helen to bed with her and found the baby infinitely cosier than a hot water bottle.

On Friday, after shopping, Annie walked around the harbour and along to the swimming pool pushing the smooth bouncing pram ahead of her. The fresh air was like wine and she felt buoyant and strong. She was amused to find that everyone that passed, even people that she did not know, but who obviously knew her, stopped her and admired the baby, as if they had never seen such a fine example before. She remembered the feelings of heroism that she had experienced in the nursing home. Those had not lasted long after she had returned home, she thought bitterly. She quickly put that Glasgow life out of her mind and concentrated on enjoying the friendly folk that she met, the brilliant blue of the sea and sky, the sounds of seagulls and the pebbles tumbled by the waves. It was lovely to be here again and to be so free of the strains of that other life in Glasgow. And though the pram was bumped over grassy verges and stony paths and up and down wynds and stairways, and though the wind blew strongly and the waves crashed loudly, Helen slept peacefully on. That afternoon Annie went to bed and slept for three hours and Helen obediently slept too.

At ten o'clock on Saturday morning, Annie had just finished cutting the grass. As the mower was blunt and the grass was long, it had been hard work. She decided to sit in the garden and knit or perhaps read for the rest of that beautiful sunny day. The wind had died down and it seemed like summer in the sheltered garden. She had arranged for a friend, Katey, to visit her in the evening. She was specially looking forward to the visit, because Katey also had a baby girl. She was just a few months older than Helen and Annie keenly anticipated her first real conversation with another young mother. They also shared an interest in knitting and no doubt the pins would be clicking as they discussed their respective offspring.

Annie made herself a cup of Camp coffee, collected her knitting bag and book, and laughed out loud as she settled herself amongst the faded garden cushions on the wooden bench. What a great life it was! What a lovely holiday she was having! .Beside her, Helen in her little knitted suit lay in the pram like a small fat angel and concentrated her energies on sleeping.

As Annie sipped the hot coffee, there was a loud knock at the front door. For a wild moment she was tempted to hide in a corner of the garden, but she dutifully put down her cup and made her way to the door. She was speechless to see Bruce looking through the window, his white teeth brilliant in a wide grin. He seemed very excited and happy, laughing and nodding and apparently hopping from one foot to the other. Annie's euphoric mood was wiped away in an instant. She was devastated at the sight of her husband. She felt attacked and wounded by his unexpected invasion of her paradise. On a different level, she realised how sad and unnatural it was, that she should feel so unhappy. What sort of wife was she to feel so dismayed at her husband's surprise visit. What future was there for their marriage?

She assumed a not altogether successful smile as she struggled to open the stiff door.

"Well, are you pleased to see me, Honeybun? My God, am I glad to get here, that's a wee bugger of a car, that Ford, you need to be a bloody genius to change gear in it. When I get a car I'll make damn sure it's not a wee bastard like that one. This is a surprise, isn't it? I was missing my two wee lassies and I thought you might be a bitty lonely too, here all by yourself, so I borrowed Sandy's damned car and anyway ... never buy a Ford whatever ye do. And I brought you a present, too. Wouldn't come empty-handed, would I? A lovely day isn't it. It's great to be at the coast again. I'm hungry as a hunter. Is there a bite for me to eat?"

No double-declutching, no "feeling" for gears, no pause in neutral, no noise--never a bad gear change with the Vauxhall Cadet. No judging of engine speed, no slowing down as you change-it's as simple as applying the brake. The Synchro-mesh gears give you a feeling of expert control.

1932 Advertisement for Vauxhall Cadet 17 hp 6 cylinders

Annie had gained control of herself and made the proper welcoming responses of a loving wife. Her suggestion of a quick snack was well received.

"Great, great! A bacon and egg roll sounds just great to me as long as it doesn't take too long to make. How's the wee one? Sookin' away grand style, I bet!"

Bruce's presence transformed the house. The walls seemed to close in and the low ceilings became claustrophobic. His strident voice boomed in the kitchen as Annie quickly prepared his food. He walked ceaselessly about as she cooked, often getting in her way, and commenting on various aspects of the house in a critical way.

"It's a wonder your father hasn't had that ceiling seen to yet. That crack's widened since I was here last, I'm pretty sure ... "

"Fancy your mother putting up with this wee old sink. And is there still no hot water supply? Still it's a great wee house, if it had some work done on it. What a view!"

Strange that he should take such an interest in this house, when his own seemed so unimportant to him!

He stood at the window and gazed at the sea as he munched his roll and seemed calmer when it was eaten. As he was eating the second roll,

"My God!" he suddenly shouted and Annie jumped.

"I nearly forgot your present. C'mon out to the car and see what I've got for you. I think you'll like this one. You won't be lonely with this wee present, I'll bet."

Annie followed him to the front door with some trepidation. "Here we are, Annie!" His tone was hearty and confident of her approval.

A long-nosed black and white face of infinite sorrow and longing gazed with liquid eyes from the window of the little green car. Bruce opened the door and the young Border collie changed immediately to a deafening whirlwind of demanding action, leaping out and barking loudly, as it jumped up and down, placing its paws on Bruce's chest then on Annie's, trying madly to lick their faces and hands. It was strong and heavy and pushed Annie painfully against the wall with its affectionate attack. It did not respond even slightly to Bruce's shouts and whacks, but continued to leap about and make more noise than several dogs together might have done.

"Aye, he's a lively young yin this. Just a puppy still ... aren't ye Don? Just a wee happy puppy. Down, DOWN ... down ye bugger. He's just still young and full of the joy of life, y'know. DON! QUIET! He's a great wee dog, isn't he Annie? Good boy, there's a good, good boy. QUIET ... GOOD BOY. DOWN, STOP IT ye brute, DOWN. D'ye like him, Annie? He's a lovely beast, isn't he? Quiet, Don, DON, DON ... GET DOWN. His name's Don, Annie."

But Annie had gone into the house.

She stood leaning against the kitchen table, biting her lower lip and with her hands clenched behind her back. The kitchen opened into the hall and the sitting room so that it was possible to run around the three rooms continuously. Don raced past her for the fourth time, his claws slipping and scratching on the linoleum and Bruce, bent over double, was always just behind him, never quite able to catch him. It was like a Keystone Cops comedy. At last Annie burst out laughing. It was too ridiculous. Bruce stopped when he saw her laughing and kissed her.

"You really like the wee animal, don't you?" he whispered beseechingly.

"Are you serious, Bruce? No, I do not like it. I have never wanted a dog and *I will not have* a dog."

"I think you would really grow to love him. Think how nice it

would be for the wee one. Children love dogs. Keep him for a
week or so. I'm sure you'll change your mind. He was to be put
down if a home couldn't be found for him, y'know. That would
be a tragedy, wouldn't it?"

"It would be tragedy if I had to look after him, 'cos I'd soon
murder him if he behaved like that all the time."

She could not help smiling as she spoke. It was all so crazy. A
dog was the last thing on earth that she wanted.

"Just keep him for a fortnight, Honeybun and maybe I could
find someone willing to take him. I promised Charley I would
find a home for him. But maybe you'll find you want to keep him
yourself. He's such a lovely beast, so friendly, look at him."

"No fear! I suppose I'll keep him for the fortnight though, if I
have to. Who's Charley anyway?"

"Atta girl! You're a brick. I knew you'd take the wee soul.
Charley's just a bloke I know. Don, DON! Come *here*, ye wee bugger."

And Bruce was off again, madly chasing the hysterical dog.

No doubt Charley was some passing acquaintance, but Bruce
found it hard to resist helping people. That was something in his
favour. He seemed genuinely concerned about the dog, and it
was nice of him to think of her being lonely and to take the trouble of coming through to visit her. Annie felt that she had been
unfair to him. She was unfair far too often. Perhaps they would
take a picnic to the shore this afternoon and later he might help
with some of the heavier gardening. Perhaps they could spend a
weekend together, like a real married couple.

Annie needed more bread to satisfy her hungry husband. As
she passed his car on her way to the shops, she noticed that he
had brought his golf clubs. That was fine. It would be good for
him to have a game tomorrow, at one of the several local courses.
She thought wistfully that she might have liked a game too, but it
was impossible with the baby. On her way to the baker's, Annie
popped into Katey's house and told her of Bruce's arrival.

"Niver mind that, Annie. Ah'll come in next week, an' see ye.
Maybe Tuesday nicht eh? An' the twa o' us hae a *grand* crack!"

The familiar Pittenweem accent gladdened Annie.

While she was out, Bruce had tied the dog to the fence in the
garden and his melancholy whining had wakened the baby.

"Would you like to take a picnic along to the beach, Bruce?"

"Well ... no. I won't do that, Annie, dear. As a matter of fact I had hoped to get up to St Andrews this afternoon."

"St Andrews?"

"Yes. Well you see ... mmm." He paused and scratched his head then coughed violently as though choking. "Aye, well, Bobby Forrester is there this weekend and I said I would join him for a game of golf. If that's all right with you, that is? I'll be back early tonight and we'll have a fish supper together. Just you and me. Is that fine?"

"It's perfectly all right with me. Is the doormat Peggy with him?"

"Yes, I think so."

"And Bridie too?"

"Aye she might be there. I think she probably is."

"I thought she might be. And you're leaving the dog with me?"

"He wouldn't be welcome on the course."

"He's not welcome here either, but never mind, never mind. Just get away and see your friends."

The tone of Annie's voice had changed completely and her expression was cold and distant. She did not feel jealousy or disappointment. She just felt dispirited.

She was about to retrieve the quiet peace that she had been enjoying before Bruce arrived and yet it was spoiled. She castigated herself, mentally. She was never pleased, was she? Annoyed when he arrived, annoyed when he left. What was wrong with her? Would she really have enjoyed that shared picnic of her fantasy? Probably not.

"We'll have that fish supper tonight when I get back. Eh? Just you and me."

Bruce hovered uncertainly at the front door.

"Aye, aye." Annie looked into the distance, as she said these words on an indrawn breath that expressed her disbelief. He still stood there.

"Is that all right now, Annie?"

She turned and looked full at him.

"Just go, Bruce"

The heavy front door slammed behind him and she could hear him racing the engine before he drove off with the usual spray of gravel. How depressing that his visit to Fife was as much for a game of golf with friends as it was to see his wife and baby. Probably more for the friends than for her ... and to dump that unwanted dog on her. She should look on the bright side, though, because she was alone again, with her baby and that was what she had wanted, wasn't it? Was she really so difficult to please? Bruce often said how incomprehensible she was.

She tried to recapture some of her earlier delight in the day and took the baby and the dog for a walk, but she was unused to dogs and it was a nightmare experience. Don was completely unbiddable and kept disappearing. He also seemed ready to be aggressive to any dog that he met and Annie dreaded a fight. The sky and sea grew dull and threatening. The wind blew and the seagulls sounded even sadder than usual. It was a short walk.

There was still no sign of Bruce at seven, so Annie prepared the baby for bed. She thought bitterly that most fathers would have delighted in watching their baby's evening ritual.

As she soaped Helen in her papier-mache bath in front of the roaring fire, Annie felt a return of her inner peace. The baby's smiles and plump little body always delighted her. Even the overactive dog stopped its restless pacing and sat watching the procedure with interest, its handsome head cocked. Annie found herself including the dog in the inane baby conversation and Don's intelligent eyes seemed to appreciate and understand every word.

"Just don't think you are going to wriggle your way into my affections, Don. *I do not want* a dog in my life and you are not staying here! Do you hear me? Do you understand?"

The dog tilted his head the other way and gave a sharp bark, which made Annie laugh.

After the baby was put to bed, Annie with no real hope that Bruce would return to share a fish supper, boiled herself an egg. After supper, she brought out her knitting, but there was no chance to knit. Don walked back and forth in the small over-crowded sitting room, his claws noisy and slipping on the polished lino. He barked at every distant sound from the street, and every few minutes he walked over and shoved his long nose into her knitting.

"What a restless brute you are!"

Before she could stop him he had lifted his leg and peed against an antique chair.

"You are a bloody nuisance, that's what you are."

Annie mopped it up and took him to the front door but he did not want to go out. She took him to the back door and he shrank away from the dark garden.

"Coward!"

Annie was getting impatient and shut him in the kitchen, where he moaned pathetically and scratched insistently at the closed doors. Fearful for the paintwork, she allowed him back into the sitting room, where he repeatedly tried to climb on to her lap and nearly ruined her knitting. He was a big heavy dog and determined. When he licked her face several times, she found it particularly repugnant and shut him in the coal shed.

She went to bed exhausted, with ridiculous feelings of guilt and sympathy for the poor lonely beast shut up in the dirt and darkness. She was too angry to sleep.

Bruce was very late returning that night and slept alone in the bedroom downstairs.

Next morning there was little conversation, though Annie could not stop herself from asking if the St Andrews fish suppers were as good as the Pittenweem ones."

"Oh we went to a great wee hotel that Bobby knows."

"Oh, yes. That would be a bit pricier than a fish supper, I expect."

"It was really very reasonable. A nice three course meal ..."

"I expect the liquid refreshment would add a good bit to the bill."

"Did you have a fish supper yourself, last night, Honeybun?" and he smiled ingratiatingly.

"No."

Bruce left immediately after breakfast with a mumbled excuse about a 'bit of trouble at the works', but Annie expected he would return to his friends in St Andrews for another game of golf.

Just as he was going, Annie asked,

"And what about the dog?"

"Yes, yes I'll see what can be done about that."

As he drove off, the dog was bounding and leaping at Annie and barking like an idiot. It was time for another walk.

For Annie, it was a fortnight of nerve-racking walks. Don picked fights with powerful aggressive dogs and cowered away from friendly ones. In the house there was constant cleaning up of urine puddles and worse. She shouted at and sometimes whacked the dog, but she suspected that he quite enjoyed these attentions. They certainly had no effect. There was never peace from Don's hyperactivity and demands. If he were shut in the shed, he howled as though being tortured. One evening as he prowled restlessly around the sitting room, casting pleading glances at her, she giggled as it suddenly struck her that he bore an uncanny resemblance to Bruce. That prominent bony nose, the brown sparkling close-set eyes and the inability to stay still, even the genius for doing the wrong thing, while he tried to please. Poor dog.

Only one incident resigned Annie to the dog's presence, but it was an important one and it almost cancelled out her dislike and distaste for the creature. This one action bestowed a sort of glory on the dog and created a heroic myth in the family.

The weather had become colder again and a strong East coast wind blew. If it had not been for the dog Annie might well have stayed at home that day and risked her baby suffering the deprivation of fresh air. Although the air which circulated around the draughty little house would have satisfied the most stringent of hygienists. However, Don must have his walk or his restlessness was unbearable. The baby had been well wrapped up and lay sleeping in the pram, which was parked outside the front door. While Annie locked the back door, banked up the fire, washed her hands, set the big pot of lentil soup to simmer gently on the hob, found her gloves and scarf, (which suddenly seemed a necessary in this unpredictable weather) and generally prepared for a long walk, Don was barking at the front door.

"For goodness sake be quiet. I'm just coming."

But the dog rushed back and forwards between Annie and the front door, nearly tripping her up several times and leaping against the front door in an agony of impatience.

"Shut up, you interminable dog. Don't you see I'm going as fast as I can. Hush! BE QUIET!"

Then Don started to scratch at the door in a hysterical way, throwing himself sideways and whining and moaning.

When Annie eventually opened the door, the dog shot out like a bullet and Annie's heart lurched with terror.

The pram was gone!

It was a brief split second of horror for Annie, because Don was racing down the street and heading for the pram, which was less than fifty yards away. It was parked at an awkward angle against the corner of a house which jutted beyond the neighbouring houses. Annie covered the ground almost as quickly as the dog. Snuggled deep in the pram, Helen slept in her usual calm oblivion.

What had happened? Had someone played a horrible trick? Surely not.

Had she herself been at fault? No, the pram brakes were safely on.

As Annie stood gazing and wondering, a sudden gust of wind blew along the High Street and its force lifted the rear wheels of the pram slightly from the ground. As the brake was on the rear wheels only, the wind was able to move the pram forward. Annie brought the pram back to her own front door and stood waiting for the next rush of wind. Sure enough, when the strong wind blew, the pram was lifted off its back wheels and blown a few yards along the pavement on its front wheels.

Annie was aghast at such bad design!

And she had thought this was a wonderful pram!

What a terrible mistake to make!

She had put her baby in such danger!

The firm should be sued!

All babies in these prams in this windy country were at risk.

It was monstrous!

It was nothing but downright infanticide!

Then her fury changed to fear and she wanted to take Helen out and hold her solid little body close, but she would not disturb the soundly sleeping baby.

Suddenly a soft whine reminded her of Don. He sat quietly beside the pram, gazing up at her, his long pink tongue licking his nose anxiously.

Annie was struck by remorse!

That's what the dog had been making such a fuss about! He had not been nagging about his walk at all. He had known that the pram was blowing away outside and had tried to tell her! Don, the biggest nuisance that she had ever had to deal with in her life, had actually proved his worth that morning, and all she had done was shout at him. She felt such regret that she bent and cuddled him and even allowed him to lick her face which was always his ambition. She found it revolting, but what a marvellous dog he had been. She would take him for a wonderful walk now, though she froze in the process. Later she would buy him a special juicy bone at the butcher and they would share a bar of chocolate in the evening.

Although she could never love Don, she did feel respect for him and deep gratitude too.

They set off on their walk. As they passed the house where the pram had been so lightly caught by the corner of the building, Annie suddenly started to tremble. Beyond this house was the West Wynd, one of several very steep paths which led directly downhill from the High Street to the sea-front below. It had not struck her at first, but if the pram had not been stopped by the house, the wind would have trundled it further along the High Street and when it reached the top of the wynd, it would have hurtled downhill, bouncing from one curving wall to the other!

She could not bear to think about it

She felt physically sick.

She continued her walk in an agonised dream, unable to banish from her mind's eye the vision of the runaway pram rushing headlong down the narrow wynd, with her little darling tossing helplessly in her blankets, finally to be ejected and broken against the sea wall.

She watched Don enviously as he capered and smiled and begged for thrown sticks and stones as though nothing had happened.

How good to have a short canine memory and no imagination.

Although she had no intention of keeping him, she admitted that he was a good dog.

A heroic dog.

At the end of May, Bruce made a brief visit to collect the dog before Annie and the baby returned to Glasgow by train. A home had been arranged for Don at a farm in Lanarkshire. Annie would never see Don again, but she often thought of him and hoped that he was happy, with lots of sheep to look after.

The Letter

On her return, it was arranged that Annie would stay with her parents until the summer. Bruce had been very understanding about her mother's need for her.

"Of course you must help your mother. 'Honour thy Mother and thy Father ...' you know. You have the baby to care for as well and we don't want you too exhausted, do we. Mother will be pleased to have me home. I think she misses my cheeriness in the house. Dad and Stewart are such serious blokes. I'll pop up to Renfrew Street every other day and see you both."

It was spectacularly good weather in June and the Mackays decided to go to Fife as soon as possible. Mary was unable to do much preparation so Annie cleaned and packed, as well as cooking light tempting meals for her mother and more sustaining food for the rest of the family. She was still feeding the baby herself and she sometimes thought wryly that it was just as well that she had this justification for sitting down at least three times each day.

One day John Mackay had announced,

"I'm particularly anxious to get through to Pittenweem because I've decided to paint you, Annie, with your new wee baby. It's my first grandchild and I'm not going to let this opportunity slip through my fingers."

Annie's first reaction was that it would be another chance for her to sit down, and she nodded and smiled to him. Before she could say anything her mother spoke.

"Oh, John, I don't think that would be convenient. Annie will have plenty to do, without sitting for you. She has all the baby's washing for one thing. Then if she gives some help in the house, she just won't have the time, will she? You mustn't be selfish."

John, in his usual mild way was apologetic,

"Oh, I'm sorry, I didn't think of the work she has to do. I don't want to tire her out. Perhaps we could get a woman in to give a hand with things?"

"That wouldn't be easy and it would be expensive."

"Well, I'll never have a first little granddaughter again and

I'm determined to paint her. She's such a pretty wee soul. You never know, her picture might catch a few eyes in the Autumn Exhibition and the commissions for baby portraits might come tumbling in! She might make our fortune before she's one year old!"

"Perhaps, as I'm not well enough to do heavy work, I could hold the baby?"

Mary was fifty now and even before illness had ravaged her looks, it was some years since John had asked her to sit for a painting.

"No, I don't think so, my lass. The painting would be a *riddle*, because you don't look nearly old enough to be a grandmother and yet you're not ... quite ... eh ..."

"Not young enough to be the mother, I suppose you mean."

"Ah, mmm well, realistically, no."

Nothing more was said that day about the painting. Mary withdrew into her private world of fury and would eat nothing at lunch, tea or suppertime.

Annie was cross with her father for having upset her mother, and furious with her mother for being so sulky and obstinate. It was like dealing with children.

◊

The dust sheets shrouded the furniture in the flat at Charing Cross. The Mackays, with Annie and the baby, were settled in Pittenweem.

Before they were properly settled in, John started talking about the portrait again, just as though there had been no problems before.

He produced some clothes for Annie and the baby to wear, national costume that he had brought back from a painting trip in the Netherlands.

"Are you sure that you want us to look like a Dutch mother and child, Paw?"

"Oh, I think it would be rather pretty and romantic and the little cap would shade the wee one's head in the hot sun."

Annie looked at Helen doubtfully. It seemed to her that the baby was getting fatter and fatter. In fact she had mentioned it to her mother.

"Don't you think Helen is becoming awfully fat? She's starting to look very like a little pig!"

"Oh, no she's not, the wee sweetheart. Though I did think she wasn't quite so pretty these days."

"Fat as a little porker, I think."

The miniature linen cap sat on top of the round babyface and Annie did not think it an improvement. It accentuated the several chins which the baby had developed. However her father was adamant and they were painted in Dutch costume. The painting was to be called 'The Letter' and Annie held a sheet of writing paper. As she gazed down at the blank page, she wished that Bruce would get in touch. He had been very distant and she had seen little of him, since the disastrous visit with the dog in May. Perhaps it was her fault for returning to Pittenweem again so soon. She felt very torn between her marriage and her mother's physical weakness.

If she and Bruce could only have some time to themselves they might discuss what sort of future, if any, there was for them.

Although it was quite pleasant to sit for her father, it meant that she had to work extra quickly to get other things accomplished. The baby tended to sleep while the sittings proceeded and needed attention immediately afterwards. Annie seemed always to be racing to catch the shops before they closed, grabbing in washing to air and iron, or producing meals in a great hurry, because visitors had arrived and everyone was ravenous. The house was much more difficult to run than the Glasgow house and, of course, no domestic help was hired

As always, the Mackays had a lot of visitors that summer, mainly other artists who came to Fife to paint. There were also clients who must be entertained as well as local friends who popped in informally at any time of day

Everyone was delighted with the painting

Mary lay languidly in the hammock for most of the three months, giving out orders in a weak resigned voice. She certainly was not a well woman and her obvious deterioration made her daughter a determined slave.

Bruce arrived on his motorbike, two or three times, but he did not stay overnight and most of his conversation was with his parents-in-law.

In September the sad family returned to Glasgow.

Difficult Months

The three months at the seaside had not helped Mary Mackay. She had grown thinner and weaker and her sun-burned face looked old and wizened. In September, Annie moved back to Renfrew Street, to look after her mother and Bruce continued to stay with his parents. Bruce seemed very understanding and assured Annie that it was obvious she was needed at home.

Although the words were not spoken, they both felt that Mary was dying.

Annie was heartbroken when she looked at her mother. She pushed herself beyond all limits to please the invalid and to tempt her with delicacies to eat. Annie herself was thin and worn with the many domestic and emotional demands.

By October, Helen was weaned and at the messy, time-consuming stage of mashed banana and milk from a cup. She was also learning to crawl, when her mother could find time to watch her.

John Mackay had an important portrait commission and the house must be perfect when the sitter arrived.

Mary worried and nagged that the meals should be prompt, though she ate so little herself.

Annie felt that she had never worked so hard in her life before and her mother's constant small criticisms and querulous remarks saddened and depressed her. At bedtime she often wept, sometimes for her dying mother, sometimes for herself, as she thought of the happy carefree life she might have had in her nice little colourful flat with her new lovely baby.

Once a week, Annie trundled the baby in the pram to the house in King's Park to open windows and dust her precious belongings. These visits, though strenuous, were like a little holiday to Annie and gave her back a feeling of reality about the marriage and her own life.

The baby was always very happy in the small flat, crawling industriously or sleeping contentedly.

The phrase 'the might have been' often echoed through Annie's mind as she worked, but she sternly rejected such negative thoughts and polished harder. She tried to be smiling and cheerful when dealing with Helen.

Very occasionally, Bruce would manage to get away from the works and meet her there for an hour or so.

Bruce visited the Mackay's flat two or three times a week. These were usually brief visits, sometimes no more than twenty minutes and they brought no comfort or companionship to Annie. A strange, awkward emptiness hung between them.

Bruce always seemed delighted to see Helen and made a great fuss of her, throwing her into the air and twirling her round and round in the way that made Annie nervous, both for the child's safety and for her mother's many ornaments. Helen screamed delightedly and shrieked with laughter, but to Annie there was an underlying note of hysteria in these sounds. Then Bruce would pretend to be some sort of animal and gallop around on his hands and knees. Helen was entranced with her mad daddy and even Annie would have to laugh. He seemed happy to caper about and play the fool.

In private, Bruce would complain to his wife that he felt inhibited with her parents around, but Annie saw no sign of inhibitions. In fact he seemed to be even louder and more boisterous when Mary Mackay's critical eye was on him.

"Be careful of the child, Bruce!" his mother-in-law would exclaim sharply, but Bruce would reply with a wide grin,

"Oh, she's fine an' dandy, the wee monkey. She's having a rare old time here! Aren't ye, Tuppenny? Loving every minute, aren't ye."

It was impossible for Bruce to believe that anyone might disapprove of his actions.

As she watched Bruce clown around, Annie would think of his staid unhappy brother, who seemed to be turning into a recluse and a miser before he was thirty, if everything Bruce said was to be believed. How could two brothers be so very different

Annie always had a guilty sense of relief when Bruce left with his usual profuse apologies and excuses. She knew that her mother would almost certainly comment on what a damned idiot that man was.

Helen generally slept fitfully the night after her father's visit and Annie would face the next day with a yearning for another hour or two in bed.

Cleaning the flat in King's Park seemed to be all that was left of the life which Annie had thought she would share with Bruce. She took a bittersweet pleasure in polishing and dusting its contents. Bruce joined her there more and more rarely. Sometimes, after arranging a rendezvous, he would not turn up and Annie would wait for an extra hour. The long walk home with the pram would be swift, her feelings a bitter mixture of anger and sadness. At their next meeting he would be full of remorse. Unexpected problems at the works would usually be the justification for his non-arrival, but Annie hardly believed him. Without a phone, it was impossible to get in touch.

There was an unhappy episode when Helen was nine months old.

In November, because of bad weather, Annie had not visited the house for nearly three weeks. When she unlocked the front door and stepped inside she was aware of a strangeness. She manoeuvred the big pram into the little hall before turning on the lights.

In the sitting room, she stared for a moment before she could understand what she was seeing. Every piece of furniture had a large white label stuck to it! On each label, badly written in pencil, was a sum of money, generally about a pound or thirty shillings. Some of the smaller items a footstool, a lamp and a table, had 2/6 or 5/- chalked directly on the polished wooden surface.

Annie sat down and tried to puzzle out what Bruce, who was the only other person with a key, had been doing. Had he been drunk? Was it some sort of game? Truthfully the place looked too tidy for Bruce to have been there. The leather couch had a label with 17/6 marked on it which bore no relation to its value. Could it be its second-hand value? She had no idea, but that gave her the clue.

Bruce had not paid the rent.

How could he forget to do that?

And now, because they were in arrears, the bailiffs had come in and marked their furniture ready for a warrant sale. She had heard of these terrible sales, when a family lost all its furniture for a comparatively small debt. That must be the explanation of these horrible labels and chalkmarks. How could he? Did their lives together mean so little to him?

She was panting and her heart was pounding.

How shameful!

The bailiffs!

She could not believe that Bruce could have allowed this to happen. All her beautiful furniture, defiled!

She could never forgive him.

Was this his way of telling her that the marriage was at an end?

Surely he would not be so cruel!

She wandered through the house and found everything marked at ridiculously low prices.

It was ludicrous and tragic at the same time.

She was in danger of losing all this valuable furniture for the sake of a few pounds of rent!

Thank God she had come to King's Park today. Next week might have been too late. She had no idea of the process, but surely her parents would be able to pay the rent and save the furniture, if Bruce were not willing.

She left the house quickly and walked home in record time. She did not cry and she did not feel the cold wind in her face. She dreaded explaining the situation to her parents. Her mother was too ill to be troubled by this problem, though her father would no doubt help her, but he would be furious.

What a mess.

She felt ashamed for Bruce and for herself.

◊

By the time that Helen was one in February, Mary Mackay had been diagnosed as having pernicious anaemia. Only three years earlier this disease would have been fatal, but now, with the discovery of an antidote for the B12 deficiency, that fear was removed. Within weeks she was on the way to recovery, although the injections must continue throughout her lifetime.

There was an element of the miraculous in the immediate change in Mary's health after she started these life-saving injections. Annie could hardly make enough food to satisfy her mother. Porridge, milk puddings and pancakes were daily additions to the generous meat and vegetable meals which Mary ate twice daily. Annie was delighted and stood at the stove for hours each day.

The problem with the unpaid rent had been fixed. Bruce had

just been a bit forgetful and he apologised endlessly to Annie and to her parents. He was good at apologising and sounded truly regretful.

Annie did not tell him of her suspicions that it was his way of ending the relationship. She was ashamed to have considered it. Unusually, Mrs Mackay was inclined to excuse Bruce. Certainly her own son had a longer and darker list of misdeeds.

"He's still a very young man, Annie."

But Annie knew his apologies too well. She had no faith in them. They sprang to his lips so easily and were soon forgotten. And yet she felt it wrong to doubt her husband who seemed so anxious to make amends.

As Annie was still helping her mother, the King's Park flat was given up and the furniture put into storage. Bruce was decisive,

"Best if you just stay at your mother's just now, Annie, and I'm settled at Doune Terrace. It's more practical. I'll pop in and see my two girlies every day or so, unless there are problems at the works of course. You know how tied up I get. Anyway you've got enough on your hands without looking after me and Mother is always delighted to have me at home, y'know. Ha, ha, not so sure about Stewart and the old man, of course. They always say I'm noisy!" He laughed uproariously for a few moments and slapped his knees. Then he searched in all his pockets with serious concentration, shaking his head and muttering.

"What have you lost?" Annie asked.

"Oh nothing, doesn't matter anyway. Later on when things are more settled and your mother is back on her feet, we'll look for a flat in the West End, Honeybun. Nearer our folk. We were too far away from friends and family out there. I never really liked it."

That remark hurt Annie terribly. She very much regretted parting with her modern little flat and she was not sure that being near their folk was at all what she wanted. However she was too busy coping with life to argue with him. Besides she was learning that discussion and compromise were not what Bruce considered part of married life.

Eventually, after searching in every pocket twice, Bruce found his car keys.

◊

Mary was up and about again in the afternoons, not strong enough to do much, but certainly able to direct and criticise.

William had returned from working in Manchester and made a fourth adult in the house.

He and Helen were great friends. He was less frantic than her father and could amuse her with all sorts of little tricks and games with his handkerchief or a newspaper.

Annie liked to see them together. She was reminded of the good times of their childhood years when they had been great friends. Every night Willie would enjoy a long exciting story told by his big sister. When she suspected him of going to sleep, she would advise him to lick his fingers and put spit on his eyelids to keep himself awake.

She still always laughed to herself when she thought of the day that Willie had broken the mirror. He was just ten and had been horsing around and knew his mother's fury would descend upon him, for she had no sympathy with accidents.

The Pittenweem maid had exclaimed with horror,

"Oh, Wullie! Yer mither'll no' be pleased. An a broken mirror, tae. Ye ken, that's seeven years' bad luck!"

Quick as a flash, Willie had replied,

"Yes, and the first seven minutes will be the worst!"

It was long ago, but his smart wit still sometimes softened the resentment that she felt towards her demanding brother. Older sisters and younger brothers seemed to be a difficult relationship. Annie wondered if she might some day provide Helen with a small sister, who would prove a more satisfactory sibling.

As things stood at the moment, it seemed very unlikely that there would be any siblings for Helen.

Every day, lunch must be ready at one o'clock sharp. Willie was now working in Coplands department store and he came home for his short lunch break. He could have eaten in the staff canteen, but it saved him money and Mary had a snobbish dislike of the idea of her noble son eating in a canteen. Once again, Mary's concern for her son's convenience seemed to blind her to her daughter's heavy workload.

John Mackay had started the important portrait and the large flat must be kept to a high standard of cleanliness for the sittings. The public rooms required dusting twice daily in the city centre grime. Annie had forgotten how much dirtier it was in the centre of town.

She struggled with the immense amount of washing for her parents and William, as well as the baby's laundry. There was a primitive mechanical washing machine, but she found filling and emptying it more trouble than it was worth, though the wringer was helpful. The pulleys were always laden and the neat little winter-dyke, that Bruce had made, stood permanently in front of the fire airing nappies and small garments.

Annie did suggest tentatively that a charwoman once or twice a week would be helpful. Her mother had employed one when Annie left home to get married.

"Well, you know how bad things are just now, Annie. These are difficult times and the pictures are just not selling."

"But my father's got this big portrait to do and an exhibition in October. I thought you were doing quite well just now."

"No, I don't think we can afford a charwoman. I wouldn't like to ask your father for that sort of outlay just now when I'm out of action and we have you and the baby to provide for. And William too."

"Isn't Bruce giving you an allowance for us?"

"Yes, I believe he did give your father a token amount. Your father wasn't keen to take it, of course."

"But Bruce is due to pay something and I'm sure he's pleased to do it and William's working. Surely he pays his way when he's working?"

But Mary swept from the room in her usual stately way and did not answer that question.

Annie guessed that William made no contribution. Grimly she thought it more likely that the usual stray fivers would be handed to him to help with his gambling debts.

Most days there were two outings with the pram, to the shops in the morning and to the park in the afternoon. Mary generally spent the morning in bed. It did not seem to occur to her to look after the baby while her daughter shopped. Anyway, Annie felt that Helen's daily outings were vital for both of them. Twice a day, she bumped the pram up and down the six flights of stairs with dogged determination and some satisfaction in her own strength.

Much of the time, while in the flat, she felt oppressed and a prisoner. Almost a slave. Her mother was extraordinarily demanding over what seemed to Annie to be unimportant details. Her father was immersed in his painting and must not be disturbed, for he was the very competent breadwinner. William lived his usual princely life, perhaps occasionally, as a favour, stoking the fire and always escaping each evening to some doubtful place of pleasure, not to return until the small hours of the morning.

The never-ending pressure of domestic toil meant that Annie had virtually no leisure or social contacts,. She had no energy to go swimming or join her friends at the Wednesday night sewing bee. Anyway, who would look after Helen if she woke up? Her mother was hardly fit enough.

Annie knew that she was giving up on her appearance. Old clothes were all that were required for the life that she was living and she had not gone to the hairdresser for months. When she looked in the mirror, she thought her appearance reflected her mental state. She had forgotten all her jokes and limericks. She did not read or play cards, she did not even knit these days. No wonder Bruce had become cooler to her and seemed to have lost interest in her almost completely.

Perhaps if her mother had been appreciative, the hard grind would have been more satisfying. A word of praise here and there would have been so sustaining. If only her mother's returning strength had not accentuated those always critical faculties!

Sometimes Annie would remember how ill Mary had been and feel guilty. She should be delighted that her mother's life had been saved by the wonderful injection. Then she would roll up her sleeves and start preparing another tasty meal to satisfy her mother's ravenous appetite.

She told herself that she really was overjoyed that her mother was regaining her health. She was also not a little amused at the speed with which Mary was regaining her lost pounds. Daily, Annie watched Mary fill out her clothes more and more until, truthfully, they were far too tight.

Annie's only real pleasure in life was the baby who was a particularly jolly little soul. Annie found it hilarious that Helen ate her mashed banana with the same sort of delirious happiness that her Grandma showed at mealtimes.

Strangely, Bruce, when he visited, seemed extra friendly to the rest of the family. He was in good spirits, but he showed no inclination to save her from her servitude. He spoke of flats to rent in various areas of the West End, but the time was never right for him to look at those flats. He was always too busy.

She thought, in her gloomier moments, that it suited him very well to have her at her parents' house. It saved him money and he could look in and play with the baby for short periods when it was convenient for him. It was a bachelor existence again for him and she knew that he had renewed his friendship with the Forresters.

When the summer of 1933 arrived, it was taken for granted that Annie and the baby would go to Pittenweem with her parents. Bruce's plans were vague, but he had acquired a little green Austin car in May.

"I'll be able to pop through and visit you every weekend throughout the summer!"

He made this statement to John and Mary, as well as Annie and he looked terribly excited and happy as he said it, shrugging his shoulders inside his jacket. His cheeks were extra red and his wide enthusiastic grin showed his splendid white teeth.

Somehow Annie could not mirror his enthusiasm, for she did not believe that it would happen that way.

She was right.

◊

One afternoon in mid-July, after a fortnight of the fresh sea breezes of the Fife coast, Mary felt well enough to shop.

"I thought I'd go along the High Street today, Annie. Show them that I'm fully recovered from my illness."

"Good idea. You're looking very splendid!"

Mary wore a green silk print dress which had always been a favourite. To the sharply observant eye, it was a little strained across the bosom and hips, but it did fasten and she knew that the colour suited her. It was a lovely dress and she wore a smart straw hat which had cost nearly four pounds, though John had been protected from knowledge of that particular purchase.

Unlike her daughter, whose daily shopping was necessarily brief and business-like and accomplished in workaday clothes, Mrs Mackay had a reputation for elegance to maintain. Even shopping for mince and chops in the village butcher shop, required the correct outfit and accessories.

"Aye, aye Mussus Mackay, yer lookin' weel!" The brawny

butcher welcomed her, pleased to see the return of such an excellent customer. "Ah heard ye were gey faur gone in the wintur! But yer lookin jist fine the noo."

"Yes, Mr Thomson, I did have rather a bad time of it. The family was very worried. And of course I shall never be completely cured. It's a terrible thing to think that I must have these horrible injections for the rest of my life. But I suppose I shouldn't complain, because in fact I was dying! Now this treatment has really saved my life and I'm practically as good as ever again!"

She smiled and waited coyly for his next compliment. She knew her colour was good and the hat flattering.

"Aye, thur's nae doot, Mrs Mackay, yer the pictur o'health noo, an' yer lookin' really awfy weel, awfy weel, Ah'm happy tae tell ye ... Ah congratulate ye oan yer recovery. Yer fair pittin' oan the beef, though!"

It took Mary a moment to understand his meaning.

"Well, yes, I have gained some weight, I suppose. You see I got so terribly thin ..."

"If ye let me luft ye, Ah'll tell ye whit ye wey."

"You're certainly not going to lift me."

"Wull ye no' let me luft ye?"

"No, no, certainly not."

"Weel, hm," he rubbed his chin and looked her up and down in a way that she did not care for.

"Weel ... judgin' by cattlebeasts, Ah'd say ye wur aboot thurteen stane."

"Oh!" she screamed, "I'm certainly not that weight!"

But later that day, when she stepped on the chemist's scales, she was twelve stone thirteen pounds.

It must be said in Mary's favour that she told this story to all her friends. It was too good a story to waste and her inimitable telling of it, and the fact that it was against herself, was the source of much uproarious laughter.

From that day onwards, she curbed her voracious appetite somewhat, though she would never again be a slender woman until extreme old age overtook her.

Misunderstandings

The summer passed in a sort of haze for Annie. The weather was lovely, and Helen left her fat babyhood behind as she marched sturdily up and down the steep wynds and clambered unsteadily over the rocky beaches with her grandfather. She was a child whose skin quickly turned brown in the sea air and her dark eyes and eyebrows contrasted with the thick cap of straight silver hair. People did notice her unusual colouring and of course, Annie and the Mackays thought she was perfect.

Bruce drove noisily up in his little green car on three weekends. His visits were unannounced and not always convenient.

One of John Mackay's friends and patrons, George Findlay, was visiting when Bruce arrived the third time.

Mr Findlay, as he was always referred to in the family, was a wealthy though uneducated man, now in his mid-fifties, who had made a fortune in the soft drinks trade. He was unmarried and lived on a small estate with an extensive and beautiful garden which he adored. Although he employed five gardeners, he worked democratically beside them and took his full share of the heavy work.

He had bought several paintings and had his portrait painted by John. They were personal friends, golfing and often playing billiards at the Art Club together.

Unfortunately, George Findlay detested Bruce Corning. He had met Bruce when the engagement was first announced and Mary remembered it all very clearly. Although twenty years older than Annie, Mr Findlay had always been very fond of her. To her he had seemed like an old man, but Mary, intuitive as always, had often wondered if this wealthy client had romantic feelings for her daughter. Nothing had ever been said, but when Annie had become engaged, Mr Findlay had expressed a strong dislike of the younger man. He had astonished John and Mary with his vehemence.

"I don't like the look of that young fellow-me-lad that's after Annie. I doubt you'll have to put a stop to that match, Mackay."

"I'm afraid it's a bit late now to stop things, Findlay. They're engaged, man."

"Never too late until the knot is tied. I don't like him and I don't trust him. That hail-fellow-well-met attitude cuts no ice with me. He's far too *damned* pleased with himself and he hasn't realised his luck. I don't see him going far in life and he doesn't appreciate your lovely girl. It's simply casting pearls before swine! Letting a lady like Annie marry *that* ... indeed! It's preposterous! You'll have to stop it, Mackay. You'll have to ... or you'll be sorry. He's not the man for your girl. He'll let her down, I'm telling you."

After the wedding Mary and John had discussed it. How emotional Mr Findlay had been! They had no idea that he could become so worked up.

"John, I've often wondered about Findlay. It was a wonderful present that he gave Annie, but he didn't come to the wedding. Do you think he would have liked Annie for himself?"

"That's certainly never occurred to me. He's too old for a start."

"Not so very much different from us, John, just a few more years between them. It's worked fine for us. He'd certainly have been a great match as far as worldly goods are concerned. Bruce will never make much money in that Gallowgate business. I've never seen the place, but it sounds antediluvian. He's twenty-seven and he only makes about three pounds a week, not much more than a working man. And he's filthy at night."

"Och, I don't think old Findlay is the marrying type. I think he's just fond of Annie in a fatherly way."

"I'm not convinced of that, John. And what about his ideas of Bruce? You don't think he's a bad bet for a husband, do you?"

"No doubt he's a bumptious sort of fellow. I think he's trustworthy enough, but I was surprised that Annie would have chosen someone like that. Anyway, it's too late now."

"Oh, you can never tell what will attract a young woman. He's full of life and so energetic ... quite handsome in a way. Well, I don't know ... there's nothing we can do about it now, anyway."

◊

On his third visit that summer, Bruce arrived in Pittenweem at the same time as Mr Findlay was visiting. It was very awkward.

Annie had the unpleasant and almost impossible task of convincing Bruce that his visit was inconvevient, that particular weekend.

"What do you mean, it's inconvenient. I call that a bit thick."

"If you had just sent a wire, Bruce, I could have let you know not to come."

"Surely I can come and visit my wife and child when I want to!"

"Yes, but ... oh it's not my house and I'm extra busy cooking and it's awfully difficult. He's a strange old fellow and he's an important buyer and a friend of my father's."

"But where's the difficulty? I'm jiggered if I see what the problem is. Surely we can both stay in the same house? I'm your husband!"

Suddenly he laughed loudly and slapped his thigh several times.

"Ye're not telling me he doesn't like to see you with your husband? Does the old geezer still have a fancy for you himself? What a nerve! I always thought that old Methuselah might be after you! That's what it is, isn't it. I'll be blowed if he's not jealous. The dirty old bugger."

Bruce laughed long and heartily, while Annie shook her head and tried to quieten him. Then his face changed.

"Maybe you like him too. Do you, Annie? Maybe *you'd* prefer me to get away out the road?"

"Nonsense, Bruce. Don't be ridiculous. It would just be easier if you went to those friends of yours and came back next weekend. It would be simpler all round. You've spent plenty of time with them already this summer, when it suited you. I haven't seen or heard from you for over three weeks, Bruce."

"Don't worry, I won't stay here. Not where I'm not welcome!"

"Oh, Bruce ...!"

"I'll be in touch."

He jumped into his car and his wheels sent a hurricane of gravel spurting, as he drove away. He did not return to Pittenweem that summer.

As usual, Annie was left with mixed feelings of pity, anger, regret and relief, with the last most predominant, for she felt it almost beyond her capacity to deal with Bruce and her parents at the same time.

◊

Annie had no idea of Bruce's plans when she returned to Glasgow with her parents in September. She had received one brief and cold letter from him since he had driven off at the time of Mr Findlay's visit.

Unpredictable as ever, Bruce arrived at Renfrew Street the day after their return, with flowers for her, chocolates for her mother and a large teddybear for Helen. He was in an ebullient mood and spoke of three different flats that they would view on Saturday.

"Now that we see you fully recovered, Mrs Mackay, it's time to get all that dusty furniture out of store. Isn't that right, Annie? Make a home for our wee yin. Just as soon as possible."

It was as though the rebuff in Pittenweem had never happened.

However, finding a flat would not be simple. The flats they visited were all shabby and in poor areas.

"Never mind Honeybun, you and me and the kiddie will get settled down soon, just like a real wee family. We'll get all our furniture out of store and just you wait and see, everything will be fine and dandy."

He looked at her with his fond, intense look and Annie wanted to believe him. It was more than four years since their wedding and a very small proportion of those years had been lived as a normal married couple.

Her mother seemed well on the way to regaining her strength and Annie longed to leave the life of servant to her parents and brother. Now that Helen was mobile, too, she required more looking after and Annie dreamed of her own home.

The months passed, but when possible flats were advertised, Bruce was not always available to look at them. Annie watched the papers herself, and when she saw something likely, she would put the baby in the pram and walk to see what sort of place it was. In this way she started to get an idea of the areas in which she would or would not want to stay. But it was impossible to depend on Bruce's availability in the evening. He sometimes phoned at the last minute to cancel, which she found infuriating after she had, with some difficulty, persuaded her mother to look after Helen.

One night she was just leaving the house to meet him, when he rang to cancel the appointment.

"Really, Bruce, I sometimes get the feeling that you don't want to get settled. What is the problem tonight that you can't make it? Is it Bobby Forrester that you have to visit some pub with?"

"No, Annie. It is nothing like that. My Uncle Gordon has been taken very ill and I am going to the hospital."

"Oh, I'm sorry, Bruce. I shouldn't have said that. Who is your Uncle Gordon? I don't think I've met him, have I? Is that your mother's brother? Or your father's? I hope he's all right."

There was smothered laughter at the other end of the phone, then Bruce said very seriously,

"Yes, I think he will recover this time."

There was more laughter and he hung up.

Annie burst into tears, but hid them from her mother.

Last Days in Renfrew Street

Just before Christmas, Annie walked out to the suburb of Hyndland. It was a crisp wintry day with pale sunshine and she enjoyed the two-mile hike. She walked through Kelvingrove Park and over the hill past the University. The well-sprung pram bounded along and she seemed to float behind it. This time she had arranged to view the flat herself, as it was getting more and more difficult to pin her husband down.

It was a ground floor flat, halfway down a hill and opposite a school. Annie thought to herself that a school would be handy, for though the child sleeping in the pram was just a toddler, in a very few years Helen would be a schoolgirl.

The young man who showed her round was singing the praises of the three large square rooms, the airy kitchen, the generous cupboard space and the conveniences of the area. There was a school opposite, shops, lending library and post office just up the hill, two banks at the top of the road and the tram and bus stops were just at the door. Two train stations were within five minutes' walk.

"Yes, I can see it is very conveniently located but surely ... is there no electricity in this flat?"

Annie could hardly believe her eyes. She had lived all her life in Glasgow flats with electricity, much older flats than this one.

"I believe it was an elderly couple who were the former tenants, Madam, and perhaps they never got around to arranging electric installation."

"It seems quite a nice flat, but I certainly wouldn't be interested in renting it without electric light. That would be the landlord's responsibility wouldn't it? And it is very grubby."

"I would need to make inquiries about that, Madam."

"The walls and paintwork are really filthy."

However, she saw that it was a very spacious flat and the cupboards were terrific. The shops across the street looked excellent and altogether it was much better than anywhere else that she had seen.

Eventually, Bruce saw it and liked it too.

It was only two miles from Charing Cross, but few people seemed to want to move so far from the centre of town and these flats were not renting easily.

The factor agreed to install electric light and repaint the entire flat if they would take it. It would be ready for them in March and they congratulated themselves on an excellent bargain.

With these arrangements made, their relationship improved and the couple spent more time together planning their future, although it was almost impossible for them to have any privacy.

"I'm longing for March and our own wee place, just the three of us." Bruce would whisper and Annie would smile secretly and lean against him. They did a lot of walking and talking. Fortunately the weather was not too extreme that winter because wee Helen spent most of Saturday and Sunday running along the paths of the Botanic Gardens or Kelvingrove Park. When her short legs grew tired, she was pushed for miles in her high black pram.

On the colder days they would visit one of the Italian ice-cream cafes in Byres Road for coffee and a plate of savoury hot peas cooked with a ham bone, then liberally dressed with cheap vinegar.

"Here, I hope this isn't acetic acid on these peas, Annie!"

"Well, you should know!"

"Mmm, yes it could be, y'know."

They would laugh and sniff the vinegar suspiciously and eat the peas while they were still too hot.

"Wonder when the wee yin'll enjoy a plate of peas, eh, Annie?"

And he looked lovingly into the pram at the sleeping child. It was a happy time for Annie. Bruce could be very tender and beguiling when he tried and she started to feel young again and positive about the future.

A Special Doll

Just before Annie and Helen left the Mackay home, Mary was in town shopping. The buying of food was still Annie's responsibility, but with her regained strength Mary enjoyed a day in town rooting around for bargains. The renewal of household supplies and also her wardrobe, which had been neglected during the two years of her illness, justified her many purchases.

As she walked along Sauchiehall Street, her mind dwelt on the unpleasant emptiness that would envelop the house once Annie and the baby had left. Her life would change in so many ways. Cooking and cleaning would become her entire responsibility and she would lose all those charming hours spent playing with the child, enjoying her quaint little ways. Helen knew so well where the box of chocolates was kept and how to wheedle one from her Grandma. She could implore, speechlessly always, as the child refused to say a word, *implore* her doting grandparent to peel the large green grapes and pop them into that sweet little mouth. Mary could never understand why Annie was so against those chocolates and grapes. It was possibly jealousy. She had always suspected Annie of jealousy, especially where her brother was concerned.

Annie fussed about other things. The bread and butter with sugar sprinkled on it and the sweet milky tea that Mary herself enjoyed and gave to the wee one in a saucer. Helen just loved these treats and what harm could they do to the child, she wondered? No doubt her little granddaughter was rather difficult at mealtimes and ate very little, but Mary worried about that just as much as Annie did.

The biggest row that Annie had made was about the chocolate granules. This was Mary's iron tonic. Chocolate was wrapped around the granules of medicine to hide any unpleasant taste. It came in a small tin box and when Mary rattled the box, wee Helen would come running from the furthest part of the house, even John's studio. It was so sweet and the little thing must have exceptional hearing. It was amusing and exactly like Smoky, the

Persian cat, who would come tearing through the house if he heard the grinding of the mincing machine.

Without interrupting her sharp inspection of the goods on display in each window that she passed, Mary smiled to herself, as she thought of them both and their similar, greedy reactions to a distant noise in the big flat.

When Helen would arrive, breathless and with a bright expectant smile on her wee face, Mary would give the child a tiny amount of her medicine, just a few granules in the palm of her hand to lick and taste the chocolate. The kid did enjoy it so much and surely a little iron tonic was not a such bad thing for anyone.

However Annie, when she had found out, had kicked up absolute hell. She was more furious than Mary had ever seen her! And over such a trifle!

"That's just about the most poisonous thing you could give her!" Annie had almost screamed.

"Nonsense, Annie. It's a tonic and I only give her a totie wee amount. Calm yourself down, for God's sake. What a state to get into."

"If children eat iron pills by mistake, there is very little hope of saving their lives. Children die every year from eating iron pills."

Annie tried to control herself but her voice was high.

"But Annie, these are not pills, are they? They're granules."

"Yes and much more tempting and more palatable with the chocolate coating, but just as damned poisonous."

"I always keep the tin in a safe place, well away from the child. You know how precious she is to me. I would never allow anything to happen to my wee jewel. Would I, darling? Look, you've upset the baby with your ridiculous screaming."

"I was not screaming and it doesn't matter where you keep things, mistakes happen and children can get into anything."

Mary looked away from her daughter into the fire. Her lips were thin and tightly pressed and she inhaled and exhaled slowly and deeply, the sign that she was very displeased and did not intend to speak to anyone for the next few hours. For once, Annie was not intimidated.

"I want you to promise me that you will never give Helen any more of those iron granules."

This was very brave of Annie.

Mary shrugged one shoulder slightly without looking round and breathed hard.

"Promise me that you won't give her any more and you'll tell her that they are bad for little girls."

This was heroically brave.

"I promise then. Now take the child away and leave me alone."

The tone was snappish and ungracious, but Annie left the room with a distinct and previously unknown feeling of victory.

As Mary went over the incident in her mind, she blurred the ending of the story slightly. Without realising it, her attitude to her daughter had changed since that incident. It was an infinitesimal change, but a change nevertheless.

Just then, Mary saw a wonderful bargain and her musings ceased immediately.

There in the window of Trerons was an immense and eye-catching display of paper thin Japanese silk in a riot of vibrant colours. It was marked at fourpence a yard. Mary walked in and bought twenty-five yards of the sunshine yellow and forty yards of the sweetmeat pink. It was the finest of pure silk and it billowed and floated dramatically as the girl measured and, with great difficulty, struggled to fold and wrap it. Mary had no idea what she might do with this magical diaphanous fabric, but it was gorgeous, it was cheap and it crushed into a very small and light parcel, so she need not yet turn homewards.

She walked around the various departments of Trerons. It was not a shop she frequented normally, but the china department was excellent and she also bought two pairs of stockings.

In the toy department there was a special consignment of dolls. Mary was immediately attracted to one of them and bought it with hardly a moment's hesitation. It was quite expensive at a guinea, but it had a unique and fascinating face. Mary was unable to resist it and she was sure her granddaughter would feel the same way.

It was a brown velvet doll with a bright wide smile and was as far removed as possible from the golliwogs which were so popular, but which Mary hated, without quite knowing why she hated them so much. This was a female doll, made of the finest brown plush. She was dressed in an outfit more reminiscent of the South Seas than Africa, with a grass skirt and necklace, anklets and bangles of tiny green, red and gold wooden beads. Her body was square and unformed and her arms and legs were long, slender and straight, similar to the limbs of a rag doll but with a strange reality because of the soft plush and finely detailed hands and feet. She had a mass of short black curly hair and was a charming doll by any standards, but it was her face which separated her from other dolls. A beautifully modelled paper mache base under the warm skin of velvet gave the face an unusual reality. Magically enlivening this face were the sparkling dark brown eyes, which seemed to follow your every movement. The eyes had no mechanism for closing, but to Mary they almost seemed to dance.

It was a stupendously lively and happy little face and Mary giggled as she gazed at it.

"Where was this doll made, I wonder? Those eyes are marvellous. So life-like!"

"It was made in England, madam, and it is a named doll, created by Norah Wellings. Look, her name is here on the sole of the foot." The salesgirl removed the doll's small green shoe to show the label. "I cannot say for sure, but the traveller told me in confidence that the eyes were manufactured by a firm which makes human glass eyes. They decided not to put that fact on the label, in case some people might not like it, but I think that information is quite correct."

"Oh, I say! How interesting. I'm glad you told me that. They are so realistic, just marvellous really."

Mary always enjoyed a gruesome fact and at first, this did seem a little gruesome. Thinking it over she decided that glass eyes were a wonderful invention for those poor people unfortunate enough to require one and the doll was just delightful with her dancing eyes ...

Mary rushed home and placed the new doll at the foot of the cot where Helen was napping for her to find when she awakened.

Two and a half hours later, Helen had still not climbed out of her cot, but she could be heard laughing, crowing and crooning to her new friend.

It had been love at first sight.

Mary decided to call the doll Topsy and throughout Helen's childhood, Topsy, with the wide smile and the brilliant and realistic eyes, would remain the child's favourite toy beyond all other toys. Mary little realised that she had bought something that day which would play an important role in her granddaughter's life and in the lives of granddaughters and great-grand daughters yet to be born.

Charming and magical Topsy was to become an icon in the family.

◊

The preparations for the move to Hyndland were hard on Annie. In the preceding weeks her mother had found various tasks that must be accomplished before Annie left. There was a cupboard to overhaul and a bedroom to spring-clean and one or two dinner parties were arranged.

"I really owe the McKillops a meal, and the folk at the golf club have sent flowers and fruit so often. I suppose I should have them for afternoon tea, but I'd really need your help. Then there's the Robertsons too. I wonder ... "

Annie was used to helping her mother with entertaining and did not even expect to mingle with the guests.

At last, all her mother's tasks were accomplished, and the furniture was brought out of storage and delivered to the Hyndland flat. A large carpet was bought for the sitting room, and Annie spent two days arranging and polishing her new home, while Mary looked after Helen.

Annie returned on the third day, to find Mary with tears streaming down her cheeks, cuddling the little girl who was also weeping.

"What's wrong, Maw?" Annie asked anxiously.

"Oh, I'm going to miss this wee sweetheart so much. I'll miss both of you. And she'll miss me. I don't even know why you're going. You could easily stay here with us in this big place. It will seem so empty without you both!"

Annie stood looking down at her mother. She was tempted to say what she really felt, tempted to point out how powerless she felt in her mother's house and that, after working so hard for two years, she was now really looking forward to living her own life in her own home. Tempted to reproach her mother with selfishness, bossiness, bad temper, greed, with spoiling her son and grandchild and leaving Annie to deal with the consequences. Tempted to point out how little appreciation had been shown ... but what was the use?

Her mother's plump tear-streaked face looked middle-aged and vulnerable. Annie felt a wave of compassion for the woman whose persona had always depended on being the 'the artist's beautiful wife'.

"Now don't be so daft, Maw. We're only fifteen minutes away in the tram and we'll be seeing you several times each week. I can pop over any time and you and my father can visit me as well, and I can entertain you both in my own home. Remember, I'm a married woman and a mother and I need my own place! And if Bruce and I are ever to make things work, the sooner we start the better."

Mary made a sound between a grunt and a sob and Annie patted her shoulder awkwardly, realising as she did so that she was mimicking her father's action. Perhaps Mary would have appreciated a cuddle at that moment, but she was not a huggable woman.

A New Start

On the day that she moved to Clarence Drive, Annie walked with Helen in the pram from Charing Cross to Hyndland. It was a bright windy day in March. Bruce would collect their suitcases that night. Mary had wanted to come with her and take a taxi, but Annie wanted no fuss. She felt strong and powerful for the first time for ages. She had a nice bit of steak to cook for Bruce that night, onions, cabbage, potatoes, everything well wrapped and tucked into the foot of the pram.

She felt as though she were starting her life again. It was a second chance at this tricky thing called marriage and, just as important, the opportunity to bring up her daughter as she wanted.

She decided that it was the last time the pram would be trundled up or down those stairs to her mother's flat. Helen was now big enough to walk and they would take the tram or bus into town and make their visits brief.

As she looked at Helen sitting up and enjoying the scenes around her, she felt reluctant to abandon the pram completely. It seemed to make walking so enjoyable. Its easy action almost pulled you along. She had recovered from the horror of the problem with the brakes and always parked it at an angle against a wall. She must have walked an astonishing number of miles with this pram, for it was so handy to visit friends and to carry shopping. A pram was really a wonderful invention and she would not get rid of it just yet.

As they swung along, Helen suddenly pointed imperiously to a large cart horse, standing patiently at the kerb. Annie stopped and said a few gentle words to the horse. She had always liked horses very much. The horse turned towards them and, breathing noisily through its hairy lips, thumped its enormous foot on the ground.

Helen smiled and held up Topsy for the horse to admire and Annie felt inordinately happy and optimistic.

◊

The first month in the new flat was not at all easy. Helen missed her grandparents and was quite dismal and lack-lustre, in a way that Annie had not seen her before.

Strangely enough, she started to talk for the first time. She had obviously been waiting until she had the confidence to speak fluently. She surprised her mother with the wide vocabulary, which she must have been storing and practising in secret.

It was obvious that she loved to go back to the Charing Cross flat and it was always difficult when it was time to leave. Mary was delighted at the fuss that Helen made and often suggested that she would keep her for a day or two or that they should both just stay the night.

"Bruce wouldn't mind just this once. Go on, stay! You can see the wee one doesn't want to go. Do you, my little jewel? You'd like to stay with your Grandma, wouldn't you?"

When this suggestion was rejected by Annie, there were renewed tears and tantrums and she wished that her mother would be more co-operative. If they were ever to become a family, she felt that they must all live together consistently in their new home. Bruce had not once gone home to his mother in those first few weeks and it would ill-behove her to leave the marriage bed.

It would have been great if her mother would have looked after Helen for an evening in Hyndland, while she and Bruce went to the pictures, but that was never offered and Annie hesitated to suggest it. With her regained health, her mother had returned to leading a very social life and few of her evenings were free.

Nor did Bruce help Helen to adapt to her new life.

In the evenings, when he came home from work, he seemed determined to have all of Annie's attention and hardly looked at Helen. It sometimes seemed as though he resented the little girl.

"Have a wee game with the kid, Bruce, while I mash the potatoes, or maybe show her a book. She's been waiting for ages for you coming home."

But Bruce would make jokes when reading Helen's books and call the animals and characters by the wrong names, in spite of the child's protests

"It's Margaret, it's *not* Jean and it's *not* a sheep, it's a horse, it's a horse. She's riding on a horse!"

And not all Bruce's laughter and mock apologies could mollify the child.

After his meal, he was ready to turn his attention to his

daughter and the rough-house games would begin. Helen, timid and yet partly enjoying the excitement, would laugh at first. As she swooped and whirled through the air in her father's strong arms, her laugh would become exaggerated and shrill, then falter, and Annie would interrupt them.

"Bruce! Bruce! Not so wild, please. Remember she's only two and I want to get her to bed soon. If she's over-excited, she won't sleep and I'm wanting to have a bit of peace and conversation with my husband."

But the subtle flattery did not work. Bruce, determined not to be directed in any way, stepped up the tempo.

"Aw, she just loves this playtime with her old dad, don't ye, my wee Tuppenny-ha'penny."

Sometimes he would balance the child on his head and skip around the room, or perhaps he would hold her upside down by the heels and swing her like a pendulum, while Annie, expressionless, watched and felt a cold grip of fear as Helen's head swung near the furniture.

It always finished the same way. Helen would suddenly burst into hysterical tears and Bruce would make an exclamation halfway between regret and astonishment.

"What the hell's the matter with the kid? I didn't bump her, did I?"

Annie would shake her head and, with a small tight smile, silently take the child off to bed and try to pacify her with a story.

Most evenings were like that, for Bruce was determined to have his 'boisterous time', as he called it, with Helen. When Annie tried to suggest that at bedtime it was better to read a book, he would just roar and laugh and say,

"No, no, the wee one doesn't like the way I read. She doesn't seem to understand my fun! But it's comical the way she corrects me, isn't it? The cratur! She gets quite cross and pulls me up, just like a wee old woman. By Jingo, she'll be a right wee nag someday, I'll bet. She'll keep some poor man in good order!"

If Annie became too serious in her requests to keep the bedtime hour calm, Bruce's face would quickly show the old aspects of fury.

"Ye're surely not going to direct me about how I can play with my own child, Annie."

And Annie would back off and placate him. It was not easy.

Bruce often accused Annie of spoiling Helen and she hardly knew how to refute this. No doubt the child had been over-indulged by her grandparents. When living in their house, Annie had mostly given in to the child's demands in the interest of keeping the peace. If her mother were sleeping or her father had a sitter, it was important not to have the child screaming and Helen, though without words at that time, was an expert screamer. Now that they were in their own home, Annie had hoped to introduce the child to 'kindly and consistent discipline' as the books suggested, but Helen's demanding ways were entrenched and so were Annie's reactions to them. Life with Mary Mackay had not trained Annie to be assertive and 'anything for a quiet life' had always been her attitude. She gave a lot of thought to where the blame lay for Helen's behaviour, and how she might change it. Of course, in spite of his accusations, Bruce also spoiled the little girl, bringing home cheap little toys at the weekend, which charmed Helen momentarily and gave her father's homecoming a brief magic. To Annie's relief, these toys were soon discarded, for the tin cars had dangerously sharp edges and the monkeys on elastic were made of dubious scraps of fur, while the inflammable nature of the celluloid Kewpie dolls created real horror in Annie's breast. Her vivid imagination was never far from the dangers that might befall her child.

Sometimes on a Saturday afternoon Bruce would suggest a visit to an ice cream shop.

"Oh, it's great having some free time to spend with you and the wee one. I can't tell you how I appreciate these special times. Just fine and dandy. I've got fully two hours before I have to meet Sandy. Let's nip along to Byres Road and see what's on offer in that Tally's on the corner. I bet there's a great big ice cream and ginger beer waiting for us, eh Tuppenny?"

"Would it not be better just to go to a tearoom and have pancakes or a doughnut. Those drinks are far too much ... too sweet ... she's still just a wee thing, Bruce."

"No, no, she'll love it, won't you, wee Tuppenny. You're a big girl now, you'll get a great big foamy drink all to yourself, won't you . You fuss too much Annie. That's what mothers do, my wee lass. Fuss, fuss, fuss all the time ... you'll get used to it. Come along now."

Annie might have vetoed the ice cream shop more strongly if

she had not seen her daughter's trembling mouth, for she knew the consequences of those extravagant treats only too well.

Then he would hoist his child on to his shoulders and set off for Byres road with his long swift lope, using, truth to tell, a more extended stride than his legs were built for. His daughter experienced a fearsome bumping swaying ride which, had it been required, would have been an excellent preparation for camel-racing.

Shoving on her hat, Annie hurried after Bruce, marvelling once more at his astonishing strength and stamina. Though he was handicapped by the two-year-old on his shoulders, he would march at such a rate that she knew she would fall behind long before they had walked the mile to the café.

Annie would be torn between pleasure at having his company and regret that after an enormous ice cream drink, Helen would take no real food at all for several days, with the resulting bad behaviour and little sleep. She was not a child given to sickness, but sometimes Annie wondered if the reality of vomiting might have been the only way to convince Bruce that his treats were excessive for a two-year-old. Especially, if it happened while the kid was riding on his shoulders. Then she immediately castigated herself for her malicious imagination. He certainly paid no heed to her words of warning and the next day he would once more follow his own pursuits, while his wife dealt with the fractious child.

In spite of her waywardness, Helen was curiously self-sufficient and would often play by herself happily in a world of her own making, creating a little den for herself below the table or using the pattern on the large sitting room carpet as stepping stones. She loved her mother to read to her and particularly enjoyed some books which she demanded over and over again. Annie was pretty sure that some of these stories were too complicated for Helen to understand, but guessed that the child liked the sound of her mother's voice and the comfort of her arms. Annie certainly enjoyed these sessions. It was strange that, when visiting Renfrew Street, Helen was never willing to let Mary read to her. She spent a lot of time with her grandfather, who was always reading or telling her stories from his imagination. But Helen was different with her grandmother, for she would wriggle down from Mary's knee and make it quite clear that her reading was unacceptable. Annie realised this and sympathised with her mother's feelings of rejection. What could it be that Helen disliked about her grandmother's voice, was it too loud? Too dramatic? Perhaps the kid saw her grandmother's role as different, more active than a storyteller. Children were such strange little creatures. It was a puzzle and Annie realised guiltily that she was rather pleased that her mother was unacceptable as a reader.

◊

Nancy, an Art School friend of Annie's had a baby girl in the spring. It was the first baby in the Glasgow crowd after Helen and Annie hoped that the children would be friends in the future. Helen had not seen a baby before and the first visit was paid to see the new arrival. Annie had knitted a little white jacket with an edging of Fair Isle in pale blue and yellow. Helen had been terribly interested in this coat while it was being knitted, smiling and stroking it. Annie felt quite nervous that perhaps there would be a fuss when the coat was handed over to the other child, and tried to explain in advance that this was a present for another little girl called Ruth. Helen only gazed at her with one of her inscrutable looks. Annie wished that she would say something and give her a clue as to what she was thinking. Fortunately, at the presentation of the gift, Helen said nothing, although she watched it being tried on the baby with a cold eye. In fact there was a distinct lack of enthusiasm for the baby altogether and Helen did not smile once as she watched the processes of bathing, dressing or feeding. When the baby was finally asleep after twenty minutes of little hiccuping cries, Helen brought her coat and hat and her mother's hat from the bedroom and put them all firmly on her mother's knee.

"Oh, Nancy, perhaps it is time for us to be getting along. You need a wee rest while Ruth is asleep. She's just a lovely baby and you're looking awfully well. You and Alec must be terribly happy. I'll be out to see you soon again."

In spite of Helen's lack of interest in the new baby, Annie was amused and touched to see her that night at bedtime. When Helen's vest was removed, she turned away from her mother and, picking up Topsy, cuddled the doll's smiling brown face to her own flat little chest and sat for some minutes giving her a breast feed. Not a word was spoken.

Topsy was always her companion and never out of sight. She was treated like a real person and cared for like a real child. Woe betide any parent or grandparent who did not show proper respect and solicitude for Topsy. There were also two imaginary dogs that were sometimes part of Helen's life. They seemed to be large and were generally on leads. Their presence was inconsistent and those dogs held many pitfalls for the unwary adult. Tantrums were generated by the foolish mistakes of grown-ups who made much of the dogs when they were not present, or walked right through them when they were there. As far as Annie could make out, Helen was completely honest in her assertions about the dogs. She knew exactly when she had them with her, and when she had not. Mary Mackay was less sure and suggested that it was a good way to put people in the wrong and to create a rumpus. Annie thought that rather a sophisticated thought process for a two-year-old and considered that it said more about her mother's character than her daughter's. But one could never be quite sure.

Nevertheless, little Helen with all her difficulties, had many charms and a unique quaintness that Annie was sure other children did not possess. She adored her and the child responded more and more as they shared the quiet house together. The fact that Helen was so determined and assertive seemed sometimes a jolly good thing. Those were the qualities that Annie herself lacked, and perhaps Helen would make something more of her life than her mother had done. Annie was nearly thirty-two now and had never earned a penny of her own, still seemed to be in thrall to her dominant mother and had not a great deal of optimism about the future of her marriage. No matter how hard she worked, no one seemed to appreciate it. Fair Isle knitting and Readicut rugs would never bring her fame or fortune. She determined to do some house improvements as soon as the kid was older. The kitchen looked north and some bright colours might cheer it up. It would be the following winter before these improvements became a reality, but planning it brought a positive goal into her life.

She found a seventeenth century proverb in a book which seemed apt and made her smile.

He that would please all and himself too,
Undertakes what he cannot do.

She must try and bear that in mind.

A Spoilt Child

Annie was idealistic about child-rearing and she hoped to make a simple and disciplined life for her little girl when she was settled back in her own home. She knew there were many pitfalls for the parent and was aware of the responsibility to prepare a child for life, as well as clothe and nourish it properly. She remembered her own haphazard childhood, where a succession of maids had been unwillingly responsible for herself and her brother. Some had been kind, but ignorant and easily manipulated, allowing Annie and Willie to eat what they wanted and stay up till all hours. Others had been downright terrifying, with blood-curdling tales of ghosts and bogeymen. One had repeatedly threatened the children with hellfire and damnation. She determined that Helen would not be affected as she and Willie had been.

Since her teens, Annie had read everything she could about infant care, child-psychology and proper nutrition. She knew her Truby King by heart. Now she would apply all her knowledge, for her high aims had been impossible while living with two indulgent grandparents. In the Renfrew Street flat, the child was encouraged by both grandparents to behave just exactly as she wanted. Annie was anxious that Helen should not disturb her ailing mother, or her father as he pursued his profession. Helen was quick to learn that she need only scream a few times to get what she wanted, for Annie would always capitulate if Helen made enough noise. Then, because of Mary Mackay's ill health, the flat at Charing Cross was filled with tempting baskets of fruit and extravagant boxes of chocolates, which both grandparents were delighted to offer to Helen throughout the day. The child never came to a meal with any appetite. Annie despaired when her mother commented yet again,

"That child is *far* too thin. She needs a proper meal. I would worry about her if I were you."

And yet it would be Mary who would offer Helen a large creamy chocolate just as Annie was pouring the potatoes for dinner.

Although Mary's health was improving, Annie and Helen visited the Charing Cross flat several times each week. The grandparents were happy to look after the child while Annie did some of the heavier housework.

John was Helen's willing slave, taking her to his studio for hours to look at books and providing her with more apples and peppermint drops than even Annie guessed. John had a wonderful way of producing his penknife and peeling the apple skin in one long snake, that delighted Helen. The eating of the apple was only a part of a ritual of which she never tired. On cold days when the stove was burning, potatoes and occasionally chestnuts would be roasted. A small jar of salt was kept on a shelf, ready to enhance the flavour of these forbidden treats.

The time that Helen spent with her grandfather was particularly special. In later years she would realise that, although certainly her grandmother was the more dominant character, it was her grandfather's influence which remained with her and which most often affected her actions. Her very first word had been 'Drandad'. It was practically the only word that she said for many months, and the only word she ever mispronounced. Although Helen eventually took pride in talking perfectly and using long and unusual words, she clung to this infantile term of affection and continued to use it until she was eight. She knew that her schoolfellows laughed at this baby-talk, but guessed that her grandfather liked it. Helen was seldom swayed by peer pressure, though she was often made unhappy by it. She was a girl who followed her own rules with a strange tenacity. Besides it seemed too difficult to change someone's name.

From eight months onwards, her grandfather had shown her books and magazines, endlessly describing the pictures in great detail, as though she were a much older child. She would turn pages and point and pay absolute attention as he read, sometimes gazing at the page and at others times turning to watch his mouth move under the large white moustache. Annie was amused one day to overhear her elderly intellectual father obediently reading out one advertisement after another to the baby on his knee.

"Rich Lanolia Cream for Exquisite Complexions as used by many of the leading beauties of the stage, screen and aristocracy."

"Eucryl Toothpaste for Whiter than White teeth. Even heavy smokers will immediately find an improvement."

One day when Annie heard him announce,

"Lux Flakes, made of the finest soap! Eminently Suitable for Washing Ladies' Undies."

She interrupted and assured him that he did not need to read those silly ads if he was tired or fed up.

"Och, the wee one likes it fine and I don't mind at all."

Then he looked down at Helen, smiling fondly and the baby smiled her toothless smile back. They were in complete accord with each other and Annie's eyes filled with tears.

By the time she was three, Helen and her Drandad went out walking in Kelvingrove Park every day that she was in his house. Usually they went to the Art Galleries and those visits were prolonged and fascinating. Everything from Japanese armour and Eskimo kayaks, jousting spears and dinosaurs, ancient Greek pottery and Egyptian mummies, was gazed at repeatedly each week. John would give Helen all the information that he could muster, but often she was content just to gaze at things. He wondered what thoughts were passing through her little mind as she stood and looked at the beautiful models of ships, or the stuffed animals in their realistic environments, for many silent minutes. Obviously she was happy in some world of her own and fortunately he was a patient man. If the weather stayed dry, they would wander through the park and feed the ever-hungry ducks, while John told her fairy stories, classical tales and historical happenings. Helen was delighted to listen to it all, though not always able to differentiate between reality and myth. In later years she realised that there had been an unsuitably morbid strain in some of the stories, for she remembered that she had, at a very early age, learned of Mount Vesuvius erupting and the poor people who were inundated by lava and the others who were pelted by rocks and steam and gases and died as they ate their dinner or played games. Drandad even had a piece of pumice from Mount Vesuvius. He also told her of the tragedy in India called 'The Black Hole of Calcutta' where many were imprisoned and suffocated in a terrible heat. That was terrifying but enthralling. He spoke of long, long ago in China, when it was considered a great delicacy to eat live baby mice, dipped in honey. This was something that Helen definitely did not believe to be true and besides, she did not like honey. It was certainly a story that spoiled any pleasure in eating pink sugar mice.

Then there were all the sensational happenings in Greek mythology, the Cyclops with only one eye, the Gorgon with hair like snakes, the two rocks that crashed together when a ship sailed between them. Helen particularly liked that story. Yes, it was a rich and grisly cocktail which the gentle artist offered to his beloved granddaughter before she reached the age of five. Perhaps those violent and sensational stories appealed to her. They seemed to do her no harm for she had no night terrors and enjoyed listening to the stimulating tales as often as her grandfather would tell them. While other children studied pixies, elves and toadstools, Helen was laying down a very adult background of knowledge, much of which she did not completely understand.

◊

Although Helen was late in starting to talk, her pronunciation was precise and she soon showed an interest in longer words. The praise and attention which she received when using multi-syllable words encouraged her to acquire an impressive vocabulary. Her grandmother, particularly, urged her to demonstrate her talents. Visitors to Pittenweem would be guided past a certain wall, where Helen, by the time that she was three, would indicate and pronounce the presence of 'carboniferous rock'. At four she could shop alone at the chemist's and ask for a box of 'Liquorice, Linseed and Chlorodyne Lozenges'. Truly she was a child that other children would have loved to hate, but she seldom came in contact with any other child.

Mary Mackay also encouraged Helen to perform at an early age, teaching her to sing popular songs, 'Tea for two', 'Daisy, Daisy' were favourites. She enjoyed listening to 'Barnacle Bill the Sailor' and 'Ivan Skavinsky Skavar', without comprehending them in the slightest. Best of all, Helen loved to dance to the gramophone. She seemed to lose herself completely in the music and would dance to the point of exhaustion. There was a record which she particularly loved with 'Anitra's Dance' on one side and 'The Hall of the Mountain King' on the other. Mrs Mackay assured her friends that Helen, at only two years old, could appreciate and use appropriate movements in these contrasting pieces, matching the lyrical quality of the first and the exciting, rampaging crescendo of the second.

By the age of three, her grandmother had coached her to imitate the famous catchphrases and gestures of Greta Garbo and

Mae West. The child had a certain talent, but she did not share her grandmother's dramatic ambitions and felt uncomfortable as a mimic. Helen would always dance with joyful spontaneity, but she found the other actions embarrassing, yet was unable to resist her grandmother's determined coaxings.

"Come along my wee jewel. Just do 'Come up and see me sometime.' Put your hand on your hip now, that's the way!"

When the reluctant child at last performed, with sideways glance and hardly moving lips, Mary would grab her and hug her hard, laughing until the tears came. There would always be a chocolate in payment.

At first Helen, in spite of some awkward feelings, quite enjoyed the acclaim and adulation that these demonstrations of her abilities generated, but gradually she liked it less and less. Perhaps she grew to resent being made such an object of attention, or perhaps the hidden power behind the demands became apparent to her. Even the chocolate seemed distasteful, when earned in this way. Whatever her reasons, she was able eventually to escape the thrall of her imperious grandmother in a way that few others could do. She went on strike.

She was four when she rebelled and refused to provide the cabaret for her grandmother's friends, standing immobile and gazing steadfastly into the fire, until Mary was forced to break the embarrassing silence with a little laugh.

"I don't think Mae West is at home today, is she?"

Helen continued to regard the dancing flames.

On another occasion, Mary asked Helen for her Greta Garbo impersonation. Helen turned an expressionless face to the window and contemplated the tree in the garden. Her grandmother bit her lip and whispered pathetically,

"I know you're so good at this. I've been telling my friends all about you and they won't believe me now if you don't do it! Go on, there's a wee sweetheart and I've got something for you that you'll like ..."

But Helen just looked out at the tree. Mary realised that she had met someone with a will to match her own.

Mary, who had strong didactic tendencies, had her own method of helping her granddaughter to speak properly, sometimes using wrong grammar herself and encouraging the child to correct her. Consequently, by the time that she did start to speak,

Helen had an excellent command of language.

When she reached the age of three and a half, Helen refused to react to her Grandma's incorrect grammar. It was just a pretence and, as she felt that as she was now perfectly proficient, it was a stupid waste of time.

"Did you hear what I said just now, my jewel? I said I seen the postman coming up the street."

"Yes."

"Well, that's not right , is it?

"No,"

"I thought perhaps you didn't hear what I said."

The child remained silent and over the next few weeks, Mrs Mackay gradually accepted that Helen would not play her grandmother's educational games any more.

In India, Mr Gandhi continues his regime of passive resistance.

Glasgow Herald 13th May 1933

On one or two occasions, Helen mimicked her Grandmother's well known 'signal of displeasure' with the dropped eyelids, the majestic turn of the head, the controlled intake of breath and the slower expiration.

Astonishingly, Mary was not at all offended and gleefully described Helen's performance to her daughter in great detail.

Although Annie said little, she was interested to find out that her mother was so clear about her own behaviour when furious. Was the 'signal of displeasure' a carefully orchestrated act rather than the spontaneous and unconscious display of anger which Annie had always supposed it to be?

Grandparents

As soon as Helen was able to march along briskly, her grandmother took her regularly into town to look at the shops, which were very exciting. In spite of the poverty and deprivation of the hungry thirties, shops were crammed with every unnecessary luxury and had a glamour and decadence which would be lost with the war, and would not return for nearly forty years. Presentation was paramount, with neatly tied parcels in shining brown or brightly patterned paper. A gift of fruit would be artistically displayed in a an asymmetric green basket, with high handles extravagantly tied with striped ribbons. The Mackays received these baskets regularly at Christmas, overflowing with shining red apples, exotic hot-house grapes and always a perfect pineapple. Chocolates came in a multitude of containers, papier mache animals with removable heads, miniature chests of drawers with tiny tassels as drawer handles and pretty Chinese bowls, wrapped in cellophane, each one tied with scarlet or golden ribbons. Unknown liqueurs were presented in brightly coloured pottery bottles. Helen's favourite was a parrot with an intriguing tiny cork stuck in its beak. It was an ornament in the house for years because of its pretty colour.

Most of their morning would be spent in the large department store of Coplands. The Mackays were friendly with the directors of this business, which was probably the most comprehensive and luxurious in Glasgow. With an overabundance of underpaid but eager assistants, with charge accounts and instant delivery, with little chairs beside the counters if Madam felt tired, and with luxurious resting rooms where newspapers could be read or letters written, Coplands made shopping easy and enjoyable for those who had money to spend.

Coplands have a special delivery of smart handbags at only 7/6 each. Also umbrellas, chubby or walking at only 6/11 each.

Advertisement Glasgow Herald January 1934

After a long morning, the tearoom was a wonderful haven for the exhausted shopper, but not for Helen.

In the middle of the floor was a large round hole, about twenty feet across, an abyss which Helen found terrifying! It was protected by a waist-high railing, ornate and gilded. If you chose a table beside this railing, it was possible to look over it and down to the floor below, where dresses and hats were displayed, and even to the floor below that, the department for gloves, stockings and handbags. The customers down there looked small and remote. It made Helen feel peculiar and very unsafe to look down at those other worlds so far beneath her, though she could never resist peeping. She would always look once or twice, then try to forget that it was there and concentrate on the drifting lemon slice in her grandmother's glass of Russian tea.

At Christmas, an enormous tree grew upwards in this fearful chasm, passing through the different floors of the store with the tip just reaching the tearoom. The tree was decorated with sparkling tinsel and hundreds of delicate, gently swaying, glass ornaments. Brightly coloured parcels of all sizes hung alluringly from the branches. The beauty of the scintillating glass and the possibilities of the exciting parcels reconciled Helen to the dangerous drop, but the 'hole in the floor' inhabited her dreams unpleasantly for years. It was much safer when Grandma chose a table near the wall and Helen could relax and enjoy a creamy hazelnut meringue or a sticky pineapple cake, as she listened to the orchestra. The four ladies, who were dressed in black and had rather strange hairstyles, played very sprightly music. Helen would sometimes find it difficult to stop herself jumping up and dancing, but of course she never did do anything unseemly like that. By the time that she was three, she was a typical only child of the middle classes, well-versed in what was *comme il faut*. She also had a certain stoicism, because she kept her fears of the hole in the floor to herself and never thought of expressing her own preference for sitting far away from it, the desire with which her grandmother would have immediately complied

Although it was in Coplands that Mrs Mackay shopped mainly, there were excursions to smaller boutiques to hunt for a 'nice little jersey suit' at a moderate price. Mrs Mackay had a good eye for a bargain and was prepared to wear a more exotic outfit than most people of her full figure might have thought suitable. With her good looks and her personality, she could get away with a touch of metallic glitter or rich Austrian embroidery. She was often lucky to find something, rejected by other large ladies, but just right for her, in one of the elite little dress shops called Madame Marguerite or Madame Desiree. These shops, with perhaps just one dress, or one hat and a scarf in the window, puzzled Helen. Generally, shop windows were crammed with as many goods as possible, and as her grandma seemed to be the only customer in their hushed interiors, how did they make enough money? Helen was interested in how people made money.

Throughout her life Helen would always visualise her Grandma dressed in a jersey suit over a pale silk blouse and with a long string of amber or ivory beads. A generous amount of the blouse would show, as the jacket would not overlap but would be held in place by a matching belt loosely tied around a waist, no longer easy to define. There would always be something special about the suit, some sort of braiding or decoration that Helen was sure other grandmas did not wear, and the child liked that.

But there was one article that Helen really disliked in her grandmother's wardrobe. It was a long brown leather coat which was worn open, but belted, just like her suit jackets and no doubt for the same good reason. Helen hated the look of this coat and she hated to touch it and she could not be sure, but it seemed almost as though Mrs Mackay behaved differently when she wore it. It certainly seemed that the nightmare of 'crossing the road' was accentuated when the leather coat was worn.

'Crossing the road' was the fly in the ointment of an outing with grandma.

For half a mile, tempting shops selling every article imaginable, lined both sides of Sauchiehall Street. Traffic flowed in both directions. There was certainly less traffic than nowadays, but the vehicles were disparate and confusing. Buses were forced to wait, while crowds of tramcar passengers stepped into the road to ascend their vehicle. Slow-moving horses and carts slipped on the cobbled surfaces, while impatient private motor cars, weaving their way throughthe chaos, blew their horns in frustration. In spite of this congestion, there was no official help for the shopper who wished to cross the street, no pedestrian crossings, no lights and no traffic policeman. The Glasgow citizens teemed on the pavements and had little idea of how to cross the road, except by the use of daring, desperation and speed. Mrs Mackay was no different from the rest and she had her precious granddaughter to protect. Grabbing Helen's hand in a grip of steel, and with no idea of the limitations of the braking systems of the various vehicles, she would set off into the fearsome melee. Mrs Mackay was a very strong woman and prided herself on her strength. She had established her superiority over every maid she had ever employed, by producing a stream of water from a supposedly well-wrung towel or sheet on washday, thus demonstrating how very weak the servant was compared to her mistress. This was the powerful grasp which her grandchild dreaded and immediately struggled to escape, for the pain was extreme. Helen was an obedient child and would not have dreamed of running away from her grandmother in the middle of a busy road, but in the distress of this fearsome clasp, she pulled back and wriggled her arm and hand. She was just as scared of the traffic as anyone else, but the agony of her grandmother's determined grip was so much more immediate that trams and buses faded to insignificance and her one thought was to free her poor crushed hand. As it seemed to her grandmother that the child was bent on escaping from her with the aim of self-destruction, she gripped tighter still and rushed on through the narrow gaps and insolent drivers.

Crossing the road was the worst part of the shopping trips for both of them. It took quarter of an hour for Helen's hand to recover. She was positive that her grandmother's strength and her own consequent pain were even greater when the leather coat was worn.

But Helen liked her grandmother's dashing hats with their smartly cocked brims and decorations of feathers, folded ribbons or felt flowers. They were so different from the very simple felt pull-on hats that her mother wore. Her mother was a disappointingly plain dresser who favoured classic tweed suits and lace-up brogues. Although Helen could not bear to find any fault with her beloved mummy, she did think she might have dressed a bit more adventurously, as Grandma did.

◊

As a dutiful daughter-in law, Annie visited her mother-in-law once or twice a month. Bruce, although so devoted to his mother, was often too busy at the week-end to see her himself, but he would always ask if Annie had been recently and express surprise if she had not. She dreaded these visits, for the Corning house at Doune Terrace always seemed to have a dusty gloominess and

Annie wondered if there was ever much laughter in the house. Almost immediately realising that wherever Bruce was, there was bound to be loud laughter. She wondered if anyone joined in, or did they listen to him with serious and embarrassed faces, or perhaps with a forced little smile. She was aware that the last was often her own reaction. She determined to try and join him heartily in his laughter next time. She knew that there was sometimes an overwhelming pity in her complex feelings for her husband. She was also aware that Bruce would have been astonished to learn this and would have stoutly renounced any need for it.

There was little to interest a toddler in these visits to Doune Terrace. Topsy always accompanied them and Helen played with the several cushions on the couch. Annie had no idea what the game was, but the seven cushions were repeatedly stacked and then laid in a circle around Topsy or in a straight line in front of her, while Helen muttered under her breath. Annie would balance her cup of weak tea in the Crown Derby teacup and her papery pancake thinly spread with Mrs Corning's overcooked strawberry jam and wonder how time could move so terribly slowly. Perhaps this chap Einstein, who was said to be a genius, could have explained it to her. Meantime she must stay at least another forty minutes to be polite. Mrs Corning chatted about people at the church that Annie never had, and never would meet, and about various grocery bargains that she had found around town.

"I always get my butter at the Maypole, Annie. I buy powdered butter and it lasts better."

"Powdered butter?" Annie's eyebrows went up questioningly. She had not come across the old-fashioned phrase.

"Salt butter, you know. And their cheese is quite nice too. I usually buy half a pound at a time. I hate that nasty mould."

Annie came from a household which regularly bought a seven-pound cheese which was kept in a vast china cheese dish. Her father always averred that the cheese was at its best when green layers must be carefully sliced from its surface, but she said nothing. A bubble of boredom was starting to form in her chest and she fixed her eyes on Helen, who was beating the cushions with her little fist as she had seen her mother do with the feather filled sofa cushions at home. These small hard kapok cushions were more resilient and retained a stolid and uncomfortable squareness. Annie could not see dust but she could certainly smell it and she hoped Helen would not mention it, for the kid had a particularly strong sense of smell.

"I think that butcher in Dumbarton Road sells excellent mince and it's much cheaper than the Byres Road butcher. Well worth the extra walk, I think."

"Oh, yes."

"Where do you buy your mince, Annie?"

"Well there are two butchers in Hyndland, both good I would say. I just go to the one across the road. Very handy."

"And what do you pay for your mince, dear?"

"To tell you the truth, I've no idea. Mince is quite cheap everywhere, isn't it."

"Yes and it's so nice in a pie and that makes it go further too. Although sausage meat is also very nice in a pie and cheaper, and if you add an onion and some Bisto it really is so very tasty."

Annie winced at the thought of sausage meat and Bisto, both despised products in the Mackay household.

The conversation was always deadly and Annie would feel the boredom bubble grow dangerously large. She did not want to be outright rude to Mrs Corning, but she did not know how much more she could stand and she longed to be striding home along Great Western road.

Sometimes Annie willed Helen to indulge in some outrageous behaviour that would necessitate a sudden departure, but Helen quietly kneaded and rearranged the cushions, kissing Topsy at intervals. As Annie smiled and nodded, all the time straining to hear what her mother-in-law said in her genteel little whispery voice, she determined that it was the last time that she would come here. Bruce could bring the kid to see his mother if he wanted to.

She always felt that way and yet she continued her regular if infrequent visits, until one day in October, Annie's attention was jolted when Mrs Corning said,

"I think it's about the right time for Helen to start Sunday school now, isn't it? We have a rather nice little school at St Margaret's and I would be quite pleased to take her."

Jane Corning had been reared to think it unladylike to show enthusiasm. She used 'quite pleased' when in fact she was desperately keen to have the delicious little blonde child, offspring of her darling first-born son, to show to her friends. If she could have voiced this wish more honestly, Annie would have been pleased to arrange something, but it seemed to her that the grandmother was trying to involve Helen in early religious education and Annie did not approve of this at all. Annie had memories of the Irish maid who had threatened hell and damnation to her brother and herself, and she did not intend that Helen should ever go through such terrors.

"Oh, Mrs Corning, I don't think so. The child is not even three yet. I think it is much, much too soon for anything like that."

Annie was cross and showed it.

"I really think it's time I was getting back home to make dinner now."

It was months before Annie returned to Doune Terrace and Jane was able to complain to her husband and especially to Bruce about how strangely Annie had behaved.

"You've no idea what she was like! She became so angry all at once. Over nothing at all! Then she just left, just upped and away. Most peculiar!"

"Yes, Mother" said Bruce, in the sententious tone that he often used to her, nodding his head a little, "She can be a peculiar girl."

Peculiar was not a word that he had connected with his wife before, but it was apt and he filed it for future reference. He certainly knew how angry she could get over some small trifle, he assured his mother.

For instance there was that incident in Kingspark, before the baby was born, when he accidentally dropped the cigarette ash on the carpet. She had seemed quite normal when she pointed out that she had vacuumed the carpet that day, and that there was an ashtray just beside his chair that he could easily reach. Then her voice was quiet and she was smiling, actually smiling, when she directed his attention to the ashtray a second time. The third time that she spoke, her voice was certainly raised a bit, but there was no way of predicting what would happen next. Just to relieve the tension, Bruce laughed and dropping some more ash, deliberately this time, he ground it into the carpet with his heel and said in what anyone would have understood as a jovial joking way,

"That nicotine stuff's good for the carpet. Anyway it's your job to clean it up, isn't it?"

He had been astounded by her reaction. She was furious. More furious than he had ever seen her. He had never known that she could be like that. She had said some very hurtful and offensive things about his behaviour. Things he would always remember. Yes, peculiar was a very good word for his wife. The next time that they quarrelled, he would use it about her and see how she liked it!

Wilful Daughter

Nowhere was Annie's inability to cope with her wilful daughter more obvious than at hair-washing time. It was a nightmare. While Helen was still a baby, it had been a simple procedure. The papier mache baby bath took only two kettles to fill, then Annie held her above it while she washed her few sparse locks. But Helen's hair grew longer and thicker, and as she herself grew larger and stronger, that first method was rejected with loud shrieks and struggles.

At Renfrew Street the Victorian bath was fitted with a shower and Helen had enjoyed this 'rain' to rinse her hair, but hot water for the large bath must be heated by two hours of a blazing fire in the kitchen range or alternately the gas-fired boiler, known as the circulator, could be used. The circulator was a large copper tank fixed to the wall beside the range. In the first half of the century, daily baths and constant hot water were not seen as the necessity which they are considered in the modern household. In Mary's eyes, the extravagance of running hot water was warranted only one or two days a week. Then the range would be lit and well-stoked. In the summer the fearsome circle of raging gas flames would be set alight underneath the circulator. Otherwise kettles of water were sufficient for the day-to-day demands of dishes, household cleaning, shaving or hand-washing of small items. Annie would never have suggested that the gas boiler should be lighted more often. She often suspected that it would have been more economical in the long run than the endless kettles heated on the gas cooker. It would certainly be more convenient for her.

With the move to Hyndland, the hair washing became an insurmountable problem as there was no shower. Annie in desperation, and much to her later regret, devised a complex plan for washing Helen's hair.

Using the three brown velvet cushions from her leather couch, she made a bed in the middle of the sitting room floor. She was watched with great interest by the two-year-old.

"This is something for you to lie on, darling! Pass me a cushion from the chair, please."

Helen struggled the unwieldy cushion to her mother who laid it on top of one of the others.

"Now, you lie down there, isn't that a nice little bed?"

Helen smiled and seemed pleased with this new game.

Annie went back to the kitchen and collected two large towels.

"Jump up now, pet, and I'm going to spread these nice towels over your pillow."

The child did as she was told, but already the smile had disappeared. Towels seemed to mean something other than a game.

Next Annie collected the kettle from the kitchen. It was filled with lukewarm water and Helen started to look worried, although her curiosity kept her watching. Then Annie brought the oval enamel basin, white with navy handles and trim and usually used for washing dishes. It too held pleasantly warm water.

Lastly she brought a small cup in which she had mixed the shampoo powder. It was Evan William's Camomile shampoo for fair hair, not cheap, but it had a pleasant fresh smell. Annie thought it was the best shampoo on the market.

"Now lie down in your little bed, my jewel, and Mummy's going to wash your hair."

Helen half lay down, but she had started whimpering as soon as she smelled the shampoo.

Annie knelt, pushed the child gently down and with Helen's head poised backwards over the basin, started to wet her hair and apply the shampoo with great care.

"Now if you can just lie still for a few moments, we can do this without your face getting wet, or shampoo going in your little eyes. But shut them just in case."

Sad to say, Annie had to shout these instructions for Helen, although lying perfectly still, was making an absolute din ... crying, shouting, *roaring*.

She continued this extreme noise throughout the whole operation. Annie found herself sweating and trembling, before she had finished the final rinsing. As soon as Annie wrapped Helen's head up in a towel, the outcry stopped. Annie felt that she had been dragged through a war zone, but Helen was smiling and very co-operative about replacing cushions and carrying the cup and kettle back to the kitchen.

What an ordeal it had been! At least the child's hair was properly washed but Annie doubted if she would have the energy to repeat the treatment ever again. What a noise the kid had made! Annie blushed at the thought that anyone might have overheard such a hullabaloo. Neighbours would think she had been torturing her daughter. How did other mothers manage? Mothers with several children? None of the articles she had read had ever dealt with this basic task beyond the stage of infancy. Annie felt very inadequate, but at the same time amused. How could a grown-up, intelligent woman create such a ridiculous scenario? And how could one small two-year-old make such a terrific noise. Surely there must be a better way.

However that was the unchanging method for washing Helen's hair for several years. Helen would always start to scream when the first drops of water touched her skull and continue to shout and complain until the towel was wrapped around her head. By the time Helen was five and a schoolgirl, she felt very guilty about such behaviour and talked about it to her mother in calm moments, but during the actual hair-washing she seemed unable to stop herself. It was a Pavlovian reaction that she could not control. Annie became resigned to it and stopped worrying about what neighbours thought. They probably did not hear it anyway. It got the job done and Helen was always a willing helper to set up the scene of her agony and clear it away afterwards.

Eating was still a difficulty with Helen. Like most new mothers, Annie could not believe how little food her child required. And there were some things which Helen devoured with relish and in comparatively large amounts, while on other days she seemed to pick like a little bird. Smoked fish was a favourite always and there was a ham and chicken paste which came in a small round tin. When this was spread on minute sandwiches, it was eaten with enjoyment. Perhaps the reason for the continuing success of the paste was that one day Annie had cleaned out one of these tins and using tiny amounts of paper, stick and coal, had built a little fire which burned for quite a long time in its miniscule brazier. Helen had been entranced. It was just the right size for Topsy.

Another thing that Helen enjoyed was tartan toast, made by skilful turning of the toasting fork in front of the two-bar electric radiator. The criss-cross of tones made a very Scottish slice of toast.

When Helen visited Renfrew Street, of course there were the same treats as always. Annie did not mind the chocolates so much now, as they were not a daily temptation. However she noticed some decay on one of Helen's front teeth and pointed it out to her mother, who brushed it aside as of no importance. However from then onwards there were more tangerines and peeled grapes and pomegranates for Helen than sweets. Helen loved the jewel like pomegranate seeds and pretended that they were rubies.

On Topsy's first birthday, Annie made a little party with entirely brown food in honour of the doll's warm brown 'skin'. There were date and walnut sandwiches in brown bread, ginger snaps, chocolate drops, dried bananas and a small gingerbread with a candle, all served with cocoa in doll's china teacups. It was a great success and Annie was dumbfounded at how much Helen ate, although she only nibbled for the rest of the week.

Annie had watched films from her childhood and remembered the days when you could watch a silent movie from behind the screen for a ha'penny. The captions were back to front of course but one soon learned to read backwards. She had always enjoyed the cinema but from the time of Helen's birth and Mary's illness she had hardly 'gone to the pictures' at all. She had missed all those dramatic films with her favourites, Garbo and Joan Crawford and also several jolly musicals with the dancers making fascinating patterns for an overhead camera. Now that she was living in her own home and making her own life, Annie determined to take Helen with her some afternoon to a cinema. She would not have to pay for her and the kid might enjoy it. The worst that could happen would be that they must leave. She chose a musical and Helen sat watching it all stolidly. At one point she indicated that it was time to go home but it so happened that the screen was showing a scene of torrential rain, with dancers dressed in waterproofs and holding umbrellas and splashing gracefully through puddles.

"Look, pet, it's terribly wet outside. It's no use going away just now."

Annie felt deceitful, but her pragmatic daughter accepted the situation and settled down to enjoy the rest of the film right through to its satisfyingly romantic finish.

From then on they went regularly to the cinema twice or

thrice each week and sometimes more often, if there were a particular spate of good films. It would have been interesting to
know what Helen thought of the complicated plots which
unfolded before her young eyes but, though she watched attentively, she said little. It was cheap and warm and quite educational, Annie assured herself. The ideas of great wealth, extreme
poverty, hardship and adventure were presented to the child. She
also acquired a perception, flawed though it might be, of 'olden
times' from the many historical dramas. Helen often tried some
of the dance movements or acrobatics that she had seen and
Shirley Temple became her heroine. A film with that dimpled
prodigy was always a great success.

When Helen was three and a half, a thought suddenly struck
Annie. Her mother-in-law was one of the people she had in mind
when she warned her daughter.

"You know, darling, if anyone ever asks you how often you go
to the pictures, just say 'quite often'."

Helen gazed unsmiling at her mother for a moment then
replied with a phrase which was a favourite one of Annie's.

"Not half."

February, 14th Anniversary of founding of the Nazi Party.

March, 9,000 prisoners in concentration camps.

**March, whole youth of Germany to be combined in Hitler
Youth Movement**

April, Nazi wives must be of pure Aryan descent.

April, Nazi centre established in London.

**August, German public schoolboys to have one day off each
week for Nazi activities.**

August, the Bulletin banned in Germany.

August, all British newspapers banned in Germany.

August, anti-Nazi revolt, 1124 persons arrested, 77 shot.

1934 reports in Glasgow Herald

Toys and Games

There was no doubt that Bruce and his mother-in-law vied with each other in bestowing presents on Helen, and it seemed to Annie, that Helen resisted these gifts with an adult determination. Surely she could not possibly understand that she was the pawn in their power struggle.

Mary was out of town at Helen's birthday, but she had arranged that a red and green Triang tricycle should be delivered to the flat for her. The unwrapping of the large parcel was the most exciting part, with Helen giggling and ripping paper excitedly, while Annie laid aside the extravagant lengths of string which she would later carefully un-knot and wind into useful little hanks.

When the shiny tin trike stood revealed, Annie showed Helen how to make the bell work. It was very loud and Annie could see that Helen did not like the noise.

"Sit on it, darling and see if you can make the pedals go round."

Very gingerly, Helen climbed on to the wooden seat and Annie helped place her feet on the pedals which were located on the front wheel.

"Now, push that foot first, push hard, harder now."

Without making any effort with her feet, Helen gazed at her mother reproachfully and shook her head and climbed off the tricycle.

Annie remembered her own childish delight in a tricycle and later a bicycle and was puzzled, but thought the kid was probably still just too young.

Over the next weeks there were a few times when Helen balanced Topsy on the trike and wheeled her cautiously from one room to another. After this short journey, the vehicle would be dumped and disregarded for the rest of that day.

"I hope you'll say thank you to grandma the next time you see her!"

Annie was not optimistic when Mary returned and visited the Hyndland flat, with a bright look of expectation for the success of the present and the gratitude awaiting her.

"Well, my wee jewel, did you like the tricycle that Grandma sent you?" She exclaimed with confidence. "I bet that was a big parcel that arrived. Did you know it was from me? D'ye just love it? Can you go very fast? And ring the bell like billy-ho? Go on, show Grandma how fast you can go."

Annie could think of nothing to say as the child slipped out of the room.

"The wee thing's gone away to get it, hasn't she!" Mary chortled.

Annie smiled politely, less sure than her mother.

However Helen had remembered her mother's briefing and after a long silence, the sitting room door was pushed open and the trike wheeled in with Topsy, as usual, sitting in smiling dignity. As soon as she was through the door, Helen let go of the trike handles, removed Topsy and going to her Grandma, said,

"Thank you for the tricycle, Grandma."

Relieved, Annie thought, not for the first time, what a very tactful child she had. Mary hugged and kissed her granddaughter and commented on what a polite little girl she was, not seeming to notice that the trike was ignored for the rest of the afternoon.

When Bruce had seen the trike for the first time, he had been very scathing.

"Poor bit of workmanship there, I would say. Badly finished. It would never last the pace with a wee lad, that flimsy bauble. Shoddy, tinny, badly constructed. How do they get away with it I wonder? It wouldn't cost much I suppose, but it'll never last, never last, never stand up to much wear and tear, that wee apology for a bike. I doubt our wee one'll soon be disappointed when that falls to bits. Just hope she doesn't get injured when it collapses."

"You can set your mind at rest, Bruce for she hardly ever uses it. She shows no interest whatever in riding it and just pushes it gently from one room to another, about twice a week."

She could have said nothing that would have pleased him more and he laughed heartily for several minutes, slapping his thigh and repeating delightedly.

"No interest in riding it! Ha ha, just pushes it around! That's a good one. Never heard the like, by jove. Ho, ho ho. Old granny won't be pleased about *that*, will she now."

Annie was partly amused by his maliciousness and partly appalled because his jealousy was so obvious. She paid little attention to his next remark.

"Need to see what we can get the wee one for an Easter egg next month."

The following month, Bruce arrived one Saturday with a bright orange toy motor car for Helen. It had lights that could be switched on and off, which was probably the only point in its favour as far as Helen was concerned. It had a klaxon horn which, if the rubber bulb were properly squeezed, was even louder than the tricycle bell. It too was pedal-driven and thus of little interest to Helen. Of course there was room to put her big teddy in it as well as Topsy, and a little cupboard opened at the back where books and balls could be stored. Unfortunately it was more unwieldy to push around the house than the trike, and it kept getting stuck in doorways, or against furniture. Helen was often unable either to reach the wheel or decide which way to turn it.

Bruce gloated over the little car each time he came to the house, and remained blind to the fact that Helen was as indifferent to the car as she was to the tricycle.

She was not a stupid child and by the summer she had realised the possibilities of locomotion by pushing the pedals, but this seemed like very hard work to her and not nearly as quick as walking. It seemed pointless to put so much effort into going around slowly, bumping into furniture when running and jumping were so easy.

In the summer Bruce insisted on taking the car to Pittenweem.

"It'll be great for the wee one out in the garden!"

But the garden was impossible, too small and full of flower beds and the terrain of the sloping lawn and uneven crazy paving path quite unsuitable for the lumbering little vehicle. Nor was there any thought of taking it into the rough cobbled street with its dangerously steep wynds descending to the sea.

As far as Bruce was concerned however, the orange car served its purpose as a thorn in his mother-in-law's flesh.

Helen had other things to make her happy in Pittenweem. The flowers in the garden were a constant pleasure to her and she sang "Daisy, Daisy" with daisy chains in her hair.

She learned several of the longer flower names, geraniums were her favourite and at St Andrews' market her grandma bought her a scarlet geranium in a pot. Throughout the summer Helen watered it and drugged herself with its strong smell.

Honeysuckle, too, had a wonderful and overpowering perfume but she was warned very seriously, and several times over, by each separate member of the family, that she must *never, never* eat the red berries on that bush. She was a cautious child, if not always obedient, and she remembered that warning.

Nasturtiums with their bright colours and bitter seeds were fascinating. Snapdragons were so clever and her Grandma could make them talk and roar and bite.

When Drandad was sawing wood, Helen would collect the sawdust and make porridge for Topsy in a toy saucepan. Her mummy also showed her how to make soup with seeds, grass and torn leaves in water. Then there was the beach to visit with sand pies and wading. She was not allowed to wade too deeply, but she sat down at the edge and though soaking wet seemed unaware of the chilly water.

That was the year that the two invisible dogs joined the household. Helen held their leads when out walking and often spoke to them in a cross voice when they misbehaved. Sometimes they stopped and Helen and her accompanying adult must stop too. Annie was amused and touched when Bruce held a door open long enough to allow Helen's dogs to follow at her heels. She had not credited him with as much imagination.

On his next visit to Pittenweem he brought a complete set of cigarette cards showing the different breeds of dogs.

"How on earth did you manage that, Bruce? Even you couldn't smoke as many fags as that in a fortnight!"

Bruce tapped the side of his nose and nodded knowingly,

"A geezer I know in the Gallowgate got them for me."

Helen certainly appreciated the cards and was constantly laying them out and deciding which was her favourite dog. She found it difficult to choose for the Husky and the Dalmatian were both so beautiful.

The whole family visited the Lammas fair in St Andrews in August and Helen tasted coconut milk for the first time. Mary and Bruce vied with each other to win some large trophy for Helen. Bruce spent a fruitless fortune at the shooting gallery, while Mary spent a comparable sum at Housey-Housey, acquiring a white, plush rabbit in a blue jacket, almost as big as the three-year-old.

Modern Germany was the subject discussed yesterday, by Miss Ingeborg Ritter, a young German journalist, at the weekly luncheon of the Glasgow Rotary Club.

Other nations, she said, did not seem to believe in Hitlerism. They gave advice to Germany, but were not prepared to take advice from Germany, not realising that National Socialism was the only alternative to Bolshevism.

She spoke of work accomplished under the National Socialist regime. In one year the unemployed had been reduced by more than half. Hitler also wished the different social classes in Germany to intermingle and this was being accomplished in the Labour camps. More than 350,000,000 marks had been collected for these schemes of employment.

The world must learn to understand that Herr Hitler was the only man who could help them carry through their difficult programme and also that the German people had the utmost admiration for Herr Hitler.

Woman's page, Glasgow Herald, 20th June 1934

◊

That summer there was an unexpected visitor from Alan Horsland, one of the Mackay's wealthier friends. His family owned a large department store of which he was a managing director, though it was accepted by everyone, including himself, that his brother and cousins were the practical businessmen while he dealt with other issues.

Alan arrived in an expensive open sports-car with two charming young ladies, one of whom was unable to walk. There was no explanation of her disability or whether it was permanent or temporary. She looked healthy, though very thin. Thinner even than Annie.

Alan lifted her gently from the car and deposited her on the sitting-room couch, where her friend helped her remove her jacket and hat.

"Now where is that young lady with the silver hair, I wonder?" his voice boomed round the sitting room with the anglicised accent of a Scottish boarding school.

Helen ran in from the garden and peeped around the door.
"Aha! There she is! I see her now! Come along little Helen, we
shall visit the no doubt excellent bakery in the village and buy
your Grandmama some cakes, while she puts on the kettle and
Annie entertains these lady-friends of mine with one or two of
her amusing stories. She's an absolute mine of funny stories, you
know, just one after the other! Now Annie, not too rude a story!
Just a little naughty, perhaps? I'm sure you have a perfect one at
your fingertips, if that's the right expression for story-telling.
Come along now Princess Helen, we are all hungry for cakes!"

And Helen, who was usually shy and timid with strangers,
took this overpowering man's hand immediately with a
delighted smile.

They were gone for some time, much longer than the short
walk to the bakery warranted. When they returned it was apparent from the interesting parcel that Helen carried, that they had
taken an unnecessarily circuitous route past the toy shop, though
Annie never discovered whose idea this was.

"Now, Helen, show us what stern stuff you are made of. Sit
there with your parcel and wait till we have drunk our tea and
eaten these luscious cakes *before* you open and display your
amazing toy to the wondering eyes of your nearest and dearest
and *do not turn it over.*"

Helen sat with a smile on her face, alternately gazing at the
parcel and looking over to Alan, who would interrupt the general
conversation at intervals to warn the child,

"Careful now! Not a move. Stiff upper lip and all that. Be a
stoic child. I love children who are stoic."

Without understanding all that he said, Helen managed to sit
very still until they had finished their second cup of tea, then
Alan commanded her.

"Little stoic, you have done well and I am going to give you
half a crown for sweeties. And now you may open your treasure."

As Helen ripped off the paper, a loud bleating was heard, as if
a sheep were in the room.

Before the paper was completely removed, a duck quacked.
The toy looked like an unexciting box, a five inch cube of cardboard with bright pictures of different farmyard animal on each
of its six sides but as the toy was turned about, the appropriate

noise for whichever animal was uppermost issued from the innards of the box. It was loud and realistic and delighted Alan as much as Helen. They turned it back and forth, Helen's favourite was the cow and Alan's was the cat.

"Which is your favourite, Grandma?"

"I think I like the sheep best."

But she was sorry she had said that, because the sheep bleated interminably and there was little more conversation that day. After twenty minutes of farmyard noise, Alan decided it was time to be moving on.

He asked with great subtlety if Jean would like to tidy herself before getting back into the car, and when she said yes, he carried her upstairs to the bathroom. Annie was impressed. There was no embarrassment at all. What a gentleman he was.

Mary was nervous and talkative and reluctant to let them go. She had not found out anything about the two girls or why Jean could not walk, and her curiosity was almost unbearable.

Once the girls were safely stowed in the enormous car, Alan turned to Helen and presented her with half a crown.

"Here you are, my little stoic, and you are tactful too for not once have you mentioned that the dog in your box does not bark. It is kind of you not to complain of the defects of my gift. In fact it was explained to me at the time of purchase that the dog was a silent dog. There is a silent breed of dog, though I doubt if it would be found useful on a farm. Farmers are conventional folk and like a dog to bark and bark loudly. At any rate, the kind shopman, who had no other example of that type of toy, gave me a small rebate on the price because of the silent dog and I will hereby pass this one shilling piece on to you as you must live with only five animals instead of the promised six. That means that you now have the fine sum of three shillings and sixpence and the next time that we meet, I shall be very interested to hear what you have purchased with it, or whether you have sensibly deposited it in the savings bank."

Then with more waves and farewells, the car, which was possibly the fastest, most expensive car that Pittenweem had ever seen, pulled slowly, smoothly and silently away from the little house which it had practically hidden.

"That's a very nice man, isn't he, Mummy"

"Yes, he is. Very kind."

"I like the way he talks and I like my animal box."

Annie decided to leave that particular toy in Pittenweem, and for many years, it was rediscovered and delighted in each summer.

Another member of the Horsland family plied Helen with gifts. This was Campbell who was only three years older than Helen. Annie had been very friendly with Campbell's mother and, before her own marriage, had helped her at holiday-time with her two older boys. It was not that Campbell and Helen met often, but she must have caught his imagination because on several occasions he had demanded that his father buy some toy or other for 'little Helen'. The first had been a life-like terrier with a real leather collar, which may have given her the idea for her imaginary dogs.

When she returned to Glasgow after the summer, a most beautiful toy horse, taller than she was, with a soft hairy coat and real leather saddle and harness, awaited her. It was a present from Campbell, courtesy of his father's wallet! The horse was on small wheels and could be pulled around. From then onwards, tricycle and motor car were disregarded and the horse, with a giant rabbit and diminutive smiling Topsy perched precariously and incongruously on its back, trundled continuously around the flat.

Just before Christmas, Annie saw a very life-like baby doll. Unusually it was made of rubber and its pretty face and hands appealed to Annie although it was quite a heavy doll. She showed it to her mother,

"Don't expect it will ever replace Topsy but I couldn't resist it."

"I'll get her a cot to put it in. One of those frilly little nests. She'll like to put it to bed at night."

"Don't be too disappointed, Maw, she shows very little interest in Nancy's baby or Elsie's. She's just not very maternal, but I'll get a wee basin, because this doll is entirely washable, it says. I think splashing about with water would please her."

Bruce promised to get a pram for the baby doll.

John Mackay, without discussing it with anyone (and he was sharply criticised by his wife for spending so much money) bought a beautifully made wooden hay-wagon, pulled by a well modelled cart-horse. It was just the right size for Topsy to ride in and was the most successful of the many toys which had supposedly come from Santa Claus.

The Corning grandparents bought wooden toy soldier ninepins and also gave Bruce five pounds for clothes for Helen. Bruce completely forgot about the money, until Annie made some sarcastic remark about business surely being pretty bad at the works these days, when he produced it with many apologies.

With a metal xylophone from uncle Willie, a pop-up book from the old aunties in Kelvindale, a wonderful tin spinning top that emitted a loud humming when you plunged the handle up and down, tiny knives and forks and spoons in their own wire tray and a miniature three piece suite made of basketwork, Helen required more space for her toys than her mother needed for furniture. She was not yet four.

The baby doll was called Rosemary Daisy. Annie had suggested this cumbersome name half jokingly, after many others had been rejected, but Helen immediately liked it. Rosemary Daisy was cuddled and bathed and put to bed in the pram, but it was Topsy's brown face which smiled from the glorious frills of the cot. Topsy would always reign supreme and Rosemary Daisy was destined to play a supporting role at all times.

More Difficulties

B efore they had spent a year in the Hyndland flat, Annie and Bruce realised that they would never make a happy couple. Naturally each blamed the other.

Bruce complained that Annie did not respect him as she should. She was quite ready to argue with him if she disagreed with his opinions and she often criticised his careless noisiness. He had suffered continuous criticism from his father, of course, but he was unused to it from a woman. His mother had always appeared to enjoy his boisterous fun and she had never complained or nagged about his untidy habits or late hours.These minor faults certainly annoyed Annie, but Bruce shared the theory with many of his friends, that a girl was jolly lucky to get married and have a fellow to support her. His background of doting mother and grandmother had convinced him that Annie was particularly lucky to have landed Bruce Corning and he was amazed that she seemed to show so little gratitude.

Although Bruce's behaviour annoyed her, Annie's biggest problem was loneliness. Bruce spent little time in the flat. He left early in the morning and did not always return home for the evening meal. Sometimes Annie knew that he would not be home, but very often his dinner waited for him in the kitchen and Annie had no idea where he was or whether he would come home to eat the meal. Perhaps he would arrive only at bedtime, having eaten elsewhere. She was torn between anger that he could treat her so cavalierly and worry that this time something terrible had happened to him.

Although Helen did not seem to derive much pleasure from her father's company, she would ask where her daddy was and fuss about going to bed before he came home. She was not an easy child and was at the stage of tantrums. This period of transition, after the spoiling years with the grandparents, was difficult for mother and daughter. Annie was idealistic yet unsure. Only once did she smack Helen on the leg for bad behaviour. While the smack achieved its aim of calming the child and making her more biddable, the red weals that Annie's fingers had left on the small thigh filled Annie with such remorse and guilt, that never again was Helen physically chastised.

Though Annie adored her child, and was determined to follow all the advice which she read, it was depressing that she had acquired another demanding loved one who seemed never to appreciate her efforts. When Bruce's uneaten meal waited cold and unappetising in the kitchen, and when Helen refused to be left alone in bed, screaming for yet another story until nine at night, the old feelings of failure engulfed Annie.

It must surely be her own fault!

Weekends were little different. Bruce worked on Saturday morning and went straight to the baths club to clean up, spending the rest of the day there or on the golf course. Sunday he often went down the Clyde coast to golf. Annie would suggest a special dinner for Saturday or Sunday night, but Bruce was always vague about his plans and obviously preferred to keep his options open. Once, he had arrived unexpectedly on a Sunday when Annie, tired of seeing meals go to waste, had made a simple macaroni cheese pudding for Helen and herself. Bruce had looked at the table disbelievingly and roared with laughter.

"Ye're not going to tell me that's a dinner for a hungry man that's been golfing all day."

"There was steak and onions last Sunday but you didn't appear at all ... if you remember"

"Well, ha ha, that won't do me much good tonight, now will it!"

Bruce wolfed down most of the pudding, but laughed and commented on its inadequacy throughout the meal, until Annie could stand it no longer and jumped angrily to her feet,

"You seem to be enjoying it all right anyway!"

"Aye, aye, it's a good enough pudding. Quite a tasty pudding. It's just not what a man needs, when he's hungry as a hunter. Is it, wee Helen? It's for wee babies like you, isn't it, Tuppenny! My mother makes a lovely macaroni pudding, though maybe not just so much cheese as you've used, Annie."

But Annie had left the room.

And yet there were still times when they made each other laugh, and when they looked into each other's eyes the chemistry and the passion were there as before. And certainly Bruce seemed devoted to Helen though, like other fathers at that time, was quite prepared to see very little of her.

Perhaps if Bruce's little green car had not taken him back so regularly to his mother's house, where he was treated like a god who could do no wrong. Perhaps if his mother could have shed her preconceived notions about artists and their families and helped her son to appreciate his wife's many talents. Perhaps if Annie had not returned so regularly to her sharp-tongued, possessive mother, who thought Bruce a fool and had never considered him good enough to be John Mackay's son-in law. Perhaps if Bruce had been more willing to leave his boyish irresponsibility behind him. Perhaps if the couple had gone far away from both sets of in-laws with their prejudices and jealousies and made a new independent life elsewhere.

Perhaps, perhaps, perhaps. Who can tell?

The Corning clan narrow, parochial and church-centred and the Mackay clan, artistic, lavish and sophisticated were too different, too disparate to blend. Each family was too entrenched in its own prejudices to try and help the young couple make a match of it.

Annie wondered bitterly if the two mothers were secretly satisfied that their pessimistic prophecies had come to pass. It is always so nice to be proved right.

◊

In one of Bruce's friendlier periods, when the autumn weather was still very mild, he suggested that they might picnic at Loch Lomond on Sunday.

"That's a wonderful idea, Bruce, Helen has never been on a real picnic with a fire ... have you my darling?"

"D'ye not think October's a bit late in the year for a fire? It might rain and then where would we be?"

"I'll bring other food that doesn't need to be cooked. Just in case the rain comes on. Don't you worry. But I love cooking outdoors and I bet you'll love eating it!"

For a moment, their gazes held with the old look of pleasure and anticipation.

The moment of closeness was interrupted by a loud crash. Helen had broken a cup for the first time in her life.

The picnic was a great success, with lovely weather.

Helen smelled the woodsmoke and watched the twigs crackling and sparking with delight. Then she was fascinated by the frying pan and its sizzling contents. This was something that she had never seen before.

After an almost adult portion of sausage, bacon and beans, Helen wandered off by herself, strolling through the young birches that grew by the side of the beautiful loch.

"What d'ye think the wee one's up to in amongst the trees there? Look! She's sort of stroking that tree! Ha, ha, ha, what a funny wee blighter she is! She's a wee comic! What the *devil* is she doing? Do you know?"

"Oh, she's just a very imaginative wee girl. She'll have some story in her mind that she's acting out, maybe something that I've read to her, or my father has told her about. Maybe something about fairies or perhaps she just likes the trees...by the way there's rolls and cheese and bread and jam and bananas and apples in the basket. I expect you're still hungry?"

Bruce eagerly dived into the basket, then continued as he munched,

"Did you ever do anything like that when you were wee? Walk round touching trees, I mean. You see I never did *anything* like that. I'd have been climbing up the tree or I'd have fallen in the water by now. Ha, ha, I was always a wild wee bugger."

"*Bruce!* Watch your language. She's got ears like I don't know what ..."

"Yes, but I never did any of that walking around trees slowly. Seems an awful strange thing for such a young kid to do. Unnatural almost."

Annie had been enjoying herself thoroughly until that moment.

"*Unnatural?*"

"Well maybe that's the wrong word. I suppose I mean just not exactly normal."

"You're saying our child is not normal?"

"No, no, of course not but she's ... I don't know." Bruce scratched his head, "Arty and peculiar I suppose I mean."

Annie said nothing more but watched him coldly as he demolished the remaining food.

Her mother was right. He was a fool, and a greedy one.

Though the picnic was spoiled for her mother, Helen would always remember that day with great pleasure.

The sound and smell of the burning wood, the savoury aroma of the sausages that made her feel so very hungry and the magical environment of trees and water would be conjured up many times in the future to enhance her imaginary world.

Dance Class

Annie worried that Helen led a very narrow social life. Surrounded by adults and mixing with no-one of her own age, her daughter cowered away from other children in the playpark, in a way that saddened her mother. Two of Annie's friends were now mothers, but their infants were still too young to be of much interest to Helen.

"Why don't you send her to that place round the corner?" said Mary one day as Annie was discussing the rather lonely life that her child led.

"I expect there will be a class for wee things like her."

She referred to the dance school near the Mackay flat at Charing Cross.

Annie laughed at the thought of her small daughter attending a class.

"She certainly loves dancing. I sometimes have to put the wireless off, or she would exhaust herself."

"I doubt if that woman will be able to teach her much. Have you seen how that child can high-kick?"

The reader may remember that Mary, herself, was an expert high-kicker and had encouraged her granddaughter in this useful skill.

"Well, it's really the idea of meeting and mixing with other kids that I think is important at this stage. I've no idea what sort of dance could be taught to a three-year-old. In fact I know the teacher, she used to be the gym teacher at High school."

Her mother looked at Annie in astonishment.

"Did she? That woman with the strident voice? You never told me that before. I say, that's quite amazing. So she's a real teacher?"

"Oh yes, a real teacher. I used to be terrified of her."

"Perhaps you shouldn't send the wee one there after all."

"Oh I expect Hoppy has mellowed in her old age."

"Not from the sound of that voice. Was that really her name?"

"No, 'course not."

The voice, admittedly of a militaristic strength, belonged to

Margaret Hopkins and in summertime, when windows were open, it was certainly an intrusive presence at the back of the block of flats. Even through closed windows in colder weather, the regular rhythm of her commands to aspiring ballerinas might be felt, rather than heard, by the sensitive.

The layout of the buildings and back courts behind the Mackays' flat was highly unusual.

Albany Mansions in Renfrew Street and the splendid curve of red sandstone tenements, known as Charing Cross Mansions, had been built around a portion of a previous terrace of houses, similar to the terraces west of Charing Cross. Three of these older houses had been partly demolished and were now one-storey, two-roomed studios, used for private education. These studios were tucked away, unseeen and secretive, in the centre of the rampart of tenements, which curved from Renfrew Street around to Sauchiehall Street. They were approached from the South. A brass plate at the entrance to a Sauchiehall Street tenement directed you to the *entresol*. The studios were reached by walking through the close, up three small flights of stairs, which wound around a decorative antique lift. A heavy back door led, by another flight of stairs, to a small, enclosed courtyard at first floor level. This was overshadowed on one side by the six-story tenement and otherwise hemmed in by unexplained walls and glass roofs at different levels. From the courtyard, a short flights of steps led to each of the three studios, where tuition might be had in dancing, typewriting or foreign languages. There was more than a touch of romance in the approach to this secluded nook, so completely cut off from the noise of the city. The back windows of the studios looked North over the deep and leafy backyard of Albany Mansions in Renfrew Street, sharing this outlook with the back windows of the Mackay's tenement, which was a particularly tall one of seven storeys. The back court was a neglected and overgrown abyss, to which Annie had only once or twice descended. It was a city jungle of weeds, self-seeded shrubs and a magnificent tree, shelter to sparrows, starlings, blackbirds and countless other birds of the city. This tree grew almost to the height of the seventh storey, its branches stretching out over the entire yard. When Annie visited her parents in the warm weather, she and Helen often stood for many minutes at the open staircase window listening to the strange symphony. The tapping of many typewriters was mingled with the demanding tones of the dance mistress and her piano accompaniment, and all was overlaid and modified by the incredibly loud chirping and whistling of the myriad birds who lived in the tree. The schools closed and were silent each evening and throughout the long summer days, but the *bavardage* of the birds never ceased. Even in winter there was always a friendly hubbub coming from the large tree. The tree and the birds who lived in it were an important and delightful part of Helen's visits to her grandparent's house.

Annie learned that Helen could start dance class immediately, though she required to have the school uniform, a purple romper suit (pattern and fabric available at Coplands) and soft grey slippers.

Miss Hopkins was friendly and business-like, though a little distant. The tall straight-backed figure, the large-nosed, medieval face and aristocratic voice, the kindly but distant manner, were exactly as Annie remembered from nineteen years ago. Miss Hopkins obviously did not recognise Annie as an ex-pupil, and Annie did not enlighten her.

"I can hardly believe it, Maw, she looks exactly the same, not a day older and I've to make a romper-suit for Helen, a purple one. Heaven knows if the wee devil will wear it. You know what she's like. If it was a down-to-the-ground dress, she'd be happier."

Mary had made Helen an ankle length dress of brightly flowered fabric for 'dressing up' and for months, the child had been unwilling to wear anything else.

"Best make a romper suit for Topsy, too."

"Righto, Maw, that's a good idea."

Topsy's rompers were made first, not without some difficulty of adaptation, and Helen was delighted with her larger ones.

Sadly the classes were not a great success. Helen was often unwilling to try the exercises and never happy about joining hands with other children. She must do exactly as she was told. The music was boring compared to the The Hall of the Mountain King and the movements seemed slow and ugly compared to her own free leapings and pirouettes. She was never once asked to give a high kick. There was a shoemaker's dance, which she quite enjoyed, stretching and waxing the thread, then hammering in the nails, but it was repeated so often that she became bored. Helen did not speak to the other girls. She thought their faces looked rather funny.

She stayed until the end of the Christmas term and appeared on stage at the Athenaeum in a 'Goodnight' dance with ten other pre-school girls. She was wearing a new yellow nighty and carrying Topsy. Looking out into the vast darkness of the auditorium, Helen was unable to see her mother anywhere and a great misery overtook her. It seemed pointless to go through with the whole charade of climbing up stairs then saying her prayers, for she did neither of these things at bedtime anyway. Then she was supposed to kiss her doll and lie down to sleep on the dusty stage. It was stupid and boring and it was not her idea of dancing. She performed the routine however, and saved her tears for offstage.

After the show, her weeping was doubly renewed at sight of her mother.

"What is it, my wee pet? Did you not enjoy yourself. I thought you did wonderfully well. You looked just lovely and you remembered every bit of the dance."

"Were you there, Mummy? I couldn't see you! Did you see me?"

"Of course I did. I wouldn't have missed it for the world."

Though truthfully Annie was disappointed at the pedestrian little piece that her graceful energetic daughter had been asked to perform. The fact that Helen had formed no friends and also that she seldom danced at home since starting classes, also dismayed her.

"I don't think I like dancing very much, Mummy."

"Well you don't need to go any more if you don't like it, my pet."

Helen's face broke into a delighted grin, then became serious.

"And that girl over there tried to coup me off the seat, too."

Annie had never heard her use this colloquialism before and was hard put not to giggle.

As they left the Athenaeum, Annie was thinking of the day when Helen, as an infant, was about to have her smallpox vaccination. Annie had felt it was criminal to spoil the perfection of her baby girl. Her own vaccination scar on her upper arm was quite pronounced and she had hated it showing, when she wore the sleeveless dresses then in fashion. Some of her friends had even uglier scars, deep and pitted.

With some hesitation, Annie had asked the doctor,

"Could the vaccination be done somewhere other than her arm?"

"Why do you ask?

"Well, it seems a shame to put a scar in such an obvious place, if it could go somewhere else."

"This vaccination is a very wonderful thing, Mrs Corning, I don't know if you realise how important it is. Smallpox is a life-threatening disease. It kills and disfigures thousands daily. But, perhaps in your baby's lifetime, we can rid the world of the scourge of smallpox! It's very short-sighted of any mother to consider depriving her child..."

"I don't *want* to deprive her of a vaccination, Doctor. Not at all. I merely asked if it could be put somewhere else."

"And what would be your reason for this request?"

After the doctor's dramatic speech, Annie felt embarrassed about her reasons and was trembling slightly. Yet she had thought about it a lot, so in a quick and determined voice, she replied,

"Well, we never know what might happen in the future. My daughter might grow up to be a famous ballerina or film star and an unsightly and unnecessary scar on her arm would be a great shame and a handicap to her career."

The doctor's lips were tight and his head shook slightly. He was not impressed by these nonsensical daydreams.

"Very well, if you have such faith in your daughter's future, I shall vaccinate on her thigh. but I warn you it may not 'take' there,and you'll almost *certainly* have problems keeping it clean and dry for healing purposes."

Annie felt two inches tall, but she had gained her point and, to her relief, the scars healed with no problems.

Now however, after her daughter's first stage appearance tonight, 'famous ballerina' could certainly be crossed off that list of future successes.

It seemed that Helen had ended her dancing career at the age of three.

One afternoon as Christmas drew near, Helen was visiting her Mackay grandparents.

Mary, in a mysterious manner led her into the studio.

"There's a very special surprise here for my little girl. It's from Mrs Horsland."

A large box with the name of the family's department store printed on the lid, lay on the piano stool.

"Go on, open it up, my jewel!" urged Mary.

In the box, under a lot of tissue paper, Helen found a party dress that Shirley Temple might have envied. It was pink taffeta with puff sleeves and two tulle overskirts of different shades of lilac.

Helen was speechless. She was not even sure if it were meant for her or not.

"There's something more! Keep looking."

Helen removed more tissue paper.

Another dress was revealed. It was a similar style but in green taffeta and blue tulle.

Two dresses! It was confusing. Which one was for her and who was the other one for?

"Let's see if they fit you, the pink one is a wee bit bigger I think, let's see."

But for Helen the most exciting moment had been when the first dress was revealed. That had been so unexpected, it had been like magic. Somehow two dresses seemed silly and the green one proved to be too small. Helen wished that it had never arrived. She wore her pink party dress once or twice, but only for her family, for she had no friends of her own age to share a party with. In her mind, she often went over that wonderful moment when she had unwrapped the first dress.

What was very nice was that her Grandma bought her soft bronze-coloured party pumps to wear with the dress. They were decorated with a tiny rosette and Annie sewed on elastic which crossed at the front and twisted around her ankle, to hold them securely. She loved those pumps and thought them much prettier than the slippers she had worn at Miss Hopkins.

Now that she no longer attended dance classes, she could dance *just* the way she wanted and *any time at all.*

Break Up

Ans Christmas approached, Bruce became more and more
dour. He hardly smiled when he arrived home at night.
Dinner would be eaten without a word and he almost
ignored Helen. Strangely, it made life easier for Annie, as the
child reached bed-time without any upsets, but it was a sad,
unpleasant atmosphere. She had no idea what to do about it.

Most nights, after a brief look at the newspaper, Bruce would
fold it up with the maximum of noise and go out, often without a
word of explanation. What could be the matter? Annie knew that
things were difficult in the business, but when she had asked if
that were worrying him, he had roared out it was not and left the
house immediately.

Christmas dinner was eaten at Doune Terrace, but it was a
miserable affair. Mrs Corning obviously found it beyond her
capabilities to bring everything to the table at the right time.
Annie offered twice to give a hand in the kitchen, but was
refused with a sad smile. At first sight the table, set with the
Crown Derby dinner service, had looked very splendid, but as
the long night wore on, Annie found the pattern of vivid colours
almost unbearable. The food was overcooked and not very hot.

Old Mr Corning and his two sons sat still, while Jane Corning
struggled with carving and serving. Stewart hardly said a word
and Bruce's remarks were addressed almost entirely to his father.
Annie tried to start a conversation with Stewart about the baths
club, as she knew he spent a lot of time there, but he had no skills
of small talk and they soon fell silent. Poor Mrs Corning was
much too busy to chat.

Annie, as usual, found that time seemed to stand still in that
house. It was the longest, dullest meal that she had ever eaten.

◊

At eleven o'clock on Hogmanay, Bruce went out to first foot
the Forresters. He hesitated at the door, holding his hat in his
hand and turning it nervously round and round.

"Annie, I might not be ... probably won't be back tonight.
Don't worry if I'm not home. Bobby said we might make a night

of it and go and see some folk on the South side."

"That's all right, Bruce. Just do what you want. I'm ready for my bed now."

"It seems a bit strange just leaving you alone tonight."

He seemed unsure of himself.

"Well, I don't mind at all, Bruce. Don't feel guilty. I've never been in the habit of staying up late and drinking in the New Year. It's just another night to me. I'm tired and I'm really happy to go to bed with a book. On you go and don't worry about me. I'm fine, really."

He kissed her quite tenderly, something he had not done for some time.

Annie often wondered if she should have said something else at that moment. Perhaps if she had expressed regret, or if she had thrown her arms around his neck and begged him to stay with her, things might have turned out differently. Probably not.

When Bruce had not returned home by the following evening, Annie was worried and phoned his mother. Jane seemed even quieter and more reserved than usual.

"Yes, Annie, Bruce is here with us, but I'm afraid he cannot come to the phone just now."

"Why not. He's not still drunk is he?"

"*Annie!* What a thing to say! I've never seen my son in liquor in his life!"

There was a long pause.

"Well, why can't he come to the phone, Mrs Corning? What's the matter? I've had to come out to the call box and Helen is alone in the house. I don't want to come out again tonight. Is he all right? Has he had an accident?"

Again there was a pause. Annie knew that her two pennies' worth would soon run out. She asked, for it was the only reason she could think of.

"Is he in the bath or what ...?"

"Yes ... yes, I expect he's in the bath. I'll tell him you called."

Mrs Corning hung up.

Annie stood looking at the silent phone. What sort of strange family were they? Should she be worried about her husband? She returned to the house and wept for twenty minutes. She felt confused and very much alone. Perhaps she must face the fact that Bruce had gone home to his mother permanently.

From that time onwards, Bruce would remain a peripheral figure in Helen's childhood, difficult to understand and always slightly intimidating with his noisy laughter and nervous physical presence. His visits to his wife and child were inconsistent and unannounced. He liked to 'drop in' and seldom stayed long. He continued to support them financially, though rather less than adequately, as wages were small and his own expenses must be considered. He would at times be generous to the child and also arrange outings and excursions for them as a family, but his role was ambiguous. Helen dreaded a visit from her father as it heralded a quarrel as often as a treat. She learned not to depend on his invitations.

There would be a few brief periods of father and daughter communication in the future, but mainly there would always be a lack of sympathy. Bruce was himself ingenious and creative in his engineering profession, but he would never appreciate, or allow himself to appreciate, the creative talents of his wife and daughter. Nor did he understand the timidity of the little girl, or how his teasing and overpowering gusto frightened her. As Helen grew older, this fear would change to embarrassment and hostility, though Bruce, supremely self-centred, seemed unaware of her attitude.

Annie felt a terrible sense of failure at this final break-up of the marriage, but things did become easier for her. She could concentrate on what sort of life she wanted for herself and Helen.

The idea of divorce or legal separation, although both were considered, did not seem to have any immediate significance. It is possible that Annie, with her innate, romantic optimism, felt that sometime in the future things might improve again. She did not discuss this with anyone and was probably hardly aware of her own attitude. Bruce and his family had a horror of divorce and the stigma attached to the word. He certainly was not a bad man. After all, as Helen's father, he was still the most important man in the world to Annie, no matter how annoying and impossible he could be.

She was repelled by the thought of meeting any other man, but she dreaded lonlieness and regretted the loss of a sexual life. It made her feel an old woman at thirty two.

It was terribly frightening to think that she would have sole responsibility for Helen's well-being.

The first annual meeting of Greenock and District Child Guidance Clinic was held yesterday. The need for such clinics, the report stated, was abundantly demonstrated by the rising tide of juvenile delinquency and the number of backward and problem children in schools.

Glasgow Herald 26th February 1936

Later in January, when Bruce moved his possessions from the flat, he stipulated that he should spend time with Helen each week.

"That's fine with me, Bruce. I'll be pleased to get out of the house in the evening, for a change. How about each Thursday night and I could go for a swim if I wanted."

"Yes, yes ... I suppose that would be all right, but..."

"Maybe you don't want to tie yourself down to the same night always. I don't mind if the day changes each week, as long as I know in advance."

"It might be a wee bitty tricky, ye know. What with problems at the works and well, you know, Bobby sometimes arranges a night out at the theatre or ..."

"Oh! That's interesting. I never heard that you went to the theatre with Bobby. Does that happen often? With Bridie in attendance, I suppose?"

"Oh, if you're going over that old ground, I'm away."

"No, Bruce, don't go yet. Don't go flying off the handle. We need to arrange something, if you're really serious about looking after the kid."

"Of course I'm bloody serious about it."

"Well, say which day next week, then."

"Tuesday."

"That means I can't go to the baths, it's not a ladies' night."

"I thought you said it didn't matter."

Annie sighed.

"I suppose not. When will you get here on Tuesday?"

"That's hard to say at the moment, I'm afraid. Tuesday's a *really difficult* day for me, Old Turnbull is coming in to look at the books and there's a big wood delivery expected and ..."

"I wonder why you suggested Tuesday, when it's so awkward."

"Good God! I'll come next Tuesday, but I don't know when.

Hopefully before eight o'clock."

"Bruce, I thought you wanted to see Helen. She goes to bed at seven thirty."

"Oh aye aye. I forgot about that."

"Why don't you come here straight from your work? Come for your dinner. Then I can get away in time to see the two big pictures at the Grosvenor and you can spend time with the kid."

"Right, right you are. That's what I'll do. That's very good of you. I expect I'll get away all right. If there's a problem ... I'll ... hmm ..."

"Bruce! Just come if you can."

"Righty-ho, right you are."

Most of the arrangements followed this pattern, while Helen listened anxiously for the moment that they would start shouting. However after Bruce's departure there were fewer quarrels, for they expected less of each other. Bruce usually arrived promptly for his meal and was enthusiastic about the cooking. Annie always made a specially nice dinner and was smartly dressed to go out. As her mother's health improved and Helen grew into a well-behaved little girl, Annie's life became more relaxed and she lost the gaunt, drawn look that she had worn since Helen's birth.

It seemed easier for the couple to get along when they did not share a home. In February, Bruce arrived on Helen's birthday with an enormous teddy bear. He was smiling and joking and seemed in excellent spirits.

Helen hugged the bear and whispered to it when no one was looking.

"I was along at the Arlington tonight, Annie. Saw a lot of the fellows and it struck me that you can't get to the club much yourself, these days."

"No, haven't been there for ages. I did have one swim months and months ago, but it's been pretty impossible."

"You're still a member though, aren't you."

"Oh yes, my father has paid my sub all along, but honestly it seems a bit of a waste. Why are you asking?"

"Well, our wee daughter is four now and I've just been and joined her to the club! She's a fully paid up junior member of the Arlington Baths! So now you can both go along and you can teach our wee Tuppenny-ha'penny here how to swim. Keep up the family traditions, eh? And you can see some of your old pals, too."

There was a triumphant grin on Bruce's face.

"That's very, very thoughtful of you, Bruce. Thank you, thank you very much. That's really kind. I had still considered her a bit young to learn to swim, but I know in America they teach them when they're still practically babies. We'll go into Lumleys tomorrow and see if they have a wee toty red regulation swimsuit. Got to have her in the right gear. Then we'll go along on Thursday and I'll give you a report of her progress. I bet she'll do well.

"Aye, I bet she will."

They both smiled down proudly at their daughter, in the way that made her uncomfortable and wish that they would look away soon.

The Arlington Baths was a private club which had been established in 1871 and Annie and Bruce had been members of it since their teens. In their youth they had both been powerful swimmers, racing in the annual swimming galas and swimming for the Arlington team when it competed with the Western and the Dennistoun Baths clubs. Because the sexes were strictly segregated at all times, they had not met through being members. Originally an all male club, the men in the Arlington still had the lion's share of time allotted to them. The ladies had a full day on a Thursday with only a few hours on a Tuesday afternoon and a Saturday morning.

Annie had always enjoyed the club and had made several good friends there. Perhaps some of them had become mothers since she had last seen them? She was pretty sure that Annie Thomson had a wee girl about the same age as Helen. That would be nice if they could all go at the same time.

"Oh, Bruce this is just a lovely surprise! That's fair cheered me up. I'm raring to get back into the water. I wonder if I can still fly from one trapeze to the other?"

"Just you be canny, it's tough on your arms y'know, and ye're that wee bitty stouter than you were in your twenties."

"Oh, Bruce I hate that word stout! I'm not stout in the least, I hope."

"I'm not complaining! It suits you, suits you very well. You used to be a right skinnymalink. What was it I used to call you?

Oh yes, the Russian Famine."

Bruce went into one of his long, loud bursts of laughter as he donned his coat and hat.

"There'll be no trapeze because I'll have to look after our wee champion and show her how to do the Australian crawl!"

"You'd start with something simple though Annie, wouldn't ye, just the breast stroke or even a doggie paddle." He looked quite dismayed as he spoke.

"Of course Bruce, I was only *joking.*"

She gave him a hug and a kiss.

"Thank you again, I really appreciate it."

"The wee yin hasn't said anything at all."

"She doesn't know what fun is in store for her. Besides she's too carried away with her teddy." He suddenly looked anxiously at his watch

"But now, if you'll excuse me, I'd better get away."

He did not say where he was going and Annie was too proud to ask. It always seemed that just as they were finding some common ground, Bruce remembered another part of his life which demanded his attention. Annie regretted that she and Helen were never placed a the top of his list.

Still, that was a very nice generous gesture he had made and she looked forward to Helen's first visit to the old club.

Swimming

It was a cold, blustery day, but when Helen stepped through the swing doors of the Arlington, she seemed to have stepped into summertime. The ceiling was very high and the air was *so lovely and warm*. As well as the comforting warmth, there was a strange sort of silence that could be heard. She whispered to her mother that she had never been in a place like this before.

They pushed open another tall swing door and suddenly there was quite a lot of noise with strange unrecognisable echoes and a strong, but not unpleasant, smell. Looking to her right, Helen saw two large open arches soaring above her head and through the arches was the swimming pool. It was a beautiful greeny blue colour and there were several people jumping and splashing in the water and, very strangely, one seemed to be flying *above* the water. They all wore red swimsuits like the splendid one that her mummy had bought yesterday in the sports shop. On the front of each suit was a large white A. Helen's costume had no A because there had been none left in the shop, and truthfully Helen would rather not have one. The swimsuit seemed very smart just plain red with the white trimming round arms and legs. The idea of having a big letter on your clothing seemed bizarre and not at all *comme il faut*. At four years old, Helen had fixed ideas about what was or was not acceptable.

She and her Mummy sat in a small alcove and took off their shoes and socks and stockings, putting them neatly below the bench. Then they walked round the edge of the pool to the office where they met a bad-tempered man who hardly said 'Hullo' to her Mummy. He took the nice new swimsuit and in moments stamped three messy numbers in dark blue ink on the back of it. Helen was very agitated and near to tears. Her new costume was ruined! Why had her Mummy not stopped this man. Mummy just smiled and said,

"That's your membership number, do you think you could remember it? One, two, eight. There will be a hook with that number and you can always find your costume there when you come to the baths."

Seeing that her daughter did not understand her and was near to tears, she explained further,

"You see, after your swim you'll leave your suit here and they'll dry it for you, ready for next time. It's very handy. Everybody has a number stamped on their suit."

Helen was obviously unhappy about everything, the number on her suit, the fact that she would not have her swimsuit at home with her and the bad-tempered man. Mr Saddler the bathsmaster was positively glowering at both of them and one of the maids, whom Annie had never liked, was standing there with a bitter look on her face. Certainly it was not a very friendly atmosphere for a timid little girl.

Annie set off along the side of the pool, aware that Helen was pulling strongly away from the edge of the water.

"Mummy won't let you fall in, my pet. Stop worrying."

Annie always had a bath before her swim and she was now heading for the senior baths, which were situated in a room near the deep end of the pool. Someone jumped in right beside them and Helen was splashed and whimpered miserably.

"Hush! It's only water, Helen."

As they turned into the room where the six enormous senior baths were each housed in its own little cubicle, the maid came running up.

"Ye cannae gan in therr wi' a junior. Ye're no' allowed. It's senior members only in therr."

Annie stopped in her tracks.

"What am I supposed to do with my wee girl, then? There's nowhere safe to leave her I suppose?"

Annie felt Helen's hand tighten like a vice at the thought of being separated from her mother.

"Don't worry pet, I won't leave you. But what *am* I supposed to do? This is a real nuisance. I need a bath before I swim. That's a rule too, I believe. Surely she could just come in with me."

"Naw! Ye cannae take'er in therr. Nae juniors. S'no' allowed. An' ye'll need to hiv a shower afore ye go in the pool. Baith the two o' yez. It's the rules"

Annie sighed deeply. The Arlington staff were not noted for their manners, but this woman seemed particularly offensive.

"All right, I realise that."

Fortunately Helen really loved the Victorian shower, which wrapped around her on all sides and spurted two hundred and forty separate jets of water at her. It was hard to persuade her to leave its warm safety for the cold and noisy pool.

Annie had decided against any sort of water wings and thought that if Helen were held in the water at the right depth, she could hardly avoid learning to swim quite quickly. Annie and her brother had taught each other by this method, but they had been a few years older and more dare-devil than Helen would ever be. Helen was slow and unwilling to enter the water and then she clung around her mother's waist as if for dear life.

"Mummy wouldn't bring you anywhere that was dangerous! Just lie on your tummy in my arms and feel how nicely the water supports you."

But Helen struggled and whimpered and Annie, knowing that the maid's disagreeable eye was on her, took Helen back into the showers.

After a pep talk about being a big girl of four and how she would not like other people to think she was a cry-baby, Helen was brought back into the pool and they walked from one side to the other, Helen painfully gripping her mother's arm with two hands. Her chin was well above the water surface but Annie could see that she was terrified and exerting a supreme courage.

Just then Mr Sadler, the bathsmaster, came out of his office with a strange contraption which looked as though it might be related to a fishing line. There was a long pole with stout cords fastened to a piece of grubby-looking canvas which was dipped into the water. Helen was very interested and her hold on her mother's arm relaxed. A little girl, slightly older than Helen, came down the steps into the pool and, tummy down, positioned herself on the canvas while Mr Sadler, with a world weary expression, supported the pole as it took her weight. Then as the child made feeble arm and leg movements, Mr Sadler strolled backwards and forwards from one side of the pond to the other, showing little interest in his small 'catch'.

Very occasionally he offered a word of advice,

"Keep yer chin in the water!"

"Kick out and try no' tae splash."

"Take it slow, now."

Helen was fascinated.

"That little girl is five, just a wee bit older than you are and she's learning to swim with Mr Sadler."

Although Annie could not believe that the child was learning anything about floating or propelling herself through the water.

"Maybe *you* would like to learn to swim with Mr Sadler, rather than with your old mummy."

The look of wide-eyed horror which Helen gave her made it very clear that she much preferred her mother's tuition. Almost immediately, Helen lay on her tummy in her mother's arms and made tentative swimming movements.

"I think we'll need to practise your strokes on dry land."

However the first steps had been taken. There was practice at home, with Helen balanced on her stomach on the big leather footstool, waving her arms and legs in the designated manner for breast stroke. She slowly grew more confident in the water. Annie patiently held her daughter for many months before the child found the courage to set off on her own. For the first year, Helen found swimming more of a duty than a pleasure, although she always adored her time in the shower.

Annie had thought that the nightmare of hair-washing might be solved by the Arlington showers, but again she was frustrated, for a large notice proclaimed

NO SOAP IN THE SHOWERS

and the screaming ritual in the sitting-room continued.

◊

In March the splendid, long-awaited ship, the Queen Mary, was to say farewell to the Clyde and sail to Southampton to start her maiden voyage. The event caused great excitement. Each day the newspapers were full of little bits of information about the beautiful vessel. It was rumoured that it would have a captain and a commander on board but this was later denied. Plans and photographs of the luxurious interiors were in every magazine. There was speculation about the names of the aristocrats and celebrities who would be the first to sail in this floating palace. It really would be a historic occasion and Annie's curiosity was aroused. Why should she and Helen not take the train down to Gourock, or was it Greenock, and enjoy some of the excitement? No doubt there would be some sort of procession with bands and waving flags and banners. It would be something for Helen to be able to say in later life, "I was there." However it was not easy for Annie to find out exactly where she should go. They took the train and it was a pleasant journey, but when they arrived the crowds were daunting. Bunting was flying from every lamp post and shop front. They walked and walked and saw no bands, no procession. Eventually after nearly two miles of drifting along with the crowds, the impressive craft came into sight. It was enormous-but it was moving swiftly away into the distance. Annie felt disappointed and stupid. She should have found out more exactly where would be the best place to see it and they should have been there much earlier. Walking in the crowds had tired her and now they must make their way back to the station. There was no tearoom or ice-cream shop in sight or they might have had a snack and a rest. Fortunately Helen was a good walker and had trotted along without a word of complaint.

On the homeward train journey, Annie tried to discuss the magnificent ship, but the child seemed more interested in the fact that she had seen lots of black men, rather like Topsy.

"Why were there so many black men there, Mummy?"

"I don't really know. I didn't notice. I expect they were Lascars."

"Lascars?"

"Yes, sailors from India, I think."

"Those Lascars were very black, weren't they. Blacker than Topsy."

Helen had learned a new word that she liked and it seemed more important than a ship in the distance, no matter how large.

◊

By mid-April, Bruce was visiting the Hyndland flat regularly on Tuesday or Thursday each week. He looked after Helen while Annie went to the baths or the pictures. Quite often he took them both out at the weekend in the small green Austin car. Annie felt grateful for her evenings out and was perhaps kinder in her comments to him. Also she was not irritated by watching the insensitive way that Bruce dealt with his daughter.

Perhaps it was hard on the kid, but he was her father and she must learn to deal with him. Strangely, he seemed more anxious to please them than he ever had while sharing the home. Annie certainly felt that her life was easier, more luxurious, since Bruce had returned to his mother.

Annie wondered and hoped that there might be a future for them. But it sometimes seems that determined Fate stands ready to destroy certain relationships.

There would always be a strong attraction between Annie and Bruce, not all of it sexual, but the problems which arose between them were continuous, trivial, futile. Even though they made each other laugh and each was impressed to a certain extent by the other's industry, Annie found it hard to forgive her husband's foolish self-satisfaction. Bruce had been too strongly influenced by his mother's perception of Annie as a hopeless housewife and inadequate mate for her fine son. He felt strongly that she should be more grateful to him for having chosen her as a wife. Instead of which she criticised his habits and was often insultingly sarcastic.

Sometimes Annie would be surprised and impressed by the intelligence and excellent memory which her husband generally kept hidden under the many layers of his prejudices and assumed behaviour. Often, kindness and generosity lay underneath his insensitive ebullience and Annie would feel guilty for having misjudged him.

Occasionally it would strike Bruce that his critical mother had never decorated a room in her life, while Annie had just papered and painted the kitchen with its dauntingly high ceiling. The bright wave-patterned paper and fresh green paint had transformed the place, at very little cost. She also made smart inexpensive clothes for Helen and herself. His mother's economies in this direction were different. She had just taken a favourite winter coat to the tailor's, to be 'turned'. Bruce had been surprised at the idea of unpicking and remaking a coat, and also at how much this would cost, for it would still be the same old coat.

Annie was hooking another rug and there was always some Fair Isle knitting lying around the house. Bruce tried to convince himself how untidy these crafts were, yet he had a two very splendid pullovers that she had made him. The fellows at the club had commented on them admiringly.

"Here Bruce, that posh jumper must've cost you a penny or two!"

"It's too good for a ragamuffin like yersel'."

"Man, ye're as big a swell as the Prince of Wales any day!" they had all laughed and for a moment, Bruce had felt himself someone special, rather than the victim, that his mother considered him.

Annie had just had a little painting of roses accepted for the annual exhibition of the Glasgow Institute, which had pleased her enormously. However, compared to his mother's house, the Hyndland flat was untidy. Books, magazines and Helen's toys joined the general clutter. Often there were dishes waiting to be washed in the kitchen, while Annie was sewing in the sitting room. He counted this a terrible sign of slovenliness, for his mother washed the dinner dishes as soon as the last mouthful was consumed. Annie was certainly a very good cook, but his mother's disapproval hung like a veil between them and Bruce would never learn to tear away that veil. For Bruce, his mother's words and ways were sacrosanct.

The senior Mrs. Corning had visited Annie in Hyndland on only one or two occasions and afterwards had said plaintively to her son.

"Oh, Bruce, I can quite understand the problems you are experiencing, dear. You could never relax in an un-cared for home like that. You certainly would not want to spend much time there, I would think."

In fact, Bruce's demanding work and full social life meant that he spent very little time in his mother's home either.

Fate was even less kind with the relationship of Bruce and his daughter. There was little common ground between them. Though Bruce admired his little girl, he had no idea of how to treat her. The prejudices which he held concerning women were too strong for him to think of her as a person. Helen was not attracted to her father and was a little afraid of him. He was rough and noisy and made silly jokes.

On the nights that he looked after her, while Annie went to the cinema, the time passed slowly for both of them. Sometimes, although not particularly gifted vocally, Bruce sang to her, but Helen did not know or care for the songs he chose.

The one about the tree was boring and 'Ol' Man River' made no sense at all. His intense gaze as he sang embarrassed her, and she always declined politely if he suggested she join him in song. The very worst one for Helen was 'Daddy wouldn't buy me a Bow-wow!' She despised people who used the word bow-wow instead of dog and when he reached the lines,

> *"I've got a little cat and I'm very fond of that.*
> *But I'd rather have a Bow-wow-wow."*

He always tilted his head and smiled winningly at this point and Helen would look away and feel embarrassed and rather sick. It was such a silly song and so unlikely that anyone might prefer a dog to a cat.

He usually sang that song twice.

Bruce had no skills in story-telling, but he could describe things that he had seen. He often spoke about Blackpool. He had enjoyed his visit so much that he painted a glowing picture for his daughter, describing the wonderful coloured lights that created moving animals and people in the sky and the enormous tower that glowed and flickered all through the night. Helen enjoyed his enthusiastic description, but she found it difficult to visualise this strange town.

One night Bruce had a brilliant idea. He tilted up the big oak dining table at an angle and suggested that Helen could slide down it, just like the chute in the park. Topsy and the teddy had a few shots first in order to overcome Helen's reluctance, but once Helen started, she loved it. Bruce would swing her up each time and down she would fly, landing at the bottom on the useful brown velvet cushions from the couch.

For once, they had achieved enough physical activity to please Bruce and yet not so much as to overpower his daughter.

Helen felt excited but in control, and she laughed and enjoyed herself in a way that Bruce had never seen before. He was delighted that his child could behave as he believed children should behave.

Annie returned to unexpected sounds of merriment, though it was long past Helen's bedtime and she felt a stab of pleasure. Previously, she had always been in the middle, explaining Helen to Bruce or trying to encourage her daughter to be nicer to her father. How terrific to hear them enjoying each other's company. What had caused this magic breakthrough, she wondered?

Annie opened the sitting room door with a happy smile on her face.

"Oh, Bruce!"

Her obvious dismay silenced the father and daughter.

"Look at the table! What a mess! It'll never be the same again. My beautiful table. *What were you thinking of?"*

The limed oak table did not have a highly polished surface or the first scratch made by the two metal buttons on the back of Helen's skirt might have been more obvious, even to Bruce, but it was badly scored, marking the many times that Helen had enjoyed sliding down it ...

"Oh, Annie, I'm awful sorry, I never noticed. I'm awful sorry. We were having such a great time, wee Tuppenny and me. I'll get that fixed for you, don't you worry."

"I don't think so. It will never be the same. Really Bruce, it's your furniture too, you'd think you'd show some regard for it."

She turned on her heel and left the room to hide her tears and Helen thought sadly that she was just as much to blame as her Daddy for wasting the table and upsetting Mummy. Though she could not name it, she experienced the horrible feeling of guilt for the first time. She felt so terribly sorry, she could not even cry. She had so loved those buttons on her skirt, for they had little silver flowers on them, but she would never like them again.

Annie did not mention the table again, nor did Bruce, and for the next two months, he paid only fleeting visits to his family. Always with some pressing business to attend to, he seldom stayed for more than half an hour. Annie had not expected him to do anything about the table and she arranged to have a professional man in who made it look like new.

"I would send him the bill!" Mary advised.

"I just want to forget about it. The table's fine again. I miss my nights out, though. He never comes to look after Helen these days."

"Oh, well you can take the wee thing to the pictures with you now anyway, can't you."

"Aye, I suppose so, but it would be nice to get to the baths sometimes."

"I thought the two of you were going regularly, these days."

"Yes, but she's been like a wee old man of the sea clinging to me until just recently. It's not quite the same as going by yourself in the evening and having a swim and a blether."

Though Mary sometimes took Helen into town in the afternoon, she had never offered to give up one of her evenings to look after her.

"I really miss my 'evening off' and I suppose I've been feeling a bit lackadaisical recently."

"It's all that papering and painting. You're exhausting yourself. You should get it done professionally."

"That costs money, I'm afraid. Anyway I enjoy it and it looks great now. I'm just a bit run down. I think I'll get myself some yeast tablets, they're supposed to work wonders."

"Hmm, you're a great believer in all that health food stuff. I'm more for mince and totties myself."

"You should try that health food shop down the road. It's so interesting, all the different things they have from all over the world. I think my favourite is walnut butter. Absolutely delicious, I'll get you some to taste."

"No, don't bother. I don't think I'd like it. You *are* looking tired. What age are you now? Thirty-three is it? I remember thinking my girlhood had gone at that age. Of course you were a big well-grown girl of thirteen by then, with a bust. Practically a woman. You're lucky that Helen is still such a sweet, little thing. Wee sweetheart."

◊

Bruce went with the Forresters to the Alhambra theatre where the American musician Larry Adler was playing his harmonica.

There had been hundreds of miniature mouth organs thrown into the audience at the end of the evening and Bruce triumphantly produced one for a delighted Helen. It was just the right size for Topsy.

"I'm telling you, Tuppenny, it wasn't easy to get that wee instrument. Had to do a bit of pushing and heaving, but I was determined! Honestly, that fellow's a genius! What a player, he could play *anything* from 'Ol' Man River' to those songs that crooner sings, the one you like, ye know, boo boo boomba doo, what d'ye call him ... Ding Crosby is it? ... Anyway Larry Adler

could play anything! Jazz and all that high falutin' stuff that
you like, 'Flight of the Bumble Bee' and the 'Ride of the Fal
Keeries' or whatever it's called. Real tunes as well, 'Git along
little Doagy' and 'Silent Night'. He was really marvellous.
Stupendous! What a musician! What a bloody clever, wee joker
he was. Jewish too, mind you, but clever, very, very clever.
Bloody marvellous wee Jew boy."

"Can't quite imagine Wagner on the mouth organ, but I'll
take your word for it. It's a neat wee harmonica and the kid's
awful pleased with it."

Annie was less than enthusiastic, for she could not help but
feel hurt at the thought of Bruce at the theatre with his friends.
Apart from the disappointing dance show in the Athenaeum, it
had been years since she had been in a theatre.

Bruce must have realised her feelings, for in a couple of
weeks he dropped in one night and said,

"Oh, by the way. You know that wireless show that the wee
one's so keen on. She never misses it. You know the one?"

"D'ye mean Bandwaggon?"

"Aye that's the one. She likes it, doesn't she? Well they're
coming to the Alhambra, so I got us all tickets."

Annie flushed with pleasure.

"Oh that's lovely, Bruce. I'll enjoy that too. I'm never quite
sure how much she understands of it all, but she sits glued to
the set and talks about it afterwards. She's not interested in listening to anything else, she walks away from Children's Hour
after five minutes. Music's different of course. She's always
ready to dance. But when are we going? I'm quite excited
myself."

Unfortunately the stage Bandwaggon was very different from
the radio Bandwagon. The same performers were in it, but seeing
their faces did not seem to improve the show and somehow the
magic was lost. Annie looked smart and enjoyed being in town,
but she and Bruce agreed that it was a poor show. The jokes were
often above Helen's head and the visual gags were not funny. It
was rather a quiet journey home in the green car, though the couple were, for once, agreeably relaxed and harmonious.

"When is Bandwagon on the wireless again?" asked a small
unsteady voice from the back seat.

Now Bruce had only been able to get tickets for the same

night that the show was broadcast, but he and Annie had considered that missing it this once would not matter as she was seeing the real thing onstage.

Perhaps foolishly, he was honest and explained that she had missed it that night through going to the theatre.

There was a terrible scene. Bruce had to stop the car for Annie to move to the back seat and attempt to comfort Helen's hysterical mixture of sadness and fury.

It was another instance of unkind Fate throwing a spanner into the works. Poor Bruce! Even when trying his best, he often had little luck as far as his daughter was concerned.

The First Portrait

At the end of April, John had announced that he was going to paint a full-size portrait of Helen for the annual exhibition of the Royal Glasgow Institute.

"I don't want her in a frilly dress, just something simple and nice colour. That little suit that Annie bought in Coplands would be the sort of thing I'm looking for."

"Oh John! Not that brown corduroy thing, d'ye mean? Surely not! That's far too boyish and sombre. I bet that fabric would be very hard to paint nicely."

"You just let me worry about that, my lass. Yes, I think that wee outfit would be very striking. It would show off Helen's lovely complexion. We could put a nice curtain behind her and a bright toy in the foreground for a dash of colour."

Annie had bought the suit in the boys' department at the autumn sales. She had noticed that boys' clothing was well-made and often cheaper than similar outfits in the girls' department. For herself, she had always preferred sporty styles. This brown ensemble had been described as a 'riding suit', and with its jodhpur trousers, bloused jacket and jaunty matching beret, Annie considered it not particularly masculine. Any unfortunate boy wearing such an outfit might well have had the epithet of 'Jessie' shouted at him in the street. However she liked it very much on her daughter and Helen had worn it throughout the winter. Nevertheless, Annie herself would not have chosen that suit for the portrait.

Mary had always hated the brown suit and did her best to dissuade her husband from using it, but John would not be gainsaid. He was the artist and he retained control of this part of his life.

There was a wooden throne in Glasgow, an exact replica of the one that Helen played on in Pittenweem. She stood on it, exactly as Drandad wanted, staying as still as she possibly could. It was boring and tiring, but he took some photographs to help him and Helen was always anxious to please her grandfather.

When the sittings started and it was obvious that John intended to use the despised brown suit, Mary sulked for two days. At last she burst out,

"You know John, I think you're making a terrible mistake, dressing her like that. Everyone will take it for a portrait of a boy. At least let me curl her hair. She'll look a little more like the dear, pretty little girl that she is. Please, John, for my sake. Just a few curls."

And in spite of John's misgivings, she had her way and Helen had to undergo ten minutes with the curling tongs before each sitting. She was very nervous of the hot iron tongs, but of course Mary was careful and it soon became part of the ritual.

On the first day John started painting, he was careful not to let Helen stand for too long at a time. As the afternoon wore on, the poses shortened and the rests lengthened. During each rest, Helen wandered around the L-shaped studio admiring the many interesting things. There was a life-size lay figure that could be dressed in soldier's full dress uniform or the official robes of a Lord Provost. There was a printing press. John had always enjoyed etching and prints continued to sell well. Helen found this heavy, sinister metal structure frightening and stayed well away from it. There was a hamper full of pretty scarves and pieces of fabric, and a large chest with fisher-girls' skirts and shawls. She was not encouraged to bring any of these things out of storage, but she could open the lids and peep in. On the shelves were brown and blue vases and jugs, some holding paint brushes, others with dried flowers. The free-standing stove, with its brown and white tiles, was different from any other fireplace Helen had ever seen. You could see the pipe behind the stove where the smoke went to the chimney. After lunch, John produced a bag of nice little buns that he stuck, one at a time on a long fork and toasted at the fire. Then he brought out a small jar of jam from a cupboard and spread a spoonful on each bun. It was like a secret picnic and Helen thought they were the most delicious buns that she had ever tasted.

On the wall was a wonderful print of a procession, where everyone was very lightly dressed. It must be in a warm country. There were pretty girls with long hair and lots of flowers. A man with a flying cloak had a *leopard* walking beside him. That appealed to Helen. She would love to walk along beside a leopard.

Eventually that first day, John could see by the yawnings and fidgetings that the child was tired and the day's work pretty well finished. As he painted a last corner, he asked,

"Now, Helen if you could have three wishes, what would you wish?"

"I'd wish to get down off here and I'd wish for a peeled apple and I'd wish for a story."

She was a sensible child, whose wishes were immediately fulfilled.

On the fourth day of painting the portrait, Helen came around the side of the large canvas on the easel and uttered a cry of delight at what she saw. Since the last sitting, John had added Topsy to the painting and there she sat on a stool at Helen's feet, dressed in her original primitive outfit of raffia skirt and beads and smiling happily. Helen's attitude to her portrait changed from that moment and, instead of a boring duty, the experience became pleasurable and important. When Helen felt tired she need only peep at Topsy in the painting to feel happy and ready to stand very still again.

Mary would come in most days and stand looking at the painting for several minutes, then say nothing. John knew she was brooding about the brown corduroy and he would stop painting and smile nervously over his shoulder at her, then cough slightly and rub his moustache energetically with the back of his hand. He was always relieved when she left. One day when the painting had progressed and it was obvious that Helen was grasping the edge of the large curtain behind her, Mary asked,

"John, why did you choose that grey curtain to hang behind Helen?"

John coughed again before answering, but Mary continued,

"And what's in behind the curtain? She looks as though she has something hidden there."

"Perhaps she has! Perhaps it is magical and she will surprise us all, one day."

Mary's deeply indrawn breath signalled that the next few hours would be pregnant with her silent displeasure.

The following day when her footsteps were heard climbing the stairs to the studio, John stopped painting and braced himself, but she only stayed for few moments and all that she said was.

"I certainly think you could have found a more interesting toy, than that cheap celluloid windmill."

Apart from Topsy's beads, the windmill on a stick which Helen held in her left hand was the only spot of bright colour in the large canvas.

Mary, having shot her last bolt, did not return to the studio for a week.

Later in the year, the portrait was hung in the RGI exhibition and Helen's face, with its innocent yet mysterious expression, gazed out at the milling crowds. A large photograph of the painting was published in the middle pages of The Bulletin and it was specially praised by the art critic in the Glasgow Herald. When the compliments were read aloud, Helen enjoyed hearing the phrase 'the artist's granddaughter' though she was surprised that nothing was said about Topsy.

There were several commissions for portraits of children for John after that exhibition, but Mary always regretted the brown outfit and assured her friends that he would have had twice as many commissions, if Helen had been dressed in a pretty frock.

Summer Holidays

After Bruce left the flat, Annie saw more of her old friends. Elsie, who lived in Lambhill, had two little girls, one still an infant and the other only two. Helen found them too young to play with, but she liked Aunt Elsie's house which was very *moderne*, with a bright yellow chest of drawers and tables and chairs painted in unexpected purples and scarlet. Elsie was fond of the well behaved little four-year old and very kind and loving to her, almost more kind and loving than she was to her own two children.

One afternoon Elsie had several friends for tea.

"When d'ye think my two will become more civilised, Annie? If ever? They are both so messy, it drives me wild, cleaning up after them."

Elsie was an obsessive housewife.

"Oh, they improve all of a sudden. Just enjoy the baby stage while you can, it doesn't last long."

"Thank God for that! Can't *wait* till they start school!"

Annie wondered at her not taking more pleasure in her kids, for Elsie's husband was a hard drinker and could not be much company in the evenings. However Elsie had brought up her young sisters and brother when her mother had died, so perhaps she had done enough mothering for one life-time.

Annie smiled complacently at her daughter, who could be trusted to behave beautifully in company, though twister tantrums still sometimes wrecked their home life. Helen was handing cigarettes from a marvellous wooden box which had a little dog on the top. When the dog was twisted, a cigarette appeared miraculously from the interior of the box and Helen was encouraging the five ladies to smoke as many as possible, in order to enjoy this small wonder.

Nancy was another old friend from school and Art School. She had a three year-old daughter, Ruth. Poor Nancy was having many problems with her husband.

One afternoon in the Hyndland flat, she had confided to Annie, without going into details, that divorce was probably her only option. It seemed a terrible decision to make. Fortunately Nancy's father was comfortably off and could offer them a home, as it seemed unlikely that there would ever be any financial support from her husband. Nancy had qualified as an art teacher and would return to that, once Ruth was older.

"What bad luck! What a rotter! I'm so sorry, Nancy. I'd no idea things were so difficult for you. Well it's really fortunate that you did your training, isn't it! I wish I had stuck in and finished my diploma."

"I suppose so, but teaching isn't easy. It's not the life I would have chosen, with a child to bring up. There's such a stigma attached to divorce, too."

Nancy wept a few tears and Annie stroked her hand.

Just then Helen came in, holding one of her books open at a page which had been scribbled over with a pencil. Her face was severe.

"Excuse me, Aunty Nancy, I don't think you should allow your child to treat my book like this!"

Annie was aghast and speechless. What a little prig her daughter could be! And coming in at this tragic moment was such bad timing! It was certainly true that Helen was very careful of her books and toys. Poor Nancy! However, it took her mind off her troubles for a moment and she replied,

"Oh, Helen I am so sorry. She is a naughty girl, but remember she is still very little compared to you. Perhaps if your mummy has a rubber I could try and clean it up for you."

Though Annie was embarrassed, Nancy was really quite amused by Helen's indignation.

Vida was the only one of Annie's friends still unmarried, but Vida had seemed destined for the role of old maid since her schooldays. Always neatly dressed, law-abiding and correctly spoken, Vida had worked as a secretary in her father's firm and had not followed the social and athletic pursuits of her fellow pupils. They suspected that dust and sweat terrified her, for she did not play tennis, golf, swim or even dance much, with the result that she did not meet young men. She lived in a small apartment with carefully arranged, but overmuch, furniture. Helen enjoyed visiting Vida because her flat was so crowded and different from the emptier, more spacious flats that everyone else lived in.

Tea was served on a tray, which was balanced precariously on a stool. Tiny embroidered napkins matched the tray cloth. Lace doilies were underneath all sandwiches, cakes and biscuits. Annie always felt nervous in Vida's flat, for although Helen was generally a careful child, it was often there that milk was spilled or biscuits were dropped.

Then Vida would leap to her feet crying,

"Don't worry dear! Don't touch anything now! I'll get a cloth!"

Then laboriously, and with several rinsings with fresh water, she would mop up the milk and Annie would feel awful. Helen was less concerned. She suspected that Vida rather liked mopping up, for it seemed that she kept on doing it long after she might have stopped.

One afternoon they arrived to find her sitting room unusually untidy. She was making a bed-jacket for herself which seemed a very luxurious and unnecessary garment to Helen, who had never heard of bed-jackets. Her mother had not worn one since the relaxing fortnight following Helen's birth.

This jacket was a very splendid one in pink knitted silk with white marabou trimming. Helen was entranced by the soft fluffiness of the marabou and she liked the word, too. Vida kindly gave her a few inches of the trimming and Helen treasured it for years, never quite sure what lovely thing she could make for Topsy. It was almost too exquisite to use.

"Vida! That looks to me suspiciously like a garment for a honeymoon!"

Vida laughed and did not deny the possibility.

One outing with Vida gave Annie a good story to make her mother laugh.

"Oh Maw, I must tell you. The other day we had lunch in Coplands with Vida. You know how perjink she is, fuss, fuss, fuss. It gets a bit much, sometimes, and I always worry that the wee yin will say or do something that will shock her. But we need never worry again. What a tactful wee besom that child of mine is. The soup was served and as usual, it was far too hot, so Vida was advising Helen,

"Now careful! It's too hot yet, dear. You'll need to wait for a little while. Are you very hungry? Well, just poof on it dear, just poof on your soup and it will cool down quicker."

Mary was now roaring with laughter for 'poof' was the family word for fart.

"And what did the wee one do? I wish I had seen her face."

"Oh, she behaved like a lady and blew on her soup just the way Vida was showing her and said nothing at all, but she gave me a very knowing look."

In May, Vida asked Annie if she would like to join her for a few days' holiday in Arran. There was a new hotel in Brodick, just opened by a friend of her father's. Annie thought that it would be a nice change from the East coast and a hotel sounded luxurious.

Sadly, it was a cold, windy week of continuous showers. Various aspects of the newly opened hotel were not quite finished, the staff were rude, the food was poor and Helen hardly ate all week and was permanently bored and hungry. To make matters worse, Vida seemed terribly depressed and Annie suspected the holiday was because of some tiff with the unknown lover.

The Arran holiday was a disaster and forever after Helen considered Arran to be the worst of all possible spots in the world. Mary enjoyed teasing her,

"When are you going back to Arran? That was a lovely place for a holiday wasn't it?"

"No! A *horrible* place."

"Did you not enjoy yourself there?"

"No!"

"Would you rather go to my wee Pittenweem house, darling?"

"*Much* rather."

And her grandmother would smile fondly, for she liked to have her belongings properly appreciated.

◊

Annie really was not feeling well and constantly found herself unwilling to 'get going'. In June she had confided to Bruce about her lethargy.

"Aye, well I've always said you should be out on the golf course more, Annie. That would do you a power of good."

"*More*! Bruce, I haven't golfed for years. Chance would be a fine thing. I'd *love* a game, if someone could take care of the kid."

"Could your mother not take her for the day?"

"Oh she's always busy with friends and golfing herself and entertaining sitters, I suppose. If I ever ask her for help, she's always tied up."

"Is your father still busy with portraits?"

"Yes, he has a couple on the go at the moment. Not so remunerative as that London millionaire, last year but good bread and butter. What about your mother? Couldn't she take Helen some weekend? Then we could have a game together sometime. That would be nice."

"Aye, Honeybun, that would be great wouldn't it. Of course mother always has church on a Sunday."

"Or you could take the kid some Saturday afternoon and I'd ask Nan Toner to join me for a game."

"We'll see, we'll see. That could be tricky y'know. But I'm sure a game would gee you up, lassie. Nothing like getting out on the course y'know."

Nothing was ever arranged and Annie was not altogether disappointed, for the idea of getting herself to a golf course and playing eighteen holes seemed like a great deal of effort. Then she would still have to come home and look after Helen.

Virol, the disgusting health drink which Annie drank daily was not working any magic, nor had the yeast tablets helped, though her mother's cat enjoyed both these health aids.

◊

Summer arrived and Helen was delighted. The interminable train journey to the East Neuk was accomplished, then the long walk from the station and finally the special moment when she stepped over the threshold of her grandmother's house was reached. The damp seaside smell of the house was delicious in her nostrils and the low ceilings were so excitingly different from the remote ten feet high ceilings in Glasgow. It was like living in a hatbox. She rushed out to the garden and checked that the honeysuckle, snapdragon and marigolds were in bloom. She pulled a sprig of aippleringie and, crushing it, breathed its pungent smell. Next was the ritual of climbing the secret steps, three jutting stones in the wall, to her lookout post where she could gaze out to sea. Unsure of what she was looking for, she enjoyed the drama of her lofty stance and the vista of choppy waves stretching before her.

Another lovely summer in Pittenweem had started.

Annie was less enthusiastic about her arrival in Pittenweem. She knew that the next eight weeks would be no holiday. Before her hat was off, her mother told her of various tasks that awaited her. She would work far harder physically than normal, for the holiday house was domestically inconvenient compared to Glasgow and her mother's standards were high. Mary might allow herself some leniency, but she had rigid ideas about the methods to be used by others. She was an almost impossible mistress, for she was a martinet, yet indecisive and erratic in her orders, often countermanding or adjusting previous priorities.

Annie knew there would be little knitting or sewing done, certainly no painting of pictures and she would have less time to spend with Helen. There would be no afternoon cinema. In the evenings, Mary expected to have an appreciative audience for her anecdotes. No doubt she could be very entertaining, but a nightly show, with much repetition, stretched ahead uninvitingly for Annie. She fervently hoped that the sea air would improve her health and energy.

Before she drank a coffee she had an apron tied around her waist.

"If you could just rinse through those dish-towels that are soaking there, Annie, and wash those few cups before we put the potatoes on. Ye're looking extra peely-wally, aren't you."

"It's a long journey. I'm counting on the sea breezes to buck me up, Maw."

"Well we'd better hurry, for it's long past lunch-time. Your father's up in the studio and I expect his stomach thinks his throat's cut. I never thought you'd be so late getting here. That train must have been extra slow."

At that moment two plates slipped from Annie's grasp and crashed to the floor. Her mother tut-tutted irritably and marched out of the kitchen, frowning. They were everyday plates, but Mary was unforgiving about breakages. As Annie swept up the shards, she thought of long ago, when Willie had broken the mirror and for a moment, smiled to herself.

Annie learned later that Willie was coming for a week's holiday and bringing Eileen, his new girl-friend with him.

"D'ye think he's serious this time, Maw?"

"I damned well hope not. She's a Roman Catholic."

Serious or not, Catholic or not, a tremendous programme of

cleaning was set in train before their arrival. The large backlog of laundry must be dealt with and the boiler in the wash-house was alight continuously for days, with the constant creak of the mangle echoing throughout the house. Floors were scrubbed, carpets beaten, brasses polished. Mary, as she did each year, sent John to buy a bucket of lime-wash. Next morning, she rose at six o'clock and painted the walls of the front of the house, before the town was astir. No one could accuse Mary of lacking energy, though it was noticeable that she chose the more dramatic tasks for herself, leaving Annie with much lifting of hot water, scrubbing and beating.

This year the lime wash was tinted a particularly strong ochre yellow which Helen disliked, preferring the faded tone of the previous year. When she complained to her mother about how horrible it was, Annie assured her,

"Don't worry! It'll get paler as the summer wears on and *don't say to Grandma* that you don't like it."

Helen made a moue of dissatisfaction, but her mother trusted her to say nothing, for Helen knew how to keep her mouth shut.

That year the Golf Open Championship was held at St Andrews.

"Is Bruce coming through for the Open?" Mary asked her daughter one day.

Annie, who had been shifting furniture and washing paintwork, sat down on the kitchen chair. The sea air had not worked any magic and she felt continuously tired. Each morning her mother proposed new household tasks for that day and Annie gritted her teeth and got on with it.

"I suppose he would like to see the golf. Nothing's been arranged so far."

"Well, write and ask him. We haven't seen him at all this summer. He could surely come for a few days."

Her mother appeared sublimely unaware of the problems inherent in this invitation. She spoke as though Annie and Bruce were a normal happy couple, living together. Where would Bruce sleep? Their relationship had been one of friendship, and not always that, for many months. And yet, how awkward to have separate beds! What if Bruce saw this invitation as a prelude to reconciliation? Annie did not want that either and she felt that she was being forced into a false situation. She was content that Bruce should stay away. The invitation was from her mother and yet she was expected to extend it. What was her mother thinking of? Annie sat gazing at her hands as they rested on the table. She was proud of her hands, they were a pretty shape and fell naturally into a graceful position, though they looked red and workworn at the moment.

"But we'd better get back upstairs and do that room before lunch, Annie. Just run along and buy some fish first, and we need bread and milk too and bacon and how are we for flour? And you'd better get a move on before the shops shut."

Though Mrs Mackay made all managerial decisions and most importantly held the purse strings, she was not an organised housekeeper.

Annie wrote to Bruce and he replied that he would be delighted to come on the Saturday, but as the Forresters were in St Andrews that weekend, he would be staying with them overnight. Annie was half relieved and yet offended that he had not suggested the visit himself.

When the Saturday arrived, Bruce came down to Pittenweem early and immediately took Annie and Helen back up to St Andrews.

"It's really exciting up there with the crowds, Annie, and you never know, we might see the Prince of Wales. He's supposed to be putting in an appearance."

"I wonder if Mrs Simpson will be there?"

"Who the hell's Mrs Simpson?"

Bruce did not read the gossip columns.

"I expect you'll hear plenty about her soon enough. I say, maybe we should have asked my mother to come with us. She looked a bit wistful as she waved us off."

"Och no, this is a wee family outing, just the three of us."

Annie was pleased and touched by this answer and found it very pleasant to be away from her mother's demands.

She felt happy and relaxed as they bowled along through the richly growing fields of Fife and determined that she would have a good day, whether they saw the Prince or not.

◊

Helen and her grandfather were always happy to spend time together. Whenever she climbed the outside stone staircase that led to his studio, there would be a peeled apple and a story waiting for her.

Sometimes they walked along the seashore to St Monance, lingering on a special part of the beach where one could find all sorts of small interesting stones, shells or finely sea-shaped arte-facts. The pebbles of the East Neuk beaches are particularly beautiful, in warm shades of cream, ochre and brown. Succeeding generations of children have enjoyed grinding the soft sandstone into 'flour' or 'sugar' for playing shops. John had infinite patience with his granddaughter and was reminded of the days when Annie and Willie had played in exactly the same way. As she played, his mind wandered sadly over the state of the family. Annie had a failed marriage and was not looking very well, while Willie ... well Willie had not really made his way in life yet and was still financially dependant on his father. Perhaps his latest venture, a menswear shop would succeed, if he put his back into it? Now he was speaking of marriage, but how would he support a wife, unless he changed his ways? And the girl was a Roman Catholic, too. That was another problem. John's father, an obsessive and bitter Presbyterian, would be whirling in his grave if he knew about that.

John felt old himself these days. As a young man, he had blithely carried his easel, canvas and paintbox, while striding for a couple of miles. Now the burden seemed weightier and more awkward, especially when going uphill, or if the wind were blowing. He was nearly sixty nine now. Next year he would reach his allotted span. He could see his beautiful wife growing older too. He had nearly lost her with that terrible illness. She had never been a calm girl and she grew more dissatisfied and demanding with the years. She was a wonderful woman, but life with her was never easy. Then the damned dealers were taking over the art world, convincing the wealthy to buy ugly distor-tions and daubs, while the masses bought prints of the work of dead artists. Meanwhile those wonderful Victorian painters, mar-vellous technicians, who had taught him as a young man were jeered at and despised. Who could understand it? John brooded, as he had done for most of his professional life, about his future. The commissions arrived and his paintings still sold, but for how much longer?

Then the political situation was something to worry about too. Surely the Germans, that clever and cultured people, would never be led astray by this madman Hitler? Where had he suddenly come from? Some people said that he had done a lot of good for his country. He certainly seemed to be revered by the ordinary people, but these theatrical, militaristic events, with massed soldiers and banners and shouting ... John shuddered though the sun was hot. Another war would finish Europe.

Life was difficult and sometimes very sad.

When Helen would draw his attention to some new object, John would forget his sombre thoughts and join her in her happy world of curiosity and imagination, explaining all he knew to the child, or taking part in a game of her devising. She was a constant source of pleasure to him and a shield against the depressive thoughts which hovered constantly.

Sometimes they walked away from the sea, past the railway station, then further on until they came to a bridge over a burn, where they clambered down a little embankment. Helen was not quite sure whether they were allowed to go there and was slightly apprehensive, but she knew that there was something very special about that path by the stream. There was a magical, quiet atmosphere, quite unlike the breezy seaside, where it was always noisy with the waves, the wind and the cries of the seagulls. It was calm here, although lots of birds twittered and sang in the trees and the water in the burn rippled along. It was as though they were all whispering and waiting. Foreboding is too strong a word for how she felt, but she was filled with an anxious yet pleasurable expectancy and held her grandfathers hand tightly.

John had grown up in the country and he showed Helen the things that he had enjoyed as a boy. The delicate primroses had a pale yellow perfume to match their appearance and the tough orange tansy had a pungent scent that suited their colour. John showed her the early leaves on the hawthorn trees.

"We used to call these bread and cheese and eat them."

They sampled the hawthorn leaves and Helen enjoyed them, but she could not agree that they tasted of bread and cheese.

"Don't worry, we'll come back at the end of the summer, when the scarlet haws are on the tree. They're like tiny apples."

"Would they be the right size of apples for Topsy?"

"Indeed, I think they would be just the right size for Topsy."

John, with the aid of his penknife, made a little musical pipe for her from a hollow stem. It played only three notes, but she thought him very clever. Then there was sort of chewing gum that he made from another twig. It tasted horrible.

One of the strangest things that they found was a puff ball. It was shrivelled and grey and looked revolting, but when it was squeezed, a little puff of dust flew out. It was fascinating.

"It's a sort of mushroom." John explained, "That's an old one and those are spores that are puffing out. They'll grow into other puffballs if they fall in the right place. But young puffballs are nice and white and plump and some are very big, as big as a melon, I believe."

"Can you eat them like mushrooms?" she looked doubtfully at the unattractive object in her hand and squirted more spores from it.

The idea of a large spherical mushroom appealed to her and she added it to the foods that she would cook in her imagination. She would be able to slice a large one up easily and fry it.

One day, returning from one of these walks, Helen ran to her grandmother who was sitting beside the fire counting the change in her purse.

"Grandma look what I found!"

"What is it my darling? Oh that *is interesting*" though truthfully it seemed to be a nondescript piece of stick. Whatever had fascinated the child was not apparent to her grandmother and when Helen ran from the room Mary threw the twig into the fire. Almost immediately she jumped to her feet with a cry of dismay. She had been holding a a ten shilling note in her other hand, and by mistake had thrown it into the flames instead of the despised morsel of wood.

Fortunately a small corner of the note with the serial number was retrieved from the ashes and the bank, after much deliberation, replaced the ten shillings. There was never any suggestion that Helen was at fault, but she herself was aware of the drama and the considerable time spent at the bank. It seemed like a terrible financial loss and she had many guilt feelings about the incident. If only she had not given her Grandma her little stick, the note would not have been thrown into the fire and there would have been no fuss. It was the first time that she was aware of the concept of the irrecoverable past and that sad phrase, 'if only'.

Her relief was enormous when the bank finally paid up.

The garden was always full of interest for Helen and she pottered there for hours. Her grandmother had put an old mirror in a flower bed where, surrounded by stones and plants, it made a delightful pool beside which Topsy might sit and admire her reflection. Topsy's personality and requirements were very clear in the imagination of this solitary child and the doll shared almost all her waking life. Annie had started to tell her little girl a bedtime story about Topsy's life in the days before she had come to live with Helen. Annie surprised herself with the wild and unlikely adventures that she created for the doll in this previous life and Helen never tired of Topsy in Africa.

It made the cheerful doll even more real to her.

Taking up more than a quarter of the ground space in the small garden was a large wooden building, known as the studio or the glass studio to differentiate it from the main workshop which was reached by an outside staircase. Half of this large structure was glazed like a greenhouse while the other half, similar to a garden shed, was a dim repository for unused furniture. It had first been built thirty years ago in a previous garden so that John might have somewhere to paint in bad weather. It had been dismantled and reassembled twice since then and had rested here for twenty five years. It now leaned somewhat to the side and had a rakish and ramshackle mien. The woodwork had long ago lost its paint, one or two of the glass panes were missing and some determined scarlet montbretia grew through cracks in the woodwork, flourishing and double the size of their unfortunate sisters who remained outside. When gales blew Mary watched the studio anxiously and swore that she could see it swaying. At intervals she became anxious that the panes of glass were unsafe and might slip and slice somebody's head off, but as the house was occupied for less than three months in the year, nothing was ever done.

Helen loved the glass studio. No matter what chilly breezes were blowing, the studio was cosy and quiet. It was extra nice on a rainy day, when the gentle sound of the rain on the glass made Helen feel terribly safe and she found herself smiling continuously. Because of its generally dilapidated condition, Helen could continue her messy garden ploys in the studio, playing with sawdust or a precious piece of strongly smelling putty, concocting doll's soup of leaves and seeds, making patterns of petals and even drawing in chalk on remote corners of the walls.

In the bright, glazed part of the shed was a four foot square wooden platform, about the height of a coffee table, called the throne. It was used to raise the sitter above eye level for easier painting, but Helen had many other uses for it. It might be a pirate ship, a storm-tossed raft, a gypsy caravan or a magic carpet for her and Topsy. Sometimes it was just a bus.

Hovering dustily in the dim part of the studio were a conglomeration of objects of which Helen was aware though she could not have described them accurately a stepladder, lawnmower, garden tools, two small tables, a rather fine lounging chair, some large and ancient books about the first world war, a horsehair sofa and many wooden and metal objects of unknown use. The sofa might have once been a resplendent piece, but was now sadly sagging, with immodest lumps of wadding and coarse black wiry bundles exploding from it. When Helen sat on it with her short skirt, it seemed the jaggiest, most uncomfortable, unwelcoming, horrible seat in the world. She seldom went near it. Nevertheless John and Mary often used it, with many rugs and cushions, for an afternoon siesta or for a Sunday morning perusal of the papers. Helen was banned from the studio when her grandparents required tranquillity and that puzzled her, as they usually seemed so overjoyed to have her company.

Another favourite employment for a rainy day was her swing, which hung in the long, dim coal shed, which, in spite of its name, was an area large enough to garage two cars, if the Mackays had ever thought to possess such things. The swing was the best kind, a simple wooden seat hung on ropes from an ancient and solid beam. It was a wonderful toy that Mary had bought for a modest sum. Helen could swing gently back and forth singing songs to herself or she could swing high enough to kick the low ceiling. She could swing side to side or in a large circular motion clockwise or anti-clockwise. She could lie on her tummy across the swing with her knees bent up, though by next year her legs would be too long for this particular manoeuvre. She could twist the swing tightly round and round in one direction and then enjoy the excitement of the mad uncontrolled unwinding. Sometimes she would swing and day dream for an hour. Swings in public parks with heavy seats hung on unyielding chains and with impatient children waiting for their turn, could never compare with the delights of Helen's Pittenweem swing.

Next to Topsy, the swing was probably the very best thing that Mary could have got for her granddaughter. Mary often spoke to her friends of what an outstanding success the swing was, as well as being such a marvellous bargain.

Her great desire to be successful, indeed the most successful in any situation, led Mary into unethical conversations with Helen.

"Does Grandma Corning have such a nice house as this one, my wee jewel?"

Naturally Helen answered in the negative. She found so many interesting delights in her grandparents' two houses that it seemed rather a silly question to her.

"Does your other Grandma make such good pancakes, my wee sweetheart?"

Again there was no contest, Mrs Mackay made better pancakes than anyone else.

"Which Grandma do you love best, my darling?"

Of course the answer was pre-ordained. Truthfully and easily, Helen was again able to give the correct reply. Nevertheless, young as she was, she had an uneasy suspicion that perhaps that question should not have been asked.

◊

On the day that Willie and his girlfriend Eileen arrived, Helen and her grandmother were both very excited. Mary spent most of the morning putting masses of flowers in vases and dressing herself and Helen in specially nice outfits, while Annie prepared the meal.

Though it was midsummer, Annie put on the fire. Mary said the fire always made the room look so nice. To look its best, the old-fashioned hearth must first be washed, then painted over with an evil-smelling mixture of whiting and sour milk, Mary insisting that this noisome application was necessary to keep the hearth sparkling white. The windows must be opened for half an hour afterwards, to rid the room of its disgusting stench. It was a job that Annie could have happily done without, for Mary had decided to have roast beef and Yorkshire pudding for lunch, an unusual menu for a weekday and a demanding one for Annie to manage herself, as well as the household chores. As the morning wore on, Annie realised that Mary was becoming more and more anxious, finding small corners that needed an extra polish, putting out special glasses and dishes, adjusting cushions and curtains. She also powdered her face twice and added a discreet smear of lipstick, applying the colour carefully to her upper lip then pressing her lips hard together to imprint the lower lip and reduce the somewhat vulgar brilliance of the vivid red make-up.

Was Mary determined to look wonderful and to have a perfect home and delicious food? Was she determined to show this girl, who dared to steal her son, just what standards she must match.

How sad to think that Mary was terrified about the meeting with this first real rival for her son's love. All this tremendous preparation was to bolster her failing courage. It was difficult to believe that her mother was so vulnerable. Annie felt sorry for her but also furious, as she herself was being used to set this elaborate scene. She did not give a damn for this girl, who was foolish enough to fall for Willie. She did not know her, she wished her good luck, but she would have preferred not to have had to work so damned hard for the last few weeks. She would have liked to stay in bed all day today, for she felt like a rag, and here she was, racing around cooking a large meal and ironing special outfits for Helen.

"What a mutt I am!" she mumbled to herself.

"What did you say, Annie?" Mary had sharp hearing.

"Oh I was just wondering why you didn't get some champagne in for the celebration today?"

Annie's sarcasm did her little good, for Mary's face changed and the flames of fury were almost visible around her, as she swept from the kitchen.

When the young couple arrived, Mary gushed an effusive welcome to her future daughter-in-law. Eileen was a petite and fashionably dressed girl, with the excellent skill of enthusiastic admiration. Mary accepted her multitude of compliments about the house, the garden, the view and her own appearance with a gratified smile and quite forgot to introduce her own daughter to the guest. Eileen, noticing the busy, untidy, young woman in the kitchen, deduced that she was the maid and was astonished when Annie, after serving the vegetables and gravy, joined them, still un-groomed, at the table.

Helen had a wonderful time with her uncle and his new girlfriend. They made a great fuss of her, treating her like a little doll.

Helen, although spoiled in many ways, was expected by the family to be quite adult. She was included in conversations and much of her interaction with her mother or grandparents was educational. Her mother had now taught her to knit and swim and Mary often allowed her to help with baking. Helen could break eggs with great skill and measure level teaspoons of spices. John, apart from all those myths and legends, had explained the workings of his plate camera to Helen and she had often watched the magical development of prints. Eileen was entirely different in her approach. She would grab Helen up and cuddle her and admire her pretty dress, counting all the buttons and exclaiming at her three silver bangles and her smart shoes. Then she would go into raptures over her silky fair hair and rub her little brown legs until they shone, declaring that she had 'never seen the like in her life'. Ice cream and sweeties were bought at any time of day and Annie resigned herself to the fact that Helen would not return to normal eating until they left. Eileen loved to make people laugh and was quick and witty. Annie appreciated her humour and it sparked off her own sense of fun. The two young women matched each other with limericks and rude stories, and Annie certainly felt cheered up by the visit. The extra work fell mainly on her shoulders, for although Eileen was always ready to wash dishes or peel potatoes, Mary would not hear of it and hustled her out of the kitchen. But Annie found it nice to have other young folk around and folk so determined to enjoy themselves. She realised that, though she was only thirty three, her life was taking on a tinge of middle-age, what with her constant tiredness and only her parents for company. She determined that she would have more *fun* when she returned to Glasgow.

Willie was obviously terribly happy and completely besotted. Perhaps Eileen, with her vivacity, her cajoling ways and her mock-bossiness, was just the incentive he needed, in order to settle down. She was always the charming centre of attention and Willie could not take his eyes off her. Annie thought that surely she was a much bigger attraction than chucking money away in some gambling den. Perhaps there was hope for him yet, if Eileen took him in hand and knocked some common sense into him. Annie hoped so, though she wondered if common sense were a favourite word of this young woman in her vivid beach-pyjamas, with her scarlet lips and nails.

On the fourth day of their visit, a thought suddenly struck Annie. Eileen's personality bore a distinct resemblance to her mother's! Their appearance could not be more different, for Eileen was tiny and slender, her movements quick and nervous. She had the brittle smartness which was now so fashionable, while Mary was tall, stately, full-bosomed, still possessing remnants of the sensuous pre-Raphaelite beauty of her youth.

But they resembled each other in other ways. Of course they did!

"By Jove, Willie's chosen a bride very like his mother!"

Annie smiled to herself. She would never mention this of course but the two women certainly enjoyed many similarities, their flamboyant dress sense, their vivacity, their charm, their need to fascinate and entertain and to be the centre of attention, their abilities as raconteurs and humourists, their impatience, energy, dominance. Rightly or wrongly, it appeared that Eileen, for the moment, managed to dominate Willie and twist him around her little finger. Did Eileen have Mary's terrible temper? Did she manipulate with hours of sulking? Annie wondered. She had seen no sign of these attributes. Anyway, even if she sulked, Willie would deal with it as he always had done. He would walk away.

It was certainly harder for Mary to appreciate Eileen and her fascination. This rival for her son's affections was also a social rival and Mary was unused to being an audience. Even Annie, who had been so dull recently, laughed more and joined in the repartee, while Mary gritted her teeth and fulfilled her function as a hostess, dressing more elaborately than usual, making her delicious pancakes for afternoon tea and smiling, albeit unenthusiastically, as the wisecracks flew back and forth.

John came down from his studio to join them and often seemed unwilling to return to his work.

One night when they were alone, Mary asked her husband,

"Do you think that girl has much in the way of good looks, John?"

"Eileen?"

"Yes of course. Who else would I be talking about."

"Oh yes, she's a very pretty girl, I would say, neat figure, lovely colouring."

"Mostly make-up. I thought you would have seen that."

"Oh, her eyes are a wonderful colour ... "

But John had noticed his wife's expression and he was a man who lived for a quiet life,

"... Of course, I wouldn't call her face *paintable*, she's very nice-looking, but she hasn't the features that would attract an artist. And of course her religion is a big drawback. I wonder what Willie will do?"

Mary grunted, but she was appeased.

One day Eileen and Willie found a clothes rope and were swinging it for Helen to skip. She was unskilful still, but there was lots of laughter.

Suddenly a small determined knock at the front door announced Audrey, the five-year-old granddaughter of the local farmer. Her annual visit to Pittenweem always coincided with Helen's and she was the only child with whom Helen had any contact in the summer. Almost a year older than Helen, Audrey was always ahead of her in the childhood skills of walking, running, hopping, skipping filling the younger girl's heart with an uncomfortable mixture of admiration and jealousy. When the clothes rope was 'ca'ed' for Audrey, she was able to jump twenty five jumps before she stumbled. Helen stood watching and biting her lips. Then Audrey who was a fund of quaint sayings announced that she could spell her name. When encouraged to demonstrate, she declaimed in a loud voice,

> *Audrey Paudrey, fan 'n faudrey,*
> *Nick or Naudrey, Boab or Audrey,*
> *That's the wey ye spell Audrey.*

The company was non-plussed for a moment but clapped politely. Mary recovered her equanimity first, though she smiled as she spoke,

"That's excellent Audrey! Can you spell any other names?"

"Aye, Ah cud spell Helen an' a'."

Encouraged to proceed, she increased her decibels,

> *Helen Pellen, fan 'n fellen*
> *Nick or Nellen, Boab or Ellen.*
> *That's the wey ye spell Helen.*

Everyone in the family had their name spelled, though single syllable names seemed less satisfactory. 'Willie Pillie' caused hysterical laughter.

Helen learned how to spell names too.

After that, the rain started and the grown-ups gathered up cushions and tea things and rushed into the house. The two little girls went into the garden studio, where Audrey chalked a nude lady on the wall in a secret corner. Helen had become very familiar with the details of the naked female figure since becoming a member of the Arlington club. It amazed her that so many fat old ladies did not mind showing their bare bottoms and titties. Still, to draw it on the wall seemed a very rude thing to do. Helen later shifted a chair in front of the drawing and no one ever mentioned it, and it remained for years in its hidden niche. It did not occur to her to wash it off. Probably she liked to peep at it occasionally.

It seemed terribly quiet and boring to Helen when Willie and Eileen returned to Glasgow, and she fantasised about the next time they would all meet again.

Audrey came to play each day, always with some little piece of village gossip.

"Pair auld Boab Thompson's awfy no' weel. The doacter disnae think he'll last oot the week."

Or it might be happier tidings,

"Jessie Hughes hid her bairn last nicht. It's a grand big bairn an' it's goat rid hair. An' Jessie's daein' jist fine an her milk's cam doon."

Another time she described her new cousin,

"That wee Richard's the bonniest bairn Ah've iver seen! He's fat as a wee puggy an' he's goat a heed o' black hair like an Indian, an' he's a *grand* sleeper. Sleeps a' thro' the nicht, ye ken!"

"What a caution that child is!" Mary exclaimed. Annie was speechless with suppressed laughter.

If it rained, the children took turns on the swing or played tiddly winks.

One day Mary put on the gramophone. Audrey liked the music, but had no desire to dance. Helen, as usual, gave a spirited performance to the Hall of the Mountain King, then the record was turned over and she danced Anitra's Dance, with a silk scarf floating and flying around her.

Audrey sat very still and silent as she watched. She seemed hypnotized.

"Did you like that, Audrey?" Mary asked.

"Aye, Ah likit it fine. She's an awfy grand wee dancer. Awfy grand fur her age."

Mary told Annie later and they agreed there had never been such an old-fashioned child as Audrey.

Since her son's visit, Mary had been more relaxed and friendly to Annie. She was much more sympathetic and suggested that she should lie down each afternoon.

"Away out to the studio, that sofa is comfortable if you put a rug over it and you'll just doze off in the heat. You should do that every afternoon for a fortnight and I'm sure you'll feel a lot better. It must just be exhaustion that's wrong with you. All that papering and painting! That's not woman's work."

Though astonished at her mother's generosity, Annie accepted the advice.

She decide to knit rather than sleep the day away. She had wanted to make a pram outfit for Helen's baby doll Rosemary-Daisy for some time. Of course, it could never replace Topsy in Helen's affections, but the fact that it could go to the beach for a swim was a big plus. Now the small garments would be light to hold and hopefully Helen would be pleased with the outfit. At the back of Annie's mind was the idea that a knitted pram suit was comprised of garments which could surely not be used for Topsy. All other dolls were stripped of their clothing for Topsy's benefit, for although Topsy could not wear all the innumerable garments that she possessed at any one time, they could now be stored in the doll's wardrobe that Bruce had given Helen in the Spring. This pale blue wardrobe had real wooden hangers and various sizes of drawers, each with a neat label describing the contents. It was a splendid piece and Helen was determined to have a big one just like it when she grew up.

Annie was not conscious of feeling jealous of the love which was heaped on Topsy, but she would have liked to feel that the baby doll was equally valued.

She had noticed that Helen was particularly attracted to the African students who attended Glasgow University and smiled brightly to them on tramcar or bus. Annie worried that they might be embarrassed, but they nearly always smiled and nodded back to the silver haired child. Annie supposed they must be lonely sometimes, being so far from home, in this cold, rainy place. Maybe a smiling little girl cheered them up so Annie smiled and nodded too. But what if Helen grew up to marry an African? She supposed that it would not be the end of the world but Mary would certainly think so. What would she say to that? But it was all due to her that Helen was so obsessed with Topsy and 'brown people'.

Then Annie would laugh at herself for having her four-year-old married off before she had started school.

Helen watched the doll's garments grow quickly with great interest. How lovely Rosemary Daisy was going to look. She liked the phrase 'pram set' and wished that the pram were in Pittenweem instead of Glasgow.

Annie found the many small garments a larger task than she had expected and though tempted to simplify the pattern, she stuck to it exactly, for Annie believed in 'going by the book'. There were tiny buttons and buttonholes on the jacket, while the bonnet, the leggings, the little fiddly bootees and mitts all had crochet drawstrings with minuscule tassels on each end and eventually Annie felt that she never wanted to see that particular shade of almond green again. When, at long last, the complete outfit, with matching white undergarments, was knitted and sewn up, Helen was terribly pleased with it, absolutely delighted, and Annie did feel that the restful afternoons had done her good.

On one of the afternoons that Annie was reclining with her knitting, Helen was sent to the shop across the road for a quarter of mint imperials. It was the first time that she had left the house without an adult accompanying her and though she felt quite afraid, she returned knowing that she had taken a big step towards being grown-up.

◊

As usual they spent a day in St Andrews at the Lammas Fair. The donkeys from the beach were in North Street, giving rides around town, and Helen was encouraged to have a ride. She was very dubious, but both her mother and grandmother worked hard to persuade her that a donkey-ride would be thoroughly enjoyable. Mary reminded her of the tune that she liked very much, called 'The Donkey Serenade' and suggested that she could sing it as she rode along. At last Helen, rather doubtfully, consented and Annie helped her to mount a small brown beast. A young boy led them away. He looked very young to Helen. Far *too* young. How could he look after a little girl on a donkey? As soon as they turned the corner and her mother was no longer in sight, Helen's worst fears were realised. The boy whacked the donkey with his stick and the donkey trotted off, leaving the boy far behind. Helen was alone on the trotting animal as it turned corners and explored streets which she had never seen before. She was completely lost! The tendons in her hands were like steel as she gripped the reins and her knees ached with tension. She had no hope of controlling the creature, for it was obviously a donkey with a mind of its own. Looking backwards nervously, she sometimes caught a glimpse of the boy, far in the distance, but then another corner was turned and he disappeared and again she was alone. She considered jumping off the donkey's back, but she might hurt herself and she did not know how to return to the starting place anyway. She feared that she would never see her mother again!

It seemed like hours later that the boy suddenly ran up and walked beside them, as though everything were fine. They turned a corner and there were her mummy and grandma waiting with big happy smiles, which faded at once when they saw Helen's tear-stained face. She had cried almost continuously throughout her nightmare journey.

Mary bought a big green melon to cheer her up. It was called a Red Parrot melon and came from a box with a picture of a red parrot on it.

"These are the very best kind of melons, my wee jewel. Very sweet and juicy and just you wait and see what I'll make for my poor wee granddaughter, who had such a terrible time on that *bad* donkey!"

Helen thought the boy was more to blame than the donkey, though she did not much care for the donkey either. She also felt some twinges of resentment against the grown-ups, who had been so insistent that she must risk such a dangerous experience.

In the evening sunshine, the melon was eaten in the garden, because it *was* very juicy.

Mary collected all the seeds, washed and dried them, then three days later dyed them pink and purple and green. Lastly she strung them into a long necklace for Helen. It was not worn much because it was rather jaggy, but it was very pretty.

◊

Just before they returned to Glasgow, Annie took Helen for a visit.

"We'll go and see Audrey's wee cousin Richard and see if he's as beautiful and fat and black-haired as she said he was. Would you like that?"

Helen was noncommittal, babies were not of any great interest to her. One seemed much like another. However she was pleased to find that they lived in a nice little house that she had often admired as she passed by. The small garden was filled with flowers and very white lace curtains hung at the tiny windows. Helen imagined it must be similar to the house in the woods where the three bears lived. Inside the house there seemed to be more furniture than air.

When the baby was brought in, he was indeed very handsome with a rosy skin, several chins and incongruously thick dark hair for one so young. Lying on his mother's knee, he gazed at Helen with that recognition of another small creature which even the youngest infant will show. Suddenly he smiled entrancingly to her. The smile vanished as quickly as it had come, but he continued to gaze at her and soon he smiled again, then again. Helen was delighted and gazed back with equal interest. Richard was dressed in beautifully knitted garments very like the ones that her mother had just finished making for Rosemary Daisy, only these were pale blue and a little bit bigger.

"Ah wis jist gaun tae gie'm his bath noo. Wid ye like tae see'm gettin' his bath, Helen?"

"Oh, yes please."

A wonderful towel printed with rosebuds on it was laid at the fire to warm and Annie held the sonsy child while the bath was filled and deftly carried around and over the packed chairs and tables. Richard continued to watch Helen as though hypnotised and she was charmed by his quaint attention.

The many buttons of his little jacket were unbuttoned, then his knitted bootees and trousers were removed, disclosing dimpled knees and legs with fatty creases. Because of his steady stare and tantalising smiles, he seemed much more interesting than any infant she had seen previously. Helen thought him quite gorgeous. He was a placid baby and lay quiescent on his mother's lap as she undressed him with proper maternal adoration. The blue ribbons of his pretty white vest were untied. When his plump body came into view, Helen had a desperate desire to kiss his well-fed healthy little tummy. He now wore only the bulky towelling nappy, secured with two large silver safety pins. Helen hoped that his mother would be careful. The pins looked very sharp and dangerous. She was aware of caring about this baby in a way that she had never felt about others. Was it because he was dressed in the same garments as her doll? Or was it because he had smiled so nicely to her and continued to watch her. Or was it because he was just such an extraordinarily splendid baby? He was just lovely.

Lastly the fierce pins were unfastened and safely laid in the hearth and the nappy was folded back and removed ... Helen looked away quickly.

How terrible!

What an awful thing!

Richard was *deformed*. She could not bear to look at him! One glimpse had been enough to show her that the poor baby had something wrong with his little front bottom. A strangely shaped lumpy thing, pink and wrinkled grew between his legs! She had heard adults talk in hushed tones of horror about people ill and dying because of a growth, without knowing what they meant. Now she knew, for she had realised instantly that *this* was a growth. How terribly, terribly sad. Poor little baby! To be so lovely in every other way and yet to have such a horrible, grotesque thing between his fat, little thighs. She felt tears coming and glared at the flames of the fire until her eyes were dry. She saw nothing of the bathing or the subsequent dressing. Only when Richard was well-wrapped up again and feeding dreamily from his mother's impressive breast, could Helen bear to look at him. How sweet he was with his clothes on! But she could never feel the same love for him now that she knew about his shocking secret.

As they walked home, Annie hoped that Helen might mention the fact that Richard was differently formed from the girl babies that Helen had seen up until now. It seemed a good opportunity to discuss some of the differences of the sexes. As Helen said nothing, Annie thought that she could not have seen the baby's male genitals, well-formed though they had been. It was strange, for Helen was usually very observant, but if she had not noticed anything unusual, the conversation would be too complicated.

Helen for her part could not bear to talk about the baby's horrible handicap and preferred not to think about it at all. For many years, she would always shudder when she walked past the small house where she had seen the poor deformed baby.

Autumn

A lthough Helen was sad to leave Pittenweem, it was nice to go back to her own house. Just at first, it seemed that the ceilings were very high with a lot of air above your head, for Pittenweem ceilings were extraordinarily low, but you soon got used to it and did not notice the difference.

Annie and Helen were also glad to return to the baths with the wonderful hot showers. Helen could nearly swim now.

The cinemas in Glasgow were much more elegant and comfortable than the Pittenweem Picture House. There was even one in town, where there was a restaurant and you might have tea and cakes, yet still watch the film. Helen noticed that the tinkle of teaspoons and china was almost as loud as the film actors' voices.

It was fun to visit the big shops, again. Lewis's Polytechnic was her favourite. It had such a splendid name and there were moving staircases to every floor and a zoo with monkeys when you reached the top floor.

In November, there were two weeks of fog. Everyone complained about it, but Helen thought it exciting. She could not see the other side of the road and could hardly recognise where they were. Of course she always held on very tightly to her mother's hand.

Annie found it easier to visit her friends now that Helen was older and good at amusing herself with a book or toy. She obviously had a wonderful imagination and seemed content to play on her own for hours. Glasgow public transport was excellent and they used trams, buses, the subway and a network of trains to visit all parts of the city.

Much of Helen's time was spent in the company of talkative adults. Two of Annie's friends, Elsie and Nancy, were now mothers, but during visits their uninteresting infants slept most of the time and Helen would sit quietly while the adults chatted. Sometimes she was given a book to look at, but she enjoyed listening and if the conversation became boring or unintelligible, she would daydream. She had a capacity for creating situations and stories in her head and she found complete satisfaction in her own fantasies.

One thing that she started to observe was that people did not always talk in the same tone. When they started to speak very softly, Helen's attention was attracted and she awakened from her imaginary world. She noticed that as their voices dropped, their bodies would lean towards each other and sideways glances would be cast at her. Perhaps they wondered if she were able to hear properly when they whispered like that. She could have reassured them, as her ears were as sharp as a little rabbit's. Sometimes Helen lost the meaning of adult conversation, because sentences would remain unfinished and pursed lips, nods and raised eyebrows would take the place of words.

Two people were often mentioned in these whispered conversations, Helen noticed. One was her Uncle Willie and the other was the Prince of Wales, although he was sometimes confusingly called the King. In fairy stories, kings were old and wise and princes were young and handsome, however she learned to accept that her mother and her friends were speaking of only one person. She felt great interest in these two men and listened carefully. She had every intention of marrying her handsome uncle when she grew up, and the Prince had waved to her in St Andrews when she was riding on her Daddy's shoulders. The Prince had been quite close to them and had looked right at her and waved and smiled. Helen could not remember if she had waved back or not, but her Daddy had been waving his arm so hard that she nearly fell off. Though the Prince had nice teeth, he was very ordinary-looking and quite old. He could easily have been a king rather than a prince. He wore a cap and just the same sort of clothes as her father wore when he played golf. In fact, the royal Fair Isle pullover was not nearly such nice colours as the one that her Mummy had knitted for Daddy.

These quiet conversations amongst her mother's friends had the word 'married' repeated over and over again because both the Prince and Willie were thinking of getting married. Nobody seemed very pleased about either wedding. Stranger still, the lady that the Prince wanted to marry looked quite like Eileen, the nice lady that her uncle had brought to Pittenweem. Eileen was much younger and prettier, of course, but they were both little and thin and had smooth dark hair waving on each side of the forehead. Helen could not understand why people were so unhappy about the Prince getting married. As for uncle Willie, she wished that he would wait till she grew up before he married anyone else.

Helen had certainly had a lovely time with Eileen, going to the beach, skipping and buying ice cream. She was terribly nice, but Helen did hope that she would not marry her uncle.

Perhaps it was only the Prince that was going to get married.

◊

In October, Annie was in Edinburgh visiting an old schoolfriend Laura, who was in the middle of turbulent marital problems and needed a shoulder to weep on.

Before taking the bus to Morningside, Annie and Helen had popped into Woolworths, the 3d and 6d store, to find something to amuse Helen throughout a long day of adult conversation.

"Are you *sure* that's what you want?" Annie asked.

Helen nodded her head enthusiastically. She thought it wonderful, a little marvel! She had never seen anything like it in her life before and she could not believe that her mother would buy it so readily. How could they afford it? Helen was well aware that money was scarce.

The prized acquisition was a small open box containing a model of a bathroom. The fixtures were of china, complete with metallic taps on the bath and washbasin, with two square inches of towelling and a minuscule toilet roll hanging on the wall, a scrap of sponge and a morsel of strong-smelling soap beside the washbasin. The WC had a hinged wooden seat. A chain on the cistern above it completed the miniature realism. The cardboard floor was printed with black and white squares, just like Grandma's bathroom floor, and a silver paper mirror hung on the apparently green tiled wall. It was just *perfect* and Helen revelled in it.

Annie was pleased that Helen was so satisfied with the sixpenny toy, though she did wonder exactly what pleasure was to be obtained from such a plaything. She wished that the soap did not stink quite so much, for Laura's house was soon permeated by the strong, rather unpleasant smell.

In future years when Helen brought out her little bathroom to play with, as she continued to do at intervals, the strong, saponaceous aroma would drift through the house and remind Annie of Laura's tears, as she told the sad tale of her husband's cruelty and betrayal.

◊

Annie found an article in a magazine about Shirley Temple. It had fascinating facts about what a nice happy, normal little girl she was and how everybody loved her. Then it told how quickly she could learn her lines for the films, how many hours of singing and tap-dancing practice she must do each day and how many frilly dresses with matching knickers she had hanging neatly in her vast wardrobe. Most important in Annie's eyes was the typical breakfast which Shirley ate each morning before her hard schedule started. Annie still worried about how little Helen ate and Mary constantly commented on how thin the child was.

Annie read parts of the article to Helen and finished by suggesting that she might like to try eating the same breakfast as her heroine.

Helen was very enthusiastic and, as would later be seen, determined.

It was a typical American breakfast and Annie bought corn flakes for the first time, deciding that though reminiscent of cardboard they had their own fascination.

Helen sat down to her work with a serious face and after a glass of orange juice, a bowl of cereal with sliced banana and a glass of milk, was about to leave the table.

"Oh no, there's more yet, jewel. Shirley has a nice big breakfast to make her strong enough to do all that dancing! I'll just bring it in a minute."

Privately she thought that Shirley's chubbiness would have benefitted from rather less breakfast, but at the moment she intended to cash in on her daughter's desire to emulate the miniature film star.

Helen looked at the plate in front of her with disbelief and then at her mother. The plate was piled with two slices of bacon, two fried eggs, a pancake, baked beans and a slice of toast. There was syrup for the pancake and butter and marmalade for the toast, if required.

Helen's eyes were pathetic in their pleading but Annie hardened her heart and said cheerfully,.

"Yes, Shirley must be a very hungry girl in the morning, mustn't she! That's what she eats, the magazine says. That's why she's so clever and famous, I expect. And such a good dancer."

Annie expected that the kid would give up after a token amount, but she would not make it easy for her.

She had underestimated her daughter.

Helen had started her mighty breakfast at eight o'clock and she did not leave the table until eleven thirty. Everything was eaten and, apart from a gentle shining aspect to her face, Helen showed no ill-effects. They took their daily walk in the park and Annie watched apprehensively as Helen ran about and enjoyed the swings as usual, shot down the chute thirty times and even had a cautious ride on the dangerous 'witch's hat' round-about. Although normally such an unenthusiastic eater, her daughter must surely have a cast iron stomach!

However, Helen did not touch food for another forty-eight hours and the Shirley Temple breakfast was never repeated.

The corn flakes went soft in their box and were eventually fed to the ducks.

One Temple film did give Annie a good idea. Shirley, an orphan yet again, had been adopted by a poor but kindly old man who lived in a primitive apartment. For the child's supper he had cut the end from a loaf of bread and, as sometimes happens, there was a hole in the middle of this slice. The bread was put into a frying pan and an egg was broken into the hole and fried. The finished dish with the egg neatly framed by fried bread looked very attractive to Helen, and once a week Annie could recreate that unsophisticated dish and be sure that Helen would greet it with delight.

◊

Bruce was inconsistent in his visits to Hyndland, sometimes out of touch for nearly three weeks at a time and at other times terribly friendly, popping in two or three times during the week and suggesting some sort of outing for the weekend. It was confusing for his wife and daughter. When he arrived, he would hug Annie and kiss her cheek, then grab up Helen and kiss her and swing her round with every sign of a loving father. He could be entertaining and his energy was always infectious. Often, Annie realised that she had enjoyed his visit very much and wondered if they might ever settle together again. Then another unexplained hiatus in his visits would infuriate her. When he did finally reappear, her coldness would alienate him and the cycle of misunderstanding would start once more. She wondered privately whether he returned to see them only when he had quarrelled with his family or his other friends. That was too horrible a theory to consider. Often, he disappeared from the Hyndland scene without there having been any apparent hostility between them. She knew he was 'touchy' of course and unconsciously *she might* have wounded him with her sharp wit. She tried not to do this, but then she also knew that her acerbity and sarcasm were what attracted him to her and made him laugh. She felt she would never understand him and she worried that Helen would be damaged by the strange hot and cold relationship of her parents.

She need not have worried. On the occasions when Bruce decided to be a dutiful father, the child was much less enthusiastic about his presence than her mother. Helen saw Bruce as a necessary evil, who came with his loud voice and his idea of what was good fun. She considered him an interruption in the quiet and enjoyable life that she shared with her mother. There was some excitement in his arrival, and he often brought sweets or gifts, but quite soon she would start to long for the moment when he would pick up his hat and start to make excuses about how busy he was. The child felt some jealousy, because her mother spoke almost exclusively to Bruce when he was there. That was boring, but even worse was the moment that Bruce would turn his attention to her and suddenly dive unexpectedly at her to throw her about, or ask questions that seemed impossible to answer. His way of 'kidding' was incomprehensible to the child. Bruce in his turn, found his daughter's lack of appreciation a challenge to throw her ever higher and act in an even more ridiculous way, in a bid to make her laugh.

After she had gone to bed one night he said very seriously to Annie,

"She's a right wee stolid thing, isn't she? D'ye think she has a sense of humour?"

"Oh, no doubt about it, she's brilliant at making me laugh, if she's in the right mood. She's got quite a mature sense of the ridiculous and she's a marvellous mimic, as long as you don't push her to perform."

"Aye, h'm, yes, well I never see much sign of that side of the wee one. D'ye think she's got what you'd call a dry sense of humour? A bit like my father, maybe."

Annie made no reply, for she did not think Helen bore the slightest resemblance to her paternal grandfather.

Starting School

Helen's Christmas presents were more grown-up that year. There was a clockwork train from her father which travelled on a circular track. It was too small for passengers and was either stopped or going and did not lead to much imaginative play. There was a set of farm animals but Helen had no knowledge of farms so that too had a limited enjoyment. There was a slide projector with brilliantly coloured pictures of exotic places. That required an adult to set it up and work it, and once the pictures were seen several times, there seemed no need to see them again, although the brilliance of the colours influenced Helen's art work throughout her childhood. There was a box of bright metallic beads for arranging in different patterns, and a silver mesh purse. The last two provided many hours of play. There was also a very nice book about a little girl with many dolls and the adventures that she shared with them and Helen found a lot of ideas in this book. The girl in the book taught her dolls lessons, nursed them when they were ill and took them on a picnic, and these ideas were soon incorporated into Helen's play.

Another doll joined the family that Christmas. Pauline was a beautiful and glamorous creature. With her soft pink velvet face, multi-frilled, lilac organza dress and garden party hat, she was like a miniature film star. She was allowed to keep her dress, as it was too big for Topsy, but Pauline spent most of her time in the cupboard and was only brought out, when crowd scenes were required.

Annie thought, not for the first time, that there were facets to Helen's personality which she would never understand.

Almost more important than Christmas was the knowledge that Helen would be starting school in February.

The green smock that all kindergarten children were required to wear had been purchased and hung on the bedroom door. It was a strong grassy green and looking at it made Helen happy and thrilled. It was a colour that she would love for the rest of her life. The school was just across the road and Helen had watched children at play in the playground each day for as long as she could remember. She probably did not think much about the changes that being a schoolgirl would bring but accepted the inevitable, as children do. She had certainly not grasped the idea that her mother would not be with her in school although Annie had tried to talk about it several times. Annie was apprehensive. She knew that Helen was too dependent on her and was unused to other children. Would she be terribly unhappy with the normal rough and tumble of childhood. No doubt, she avoided other kids at the swimming pool. Annie blamed herself for this reclusiveness and worried incessantly.

Perhaps she had coddled Helen?

Perhaps the harsh reality of school would scar her for life?

Annie hid her dread of the coming separation as best she could.

Bruce and Annie continued their uneven relationship. Sometimes Bruce would come regularly each week to look after Helen. At other times there seemed to be problems and excuses for several consecutive weeks. Annie could never make out whether the excuses were manufactured or not, but she learned not to rely on his help. One thing was sure. After one of his longer absences, he was extra friendly when he did return, bringing some little present or suggesting a weekend outing. Annie realised that he was like her mother, in that he could be generous when he felt like it. But, also like Mary, he required a lot of appreciation of his generosity, referring repeatedly to the gift and asking if it were the right kind or suitable size or acceptable colour. At each inquiry the recipients would of course reaffirm their gratitude and delight.

No doubt Bruce liked to be the centre of attention and would talk for hours.

Annie wondered if it was possible that, like her brother, she had chosen a mate whose personality was close to that of her mother's?

It was a bizarre idea and she tried to stop thinking about it.

Luckily, Annie's general health had improved tremendously and she was relieved to find her old energy returning.

Helen was to start school on the first of February and looked forward to it as something special, for Annie had prepared her well.

Much better than she had prepared herself.

Although she talked to her mother about Helen starting school and mentioned her fears that the child was still too young and dependent, Annie did not realise how deeply she herself was worried by the coming change. She started to have nightmares, in which Helen was knocked down by a tram as she crossed the steep, busy road between her home and the school. Wakening breathless and trembling, Annie would reassure herself that she would accompany her daughter every day, both to and from school, then once more fall into a troubled sleep. In her next dream, Helen was lost in an immense empty building, while Annie searched and called frantically for her, running along corridors and opening the doors of classrooms reminiscent of the High School where she had studied as a girl. Though she never found her daughter in the dream, Annie was acutely aware of the loneliness and terror which her child must be suffering in the vast, deserted space. When daylight came, she could smile ruefully and compliment herself, for the dream classrooms had the same cracked and dog-eared maps hanging on their walls that she remembered from her childhood. Even the hurtling tram in her dream had been a yellow one, the correct colour for the Hyndland route.

Her mother listened to her worries, but did not have any comfort or advice to offer and would only say,

"I daresay everything will be fine. She's such a bright wee thing and kids gets used to anything in time."

"Like the poor kids at Dotheboys Hall, d'ye mean?"

Annie, in her book-voracious teens, had read the entire works of Dickens, in the reading room of the Mitchell library. The horrors of the poor Victorian boys had impressed her indelibly. Mary did not catch the reference because although the complete works of many nineteenth century novelists weighted the studio bookshelves, there were no volumes by Dickens. John had never cared for Dickensian exaggeration and Mary preferred the lighthearted social scenes of Anthony Trollope.

Neither was Bruce any help as Helen's first day at school approached.

"Och the wee one'll just love school, Annie. All those other nice wee lassies to run about with, all giggling at their wee silly jokes and playing their daft wee games. She'll have a *whale* of a time!"

"Did you have whale of a time when you went to boarding school?"

"No, no. You're right there. I told you about that, didn't I. It was hell on earth! Absolute misery for me for a few months."

"Well, I wonder why you're so sure Helen will enjoy it."

"Oh well, I was older and more ... eh I don't know exactly ... but anyway I got over it eventually and learned to enjoy myself."

"Yes, you were a *lot* older and you got over it by joining the bad boys and getting into trouble. That's what you told me before."

He chuckled heartily,

"Oh I suppose we weren't so *very* wicked, but did I tell you about the time we went to this old farmhouse and ..."

The story lasted ten minutes and Helen was not mentioned again, except when Bruce left that night. He looked into Annie's eyes and said very seriously,

"You know, Annie, school will be the making of Helen. She'll get away from your apron strings and she'll lose all her strange ways and learn to be more like other kids. It'll just be the making of her!"

Annie looked at him coldly. She could detect the echo of his father's voice in those words and hurt, offence and fury were added to her worries.

"M-hmm." was all she said but her lips were tight and one corner of her mouth was drawn down.

Topsy's birthday party was held in January as in the previous year, and the brown menu was repeated and enjoyed. Helen wore the green school smock, which had become a favourite garment.

"Just think, Helen, next week when it's your birthday, you will be in school that day. You'll be a real schoolgirl. Won't that be exciting?"

"Oh yes!" Helen breathed.

Annie wondered exactly what Helen's perception of being a schoolgirl was.

"Can I take Topsy to school?"

"I don't know, my pet. We'll need to ask the teacher about that."

Helen's face changed immediately and Annie said hurriedly,

"Let's just enjoy her nice party today and we'll find out about that next week."

But the first possibility of the drawbacks of school had pre-sented itself to Helen, for until now her constant companion had been welcome everywhere.

A few days before the new intake, Annie and Helen went to the school to register and pay the nominal education fee.

Hyndland school was comprised of two buildings separated by a playground. The larger building higher on the hill and oppo-site their flat, was the secondary school and the building further down the hill housed the primary department. Although Annie had lived across the road for three years, she had watched chil-dren come and go without appreciating this difference. Mistakenly she made her way to the secondary school.

It smelled very funny to Helen. It smelled of a lot of things and none of them very nice.

This school, more modern than the other, was built around an inner play ground and had open corridors on two levels leading to each classroom. It was a surprise to Helen to find this hidden playground in the middle of what she had always imagined to be a very big solid building. Would she be running round it next week, she wondered?

"Excuse me!"

Annie spoke to a teacher who was rushing along with his black gown flying behind him. He stopped in his tracks with a stern expression and said,

"Yes!" in what seemed to Annie, a very intimidating tone.

Helen grabbed her mother's hand more tightly.

"Excuse me but I've come to enrol my little girl for school. Perhaps you could direct me, please?"

He glared at her and sighed as one might with an idiotic child.

"Oh dear! You've come to the *wrong* building! Tut, tut,tut."

He seemed to be at the end of his patience.

"Oh, I am very sorry. Then perhaps you would be good enough to tell me which is the right building."

Her words were polite, but her tone was steely.

"The other one, the other building, down the street. Which direction did you come from? Surely you must have passed it."

He was almost shouting. Annie turned towards the main door with a muttered 'I'll find it, thanks very much' but he called peremptorily,

"Here you, come back here. I'll take you there. It's quicker this way."

He turned with a flourish of his gown and hurried down a flight of stairs.

Mother and daughter gazed at each other, Helen was biting her lip and her eyes were wide. Annie smiled to encourage her daughter,

"What a horrible man! We might as well follow him, though, if it's quicker. Don't worry, he won't be your teacher! He teaches the older ones."

But Annie was furious. This man was treating her like naughty pupil and terrifying Helen as she took her very first educational step.

He had disappeared down a short flight of concrete stairs and they could hear him thumping down ahead of them. Obviously there were several more flights.

"Are you still there?" he shouted back to them.

"Yes" Annie replied loudly but she did not hurry. She was feeling tired and slightly dizzy and there was no banister. She did not want to risk a fall.

Several teenage children, tall as adults, overtook them suddenly, jumping down two and three steps at a time and almost knocking against them as they passed. She heard the teacher reprimanding them loudly and wondered if his fierce accents would stop them from descending at such a break-neck speed the next time.

The teacher was waiting for them, with no improvement to his temper and obviously fuming at their slowness. He opened a door with unnecessary strength, banging it noisily against the wall, then waved them through with an impatient gesture. They stepped outside into the fresh air which smelled delicious to Helen. A short flight of stairs on their left led to the primary playground but the school on the other side of the vast expanse of concrete looked very far away. Ahead of them another flight led to a heavy gate at street level and directly across the road was their *own house*. Helen could not believe her eyes for she had become quite disoriented by all the twists and turns that they had taken inside the school. It seemed like magic that they were now so close to home. How lovely it looked with the pretty yellow curtains at the bedroom window! She longed to return to Topsy and the quiet sitting room and forget all about starting school.

"Why, we are just across the road from our flat!" Annie exclaimed, "How handy, this gate will be the best one for us ... "

"Oh no, no!" the teacher rudely interrupted, glaring at her as though she had broken yet another rule, "It's against regulations for primary pupils to use that gate. You must use the *correct* gate at the foot of the hill, just like everyone else. This way. Quickly now."

As he climbed the left hand flight of stairs, the wind caught his gown and blew it into an enormous sombre balloon which seemed supernatural and very frightening to Helen.

"Excuse me, wait a moment, I can find my own way now, thank you very much. There's no necessity for you ..."

But he would not hear of it and strode off ahead of them with his long legs and sinister black garment, urging them over his shoulder to 'hurry, hurry'. Helen was almost out of breath, but Annie deliberately walked at a slower than normal pace and advised her daughter to take her time.

They reached the school and entered by the door which had the heading

MIXED INFANTS

... which reminded Annie of a funny story, though she was in no mood for humour.

The teacher pushed the door open and went in himself, scarcely holding it long enough for Annie to grab it. He looked along the corridor, then snapped,

"I expect you'll find someone here to deal with your problems. I must go now, I'm very busy."

"One moment, please," said Annie "I would like to make it clear that I came here to enrol my daughter in school and I had *no problems*, until I met you! You've been thoroughly unpleasant to us and I think you must be quite the rudest man in Glasgow."

Open-mouthed, he looked at her in astonished disbelief.

"How dare you speak to me like that!"

"And how dare you speak to me like a recalcitrant pupil!"

"This is outrageous! Do you know who I am?"

"I know that you are very impertinent and I must think very clearly about whether I want my child to attend a school which accepts you as a member of staff."

"A member of staff!!"

"Yes, you have quite upset me and also my little girl on her first day at school. I intend to report your behaviour to the headmaster."

"Madam, I am the headmaster."

"Well you are a very ungracious and boorish headmaster."

Helen was paralysed with fear.

How could her mother be so brave and angry with this important man?

What would happen to them next?

Perhaps the police would be called.

The altercation continued with flashing eyes and very loud voices.

When the janitor arrived to see what all the noise was about, he was urged to 'show this woman the door' and also to 'eject her from the building', but the janitor had more sense and probably knew the man and his temper well.

Mrs Brown the head of kindergarten was fetched and she led Annie away to a classroom, while the janitor edged the furious headmaster back towards the secondary school with calming and placatory words.

Mrs Brown was very nice and friendly, but would not be drawn into saying anything about her fellow staff member except,

"Teaching can be a very difficult profession, Mrs Corning, especially with the older boys, and this is a specially troubling time of year. I think his health is poor, too. *Ulcers* you know."

Annie felt her sympathies would always be with the pupils, rather than that brute, but said nothing.

The whole experience had traumatised Helen and she would not utter a word to Mrs Brown. She was taken to see her classroom and meet her teacher, Miss Totten, who had red hair and small piercing eyes. She smiled kindly, but Helen could not return the smile. She was confused and felt another row might break out at any moment between her mother and these lady teachers. She could not even remind her mother to ask if Topsy could come to school. She just wanted to go home. Maybe she would never go to school at all. That certainly seemed safest.

What was surprising was that her Mummy was hardly ever angry with anyone, except Daddy, and now she had seemed just as angry with that man in the black cloak, as she often was with Daddy.

After that horrible visit, Helen felt confident that her mother would decide against sending her to school at all. It did not seem a nice place.

Annie worried about what to give Helen for breakfast before she started for school. It was a long morning until twelve fifteen and it still seemed that Helen did not eat enough for the amount of running around that she did. Mary was always exclaiming over the child's thinness. The weather was cold, so a nice warm drink of cocoa would start her off well, though there would be a little bottle of milk in school later. Helen liked a banana so Annie decided to make a banana sandwich with brown bread. Perhaps that would tempt her and fill her little stomach for the strenuous hours ahead.

The first school day arrived and Helen, unable to forget the shouting match with the big man in black, and hardly believing that she really must go, donned her green smock slowly. Even one bite of sandwich and one sip of cocoa was too rich, although there would be several weeks before Helen told her mother how that mixture made her feel sick.

Topsy was left at home with many kisses. Annie was sure that other girls and boys would leave their toys at home.

"You can play with her all afternoon, darling."

Annie resolutely ignored her daughter's trembling lip and spoke of the exciting things that would happen in school. She made disparaging comments about the foolish children who cried when they went to school, and how other kids would think they were babies and laugh at them. She felt cruel, but was rewarded by a brave, though strained smile from Helen, as she joined the others and was ushered through the 'Mixed Infants' door by Miss Totten.

Helen found that school had some quite pleasant aspects.

Plasticine was interesting and fascinating. The teacher brought a box filled with little muddy coloured balls and each child took one and made it first of all into a long snake then developed it according to the child's artistic and creative ability. They were allowed to make what they wanted. It reminded Helen of the putty that her drandad sometimes gave her, though the plasticine smell was much less pleasant. Occasionally a child was lucky enough to be given a new vivid piece of plasticine, bright green, blue or red. That was a day to remember, for the bright colours were soon consolidated and lost in the general greyish-brown mixture.

One thing she liked a lot were little wooden rods of different colours. The colours were terribly nice and the smoothness of the wood was lovely to play with. They were to help you learn to count and she enjoyed counting.

There was a lot of making patterns with coloured paper shapes. You had to lick the shapes like stamps. They made a picture of a yacht, though not a very realistic one, then a house, again disappointing. Helen was rather pleased on the day that she made a bunch of bright flowers in a vase. Then there were other times when you used the paste-pot to stick larger pieces of paper together to make folders and envelopes. The paste was fascinating and smelled very like marzipan. It was a beautiful pure white, especially when the pot was newly opened, and it was difficult to believe that it was not for eating. Helen was tempted several times to nibble a little piece, but always resisted as it might well be poisonous! Sometimes they wove strips of paper in and out to make a chequered pattern.

They sang songs and learned something called doh-ray-me. Miss Totten made her hand into a special shape for each sound and the sounds went higher and higher until they came back to doh again. It was incomprehensible to Helen and a bit embarrassing. She did not mention doh-ray-me to her mother.

The best times were when the teacher told a story out of a special big book.

Happily she never again saw the man in the black cloak.

The worst times for Helen were playtime. In the unprotected environment of the playground, Helen's shyness and timidity were a terrible handicap.

In 1937 the toilet arrangements in Glasgow schools were shockingly primitive and unhygienic. The boys and girls of the infant class shared the same row of eight latrines. With nearly forty children in a class there was a scramble to find a WC. The children left the classroom in pairs and it was accepted that two girls would share a toilet, as there were no locks on the doors. One would hold the door against marauders, while the other relieved herself. As the cubicles were at such a premium, the boys generally used the gutter in the white-tiled corridor outside the toilets. Some of the naughtier boys directed their flow at the feet of the unlucky, squirming girls too late to claim a toilet. It was a scene of chaos and no teacher was ever there to exert control. Indeed with the chipped tiles, the screaming and the stench, it was not a pleasant place to be.

Helen was always one of the last arrivals and thus in most danger from pee attack. When she gained a WC, she often had no partner to keep the door closed and had to stretch her arm forward as she sat there, painfully and unsuccessfully pressing her fingertips against a series of bumps and forced entries. After this ordeal was over, she ran to the playground gate where her mummy was waiting with a smile and a word of support and she would stay happily there until the bell rang to return to the classroom. After the first week, Annie started to curtail her visits and only arrived at the gate a few minutes before the bell rang.

After two weeks, Annie's worst fears were realised, for Helen appeared to have made no friends. Other children chased each other, walked around hand in hand or huddled in cosy little cliques, while Helen was alone, walking forlornly about, with her hands in her pockets. Only when she caught sight of her mother did she run to the gate with relief and happiness in her face. Annie found it unbearably sad. She had no idea how to tackle the problem and was too concerned for her daughter to turn her back on her.

Annie spoke to other children around the gate, asking their names and trying to involve Helen. The kids were friendly to Annie, but there was no communication with her daughter and it was obvious that Helen resented her speaking to other children in the few precious minutes that they had together.

After three weeks Annie determined that she must be firm and leave Helen to her own devices. Perhaps the child *was* too tied to her apron strings.

"I'm going to see Grandma today, so I won't be there at playtime, darling. I'll see you at lunchtime as usual."

Annie did not go to the gate for four days. On the Friday, she could not see Helen at first, but at last picked her out at the rear of the playground. Helen's right hand was holding one of the metal pillars which held up the rain shelter, as she walked steadily round and round with her eyes tightly closed.

She seemed happy for there was a slight smile on her lips, but she reminded Annie of the poor oxen of olden times who were forced to grind grain by walking in a tight continuous circle.

Annie would never find out that Helen first performed a ritual before circling the pillar.

After the nightmare of the toilets was accomplished, she would walk slowly about the playground. As she walked, she would search on the outer rim of her ear for the small scab which she knew to be there. When she had summoned enough courage, she would scrape the scab off with her nail, then collecting on her finger-tip the tiny drop of blood which had oozed out, she examined it with a certain satisfaction. Only then did she run to the shelter for pole-circling and the pleasurable dizziness which it produced.

European Worries

Helen was setting the table for lunch in her grandmother's house. There were all the knives and forks to be laid out, the basket of rolls, the two kinds of butter, fresh and salt. Helen liked butter and she would have a thin sliver of fresh butter cut for her by her grandmother, then a second slice. When Annie would intervene, Grandma would look cross and say how good butter was for a growing child. By that time Helen did not want any more anyway. What she really loved were the two little glass dishes of salt with tiny bubbles mysteriously trapped in the thick glass. She took a little pinch of salt as she set the table. A jug of water was too heavy for her to carry to the dining room, but now that she was a schoolgirl she could manage the celery jug which was also pretty heavy.

The dining room was very different from any other room that she knew. It was papered to the same height as Helen, with what looked like dark reddish brown leather with a lumpy pattern on it. Above that it was dark paint, hung with lots of very big paintings, mostly portraits. One was of Annie when she was about the same age as Helen was now. She had long dark curling hair and a cream coloured dress with a pink sash. She looked very pretty, much prettier than Helen knew herself to be.

There was also a sideboard with interesting things on it. A large cheese dish always revealed a lump of blue whiskery cheese when opened. John finished every meal with a modest helping and he would cut himself a piece and carefully pare off the outer skin of mould. Seeing his grand daughter's look of horror, he would assure her,

"That's the very best way to eat the cheese, y'know. Just delicious. Try a wee piece."

She never would.

There were also several large beautiful mahogany boxes on the sideboard. They were never used but Helen had been shown their contents at different times. One tall one was velvet lined and had crystal decanters inside it. Another, when opened, was a writing desk with green leather to lean on, little drawers for pens and an empty inkwell. Another was for cutlery. There were also two old fashioned pistols which would never work again, Helen was assured by her grandfather. They might have been good for playing at pirates but Helen had not reached that stage yet, and she was discouraged from touching them by her grandmother, who felt that there might yet be some unexploded gunpowder in their crevices.

A very deep cupboard in the dining-room held untold possibilities of discoveries. Helen felt that she would never come to the end of all the interesting things that were to be found in her grandparents' house.

Her grandfather was greatly amused at her teacher's name.

"So when you learned to hop you attended Miss Hopkins and now that you need to be taught you have Miss Totten. I always knew that you were a very special little girl. Do you think you will be well-taught by Miss Totten? And learn all your numbers and your ABC?"

Then he would give her his special friendly look and laugh quietly under his moustache and perhaps pat her head.

They usually had lunch at Renfrew Street on Saturday that spring, and John nearly always said the same thing about Miss Hopkins and Miss Totten.

Mary would become irritated and tut-tut,

"We've heard that all before, John! Far too often."

Helen did not mind how often he said it. It made her feel happy and special.

Another thing that he regularly said, annoyed his wife,

"Do you know the best way to reduce your weight?"

The question was addressed to the company at large, but Helen would reply loudly in the negative meanwhile John had picked up his fork rather than his soupspoon,

"Always eat your soup with a fork. That's the best way to diet."

Then John and Helen would giggle together and Mary would frown. It was only too obvious that she was the only person at the table in need of dieting.

After lunch was eaten, Helen was sent off to play. She did not mind, because by this time the conversation was becoming boring and seemed to be mostly about people fighting in far away places. She usually went to the piano first of all and played the

'Bluebells of Scotland,'
    Next her *piece de resistance*

> *'Oh, I can wash a sailor's shirt and I can wash it clean,*
> *Oh I can wash a sailor's shirt and dry it on the green'*

Which could have the alternative words,

> *'My father died a month ago and left me all his riches.*
> *A feather bed, a wooden leg and a pair of leather breeches.'*

Her reedy voice sang this version with gusto and without any thought of applying it to her own father. She just enjoyed the words. After that she tried out her own little melodies. Because of swimming, she thought of the low notes as being at the 'deep end' and high notes at the 'shallow end'.

◊

"D'ye think things are really as bad as the papers make out, Paw? For the working classes I mean. Worse than when I was married?"

John shook his head sadly but Mary said quickly,

"Well, I don't know, but you still see them on buses and in shops so they must have some money. Certainly they're badly dressed and some of them are filthy but ... "

"Now lass," John seldom called his wife by her name, "They must eat and if they have a job to go to, they must travel. We have a terrible economic situation here in Glasgow, but just about everywhere in the world is poor and in turmoil just now."

He looked sadly down at his plate and chewed his moustache.

"Yes, things in America seem to be absolutely awful, though you'd never guess it when you watch their films. Everyone's dressed so beautifully, flying around in swell planes, dancing and sloughtering down the champagne. Helen and I enjoy them, just sort of modern fairy stories. But I suppose it's pretty unreal, when you think of those poor dustbowl farmers ... "

Apart from a deep sigh, John continued as though Annie had not spoken,

"It's Europe that I really worry about, these extremist mad-men that are in power. Just on our doorstep."

John's voice was raised more loudly than usual and after speaking, he leaned his elbow on the table and cupped the top of his head in his left hand, almost as though he wanted to protect his baldness. Next he opened his right hand and gazed at the palm as if trying to read some answer there, before clenching it and again sighing noisily.

Mary caught Annie's eye and shook her head warningly, then said with a little smile,

"Oh John, I don't think it can be as bad as you're making out. That man Hitler is certainly very theatrical with all his shrieking and jumping about and those enormous parades. They fairly put Hollywood films in the shade, don't they Annie? But surely in *some* ways, Hitler seems to have helped his country?"

As John shook his head irritably at these words, Annie realised that her mother was attempting to drag the conversation away from the edge of melancholy and tried to back her up.

"Yes, I believe he has built wonderful roads and he's great on getting all the young folk organised, camping in the fresh air and doing their strengthening exercises outside. That can't be bad. I've been wondering about joining the Health and Beauty myself. I suppose he has been pretty brutal to the Jews. Boycotting their shops and hanging placards round their necks, all sorts of horrible things. But you know, Bruce and all his friends are very down on Jews, too. Terribly prejudiced. I don't suppose Bruce would resort to violence exactly, but who knows? I remember, I knew several Jewish girls at school and was very friendly with them. One was a really lovely girl called Edelweiss Kunzle. Her family has a bakery and function rooms. They make delicious cakes. She was very clever at school and hard-working too, unlike myself. But we were great friends."

"It's a terrible thing to condemn your fellow man because of his religion." John gazed out of the window with a self-righteous expression.

Annie said nothing, but could not avoid thinking this ironic, considering the furore about Willie wanting to marry a Roman Catholic.

"Well the only Jewess that I know is Mrs Strump downstairs." said Mary, "And she seems nice enough, but she is so *fussy!* She's lost us two stair women because of her complaints. They were late or not doing the job properly, she said. And in spite of all these hard times you're talking about, it's almost *impossible* to find a woman willing to scrub stairs."

"Perhaps it earns so little that they're not prepared to travel?" Annie reluctantly scrubbed the kitchen floor daily at her mother's behest and hated it.

"Well I certainly always give them their tram-fare. Don't know about Mrs Strump, of course."

Annie's face suddenly became as serious as her father's.

"One of the things that I can never get out of my mind was a photo I saw, it was in the Picture Post, I think. This was a couple of years ago when Helen was still just a wee thing. It was a picture of Mussolini's blackshirts and in the foreground was the sweetest little boy, about the same size as my own wee girl. He was dressed just like the men, with miniature boots, striped breeches, black hat ... and this tiny wee sowl was giving a fascist salute. It made my blood run cold."

Mary glared at her daughter, for she knew that this speech would bring a fierce response from John, who had studied in Italy when a young man.

"That brute Mussolini, it's years now he's been ruling that wonderful country ... when I think of Venice and Florence and what's happened ... and what's happened in Abyssinia, too ..." John was interrupted by a violent fit of coughing and Mary looked reproachfully at her daughter.

When he had recovered, Annie dutifully changed the subject.

"Oh, I must tell you, Helen has finally made a friend at school. She brought her home yesterday!"

"Och, I knew she would settle in sooner or later. Is she a nice child?"

"Well, Maw, to be quite truthful, I don't know if you would quite approve of the poor wee soul. She looks as though her granny might well be one of your stairladies. I had to ask her name several times, what with her pronunciation and her sniffing. Her nose was far from pleasant. 'Maffer' her name sounded like, so I called her Martha and she didn't correct me. She was really pathetic, with a torn, soiled jumper and a skirt that, och I can't tell you what it was like. Her shoes were so broken down they must be soaking wet most of the time. It seems terrible that children should grow up in such poverty. She lives quite near us, too. She's got two brothers and a sister and her dad doesn't work just now, she told me. How the hell they manage to feed a brood like that I've no idea. She gobbled up some bread and jam and cocoa then went all over the house ooh-ing and aw-ing at just about everything. It brought tears to my eyes."

"What did you give her to take home?" Mary knew, without

asking, that her daughter would have wanted to help this family.

"Well, you don't want to offend people, do you. She was smaller than Helen so I gave her a coat and two jumpers that would fit her and do her wee sister next year. There was a doll she liked too that Helen never plays with. And I gave her sixpence for sweets, but I told her to give it to her mother. Don't know if she will of course. Helen and I walked her home, because I was frightened that her mother would be worrying about her. She was an hour later than usual, but the woman looked too tired to worry."

"I don't suppose Helen will be playing with her again!"

"I wouldn't stop her if she wanted to, though I'd keep my eyes peeled for nits, but I think Helen was quite bored by the way Martha walked around, exclaiming over everything instead of playing. Helen's such a funny kid and takes her play so seriously. More like a job of work."

"Is that her still playing the piano? I'm sure she'll be musical."

"Yes, though she's no Mozart, I'm afraid. The Germans have certainly produced wonderful music in their time. By the way, I really fancy a German fashion just now. Nothing to do with music. It's called the luftbad."

She pronounced it as it was spelled.

"What on earth is a luftbad, Annie?"

"Oh folk just wander around outside with no clothes on and let the fresh air circulate round their bodies."

Her mother's face changed. Mary, who thoroughly enjoyed scandalous tales or suggestive humour, displayed an unexpectedly prudish streak where nudity was concerned, but Annie continued mischievously,

"I think it would be rather charming to wander naked through forests and over meadows, arm-in-arm with your friends."

Mary stood up abruptly,

"Come along, let's get these dishes done, and John, it's time you got back up to the studio again, if that man's coming at three-thirty."

◊

'Maffer' did not come home again with Helen and Annie had mixed feelings. Had she offended the poverty stricken family with her gifts? She sincerely hoped not. Annie tried to imagine how she would have felt if Helen had returned from a visit with some other child's cast-off clothing. She would not have liked it, no matter how good the condition. Pride was a very strong emotion. But it was silly not to give them those perfectly good garments, when they were obviously in need. Were they perhaps afraid that their daughter might appear to be seeking more presents, if she returned to the house?

On the other hand Annie was relieved not to experience that snottery nose again.

"Haven't you asked your friend Martha to come home to play again, darling?"

"Oh no, I haven't asked her. She's not any good at playing games, you know. I'd rather just play by myself."

Perhaps this was the simple explanation and Annie decided to accept it.

One morning in the middle of May, Annie awakened with pins and needles in her left hand. When it did not right itself in five minutes, she massaged it and did some arm exercises, much to Helen's amusement. Nothing seemed to bring the feeling back to normal, hot water, cold water. Annie was half laughing as she tried different things, but there was an underlying worry. It was very strange for pins and needles not to clear up in a matter of moments. In fact it was worse than ordinary pins and needles because the outside edge of her pinky was particularly sensitive. She could hardly touch it without exclaiming. Her nails required trimming and, when she came to cut her left hand pinky, she gave a small shriek. The scissors cutting through the nail gave the impression of an electric shock. She quickly laughed it off, in order not to worry her daughter.

Annie told her mother about it the next day.

"And it's still there, tingling and feeling funny and numb."

"I remember Bessie Spence in Pittenweem had something like that."

"Good Heavens, she's about *eighty!* Surely this is something different. It's a bit worrying though. It hasn't got any better today. I wonder if I was lying in a strange scrunched-up sort of way and stopping the circulation? It's a bit much when you can go to bed perfectly well and waken up having damaged yourself somehow!"

"Yes, I seem to remember there was nothing the doctor could do for Bessie"

"Oh well."

Said with an in-drawn breath, it was a favourite phrase of Annie's and expressed the fatalistic resignation which had become so much a part of her personality.

> **Tokio: In an interview with foreign correspondents here today, Mr Sato, Japanese Minister for Foreign Affairs, described Anglo-Japanese friendship as "One of the pillars of World Peace."**
>
> *Glasgow Herald May 7th 1937*

School Sports

The school sports were to be held in Scotstoun Showground two weeks before the end of term. Helen liked the name Scotstoun Showground. She had no idea what it might look like, but it sounded exciting. From the start of June, Miss Totten had taken the class into the playground to practise the egg and spoon race, using a small potato instead of an egg, and also the three legged race, which Helen hated. As there was an uneven number of children in the class, Helen thankfully chose not to take part.

"You can have a turn tomorrow Helen, if you like."

Helen's response of tear-filled eyes was clear to the teacher, who had noticed the child's timidity and withdrawal from other children. It was unusual for a child who was comparatively confident in the classroom to be so unsuccessful in social skills, and Miss Totten was puzzled and unsure how to help her.

The sports day arrived and Helen was very disappointed with the showground. It was so very, very big and plain and green with white railings dividing it up everywhere. She had expected that it might be rather like the Lammas Fair in St Andrews with gaudy roundabouts and stalls selling coconuts. She was very glad that she had not told anyone about this hope for she would have seemed foolish.

There were strict rules for the management of the Sports Day. All spectators must remain in the grandstand during races. The forty-one infants of Helen's class were to run their races on a piece of grass on the far side of the circular track from the grandstand. It meant that the parents of the little ones were unable to enjoy their children's endeavour, unless they had particularly good eyesight or binoculars. Annie spoke to another mother and they agreed that it was a very stupid arrangement.

"I'll bet that headmaster organised it. Damned fool that he is."

The other mother had also had an unfortunate experience with him and they compared notes.

"Oh look, they are running the first race and I can just make out Helen, because she's wearing her bright yellow dress!"

The other mother was short-sighted and could not identify her own child.

"What a wee daftie my kid is! She'll never make an athlete, I fear. She started off really fast, then stopped and looked back to see if anyone was behind her. Then, of course, quite quickly nobody was behind her!"

They laughed and continued talking. Perhaps as they talked, the public address system informed mothers where and how to collect infants. If it did, they did not hear it. At the end of twenty minutes it was obvious that the infant races were finished, for little groups started to walk back towards the grandstand. It was quite a long walk, as the track, now busy with hurdlers, must be circumnavigated. Some groups had chosen the clockwise direction and some the anti-clockwise. Annie could no longer distinguish the yellow dress. A slight panic arose in her breast. It was such a very large place. Should she stay where she was? But one group would reach the east end of the grandstand, while the other was heading for the west side and the grandstand itself was large. Impulsively she set off to the left in a clockwise direction. If Helen were not in this group, then hopefully she could run back and meet the other group before the kid felt deserted.

The path around the outer rim of the track was much longer than it looked and it was several minutes before she met Miss Totten coming towards her with half her class, which sadly did not include Helen.

"Helen is with the *others*, Mrs Corning! Those whose surnames begin with letters in the first half of the alphabet were to go to ..." she waved a hand behind her towards the place where she had last seen Helen "Didn't you hear the announcement? You'll soon catch them up, I'm sure."

Her gesture seemed to indicate the best direction to reach Helen and Annie kept on walking past the teacher. She felt foolish that she had not heard the announcement, but also angry as it seemed ridiculous to divide the children in this way. Why had they not been brought back to some rendezvous, where all the parents could have collected all the children?

Annie now found herself wondering whether she should turn and go back to the grandstand. Surely that would be quicker than going right around the periphery of the grounds. She felt terribly unsure, but decided to increase her speed and continue walking in the same direction. It was a very hot day and the sun seemed too bright and blinding. She could not make out where the other half of the class now were. She walked doggedly onward though her legs felt stiff and heavy.

Meanwhile Helen stood forlornly underneath the grandstand. All the other children had been whipped away by mothers or fathers. Though it was cool and pleasant after the hot sun and boring races, she wondered where her mother was and if she would ever find her in this large strange place. Mrs Brown, who had brought the children to this mustering point, had other duties to perform and felt irritated that this child's mother was so slow to pick her up.

"Where can your mummy have got to, I wonder? Perhaps she's made a mistake and gone to the west gate. I really must go and help with the long jump. I'm late already. I think you should go to the west gate. Just keep running along this corridor until it stops. Miss Totten will be there, even if your mummy isn't. There's a good girl."

Helen knew immediately that this was not a good idea. Anything could go wrong now. She was to run to some strange place, which she would not recognise when she got there, and where Miss Totten might be, if her mummy wasn't. How would her mummy know to go to this other gate? Who would tell her? And what if Miss Totten were not there? What would she do if there was no one that she knew at all?

She reached the end of the corridor and, just as she had feared, no one was there!

Through a door she could see the track and all the green grass. There were lots of people running, jumping and vaulting over quite high fences with the aid of long poles.

Perhaps if she went out into the sun, her mummy would see her yellow dress and come running up and rescue her. She did not like the corridor that she had run along. It was smelly and cold.

Perhaps if she walked back round the track to where she had run the races, her mummy would come and collect her there? That seemed the best idea.

In the grandstand, the woman that Annie had been speaking to earlier, saw the small lonely figure in the bright yellow dress trudging off into the distance around the track and asked her little boy what the girl's name was but he could not remember.

"I think we had better go and find her mummy."

A distraught Annie was rushing back and forwards underneath the grandstand. She had found Mrs Brown who assured her that Helen would be with Miss Totten, but that teacher, when found, disclaimed all knowledge of Helen, saying calmly,

"Now do *not* get *flustered* Mrs Corning. The child will be *quite* all right and will turn up shortly. It's just such a pity that you did not follow the arrangements which the school had made for collecting the pupils."

The arrival of the other mother, with her welcome news of Helen, possibly stopped Annie from assaulting Miss Totten.

"Oh how wonderful that you saw her! And how kind of you to come looking for me! I shall go after her in case she stays there waiting for me, and perhaps you would be good enough to wait here in case she sets off again and I cannot make up on her."

It was fortunate that Annie thought of this because as she started off once more going clockwise, Helen had reached the opposite side of the grounds and was also going clockwise. They might have circled forever without meeting, but the other mother was able to greet Helen and tell her that if she waited with her, her mummy would come along soon.

After a tearful reunion, Helen said,

"I *hated* the sports day, mummy."

"I must say I never want to see this place again, myself."

Panic had goaded Annie to keep walking quickly until she met up with Helen, but now she felt absolutely drained. She would not allow her self to think about it just now. It was probably just too hot.

"Could we go to the pictures, now?"

"I think that would be a great idea. Not only that, I think we should always go to the pictures on sports days!"

"Oh that would be lovely, mummy."

If Helen had any natural talent as a competitive athlete, the Scotstoun experience made sure that her future would not lie in that direction.

Annie, who had golfed and swum competitively throughout her youth, was surprised to find that it took her several days to recover physically from her exertions at the sports day. She decided that it must be the emotional worry which had exhausted her.

◊

On the last day of term, the school had a party. All the primary children were seated at long wooden tables in the school hall, with a paper bag in front of each child. Each bag contained a sandwich of thick white bread spread with lavish butter and sparing meat paste. These seemed very alien to Helen, quite different from her mother's dainty brown bread sandwiches. Two jam biscuits, three toffees and a chipped iced cake were jumbled together in the same bag, mixing their flavours unpleasantly. It was hardly like food that she had ever seen before. Paper hats were handed out to everyone and a balloon, some of which were burst, intentionally or otherwise, in the first few moments. It was noisy and disorganised, with lots of shouting, laughter and delighted screams. Although Helen had looked forward to the school party, she now sat in her own little bubble of silence, pushed and jostled on either side by the other children, longing desperately for the time to pass until she could go home.

What thoughts did she have in the midst of that infantine orgy?

She dreamed of the long summer in Pittenweem which stretched ahead. There she would be alone with her dolls and her swing and the flowers in the garden. There would be walls and rocks to climb and jump from. At the beach, there would be shells to collect and sand to build and the salty, icy water to wade and swim in.

It was like a distant vision of Paradise.

Summer

Just before the family was due to go to Pittenweem, John injured his shin. He had been running to catch a moving tramcar and slipped as he stepped aboard. The sore was not healing as it should. The doctor pronounced it a varicose ulcer and advised complete bed rest, with the application of bread poultices twice daily. Mary applied the first few poultices, but any benefit from her careful nursing tended to be reduced by her continuous and irritable flow of reproaches. How could John have been so damned foolish as to run after a moving tramcar at his age? Just when they were ready to get away to Fife, too. Did he not *think*? Did he not remember when he fell a few years ago? That was running after a bus, that time. Would he never learn?. So stupid. Just not thinking. That other sore took *weeks* to heal.

On and on she went and eventually, in order to spare her father's feelings, Annie took charge of the poulticing.

Helen was intrigued by the thick slice of bread and the way it swelled to twice the size when hot water was poured over it. It seemed a very strange thing to do with a slice of bread and she could never believe that it would help her grandfather's sore leg.

The journey to Pittenweem was difficult but, once there, the hammock was set up in the garden and John lay there all day with no hope of painting for a month or so.

Because of his disability, lots of visitors came to see them and it was not an easy summer for Annie.

She noticed that, as she became tired, her right foot felt very strange. It was as heavy as lead and she could hardly lift it off the ground. In the morning she would feel fine again, then in the evening, when she was once more exhausted, the heaviness would return. She did not mention this bizarre feeling to anyone. She almost wondered if she were imagining it. Was it some strange sort of sympathy with her father's sore leg? It was his right leg, too.

By the middle of August, Annie's life had become easier. John was up and about and painting. Mary was golfing and attending auctions and bazaars and in a much better frame of mind. Only

Helen rather missed having her grandfather always there on the hammock, free and willing at all times to peel apples and tell stories.

A day's outing to St Andrews was planned and John was to be left to his work.

Helen always enjoyed these leisurely excursions to St Andrews. She found that usually adults seemed to be rushing and hurrying to finish one thing, in order to get somewhere else to meet someone, or to do something or other. They were always consulting watches, then tut-tutting and walking faster, but a day in St Andrews was never like that.

In South Street there would be visits to very nice shops. Her grandmother would try on many hats in one shop and nearly always bought something really unusual. Helen loved her grandmother's hats. Annie would buy wool or embroidery thread in another exciting shop. A perfumed fruit shop would yield raspberries and strawberries to eat as one wandered along the street. Next door, on the corner, was a wonderful book shop that looked very like a castle inside. Further west was a spectacular toy shop. It was certain that Helen would carry home a parcel from one or the other of these shops. Then eating lunch in a restaurant was quite exciting, although a surfeit of soft fruit had probably removed Helen's appetite. It was the atmosphere rather than the food which appealed to her. It might be the dark, carpeted silence of the Victoria Café on Market Street, where they always started with the interestingly named Brown Windsor soup. They might walk a little further and eat an omelette in the bright Tudor tearoom on North Street, which looked so old-fashioned outside and which had the only cuckoo clock that Helen had ever seen.

After that they would probably go down to the little open air theatre near the swimming pool and watch the Entertainers give their afternoon show.

Everything was much as usual until they reached the theatre that day where a large notice regretted that there was no show but instead there would be a

GRAND TALENT CONTEST FOR CHILDREN

Several families were waiting at the ticket office with children of all ages. Three boys were dressed in splendid Highland outfits and one of them carried a set of bagpipes. Helen had never seen bagpipes before and gazed at them with fascination. What on earth was it? Was it a toy? A little girl in a bright red shiny dress looked very proud of herself. Ribbons fluttered from the tap shoes which she carried. One boy was dressed as a clown with a red nose and a white face. Helen thought it must have been very embarrassing to walk through the streets of St Andrews like that. She was so busy looking at these interesting children that she hardly listened to the grown-ups voices. Eventually she became aware that she was the subject of their conversation and her blood ran cold as she realised its import.

"I really think our wee girl should go into this contest, don't you Annie. I think she'd be awfully good at singing one of her songs up there on the stage, wouldn't she!"

Her grandmother was using the special voice which, although not directly addressed to Helen was meant for her attention.

Annie demurred, but Mary had decided and bent down to put her face level with Helen's.

"You would like that wouldn't you, my darling! You could sing that one you sang to me yesterday, 'Can't help lovin' dat man o' mine'. I just bet that you'd win a prize too."

Before Helen could muster her forces to refuse, the whole paralysing experience was in train. Her name was written down at the box office and she climbed the stairs to the stage, which seemed very small, only slightly bigger than the kitchen table. Because of her surname, she would be one of the first to perform. She was not even wearing her prettiest dress.

> *"Fish gotta swim and' birds gotta fly*
> *Ah've gotta love one man till Ah die"*

The first lines of the song were her favourite and she belted them out with confidence, but it was downhill all the way after that. As the words faded from her mind, her voice also faded to inaudibility. She reached the end of the song, but it was the worst few moments of Helen's life so far. Even worse than the runaway donkey. The consolation prize of a toy watch (with painted hands which did not move) did not impress her and she was insulted to learn the meaning of the word consolation.

Deeply thankful to leave the stage, she huddled incognito between the two grown-ups, while she watched the other children make fools of themselves. Helen considered all the performances

were poor, although the clown was quite funny as he kept dropping the juggling balls all over the place. She thought the tap
dancer was the worst of all, in spite of her dress and ribbons. Not
a squeak was heard from the poor boy with the bagpipes for he
took stage fright and burst into tears. He was led away by his
mother, who was red in the face and looked very angry.

The last entrant was a tall skinny twelve-year-old, who mumbled the title of his song. The master of ceremonies did not catch
what the boy said, but, no doubt glad to see the end of the contest
in sight, introduced him with apparent delight and asked for a
round of applause. This enthusiasm quickly turned to horror as
the boy started to sing a song of incredible *lese-majesty*.

To the well-known tune of 'Get along little Doagy', the boy
croaked,

"Get along Mrs Simpson, get along,
You thought that you'd be Queen
But you were wrong."

As ever more personally insulting, not to say obscene, comments were sung by the tuneless but articulate voice, the MC
twisted himself into an agony of embarrassment and indecision. It
was impossible to stop the interminable song! Finally the MC in
desperation playfully dragged the boy offstage by the ear, smiling
engagingly and almost dancing as he did so. Helen was terribly
glad that she had not been hauled away like that. Surely that boy's
singing was not any worse than some of the other childrens' turns.

Back in Pittenweem, she was surprised that very little was said
to her grandfather about her song, while they talked and laughed
a lot about the poor boy who was removed from the stage.

When Bruce came the next weekend, again they talked about
the boy and his song and Helen wondered why it was all so interesting and funny. Her father laughed his loudest laugh and
slapped his thigh several times. No one mentioned her performance at all! Perhaps it would have been better if she had
danced. She knew she could certainly have danced better than
the girl in the tap shoes.

◊

Helen noticed that her dreams were changing. Until now she
had often had worry dreams, not nightmares, but dreams in
which she found herself in unpleasant situations. There was one
where she fell over a cliff and jumped so hard in her sleep that

she wakened up. Another recurring dream took place in a lift, probably in Coplands. Helen would be without any of her family, but a lot of grown-ups were crowded around her in the lift and paying her no attention. Looking down, she would find that she was wearing nothing but a vest and rather a short one. She constantly tried to pull it down at the back to cover her bare bottom. As the lift stopped at each floor and people got out, Helen's inadequate covering became more obvious to the few that were left. Nobody said anything, but they looked at her disapprovingly and her embarrassment was extreme. The dream usually finished abruptly then and she awakened with a great sense of relief that it was just a dream.

That summer, however, she experienced much more pleasant dreams. These all took place at the Pittenweem swimming pool, on the beach or in the water. She always felt particularly happy when she wakened from these dreams, although she might not remember them exactly. A favourite one would be repeated for years. In it she was convinced of her own magic power. She was lying at the bottom of a deep rock pool and looking upwards through the water, as though through a silvery ceiling. When she awakened she would wonder if she had been a mermaid in the dream, but she could never be quite sure. Perhaps she had been a little fish? Although Helen was a strong swimmer, she was timid and had never in reality submerged herself, so this dream gave her a very special feeling of power. Was that really what it looked like when you were under the water? She loved it and wished that she could dream that dream every night.

Many years later when she had finally found the courage to swim underwater, she was amazed to realise that the silvery ceiling of her dreams was exactly how the surface looked from underneath! How could she have pictured it so clearly in her childish dreams? That fact seemed pretty magical!

◊

Annie watched her five-year-old daughter swimming and the word 'sedate' sprang to mind. The kid was a sedate swimmer, making her way smoothly and purposefully through the water, much as a lady in her sixties might. Helen was a strong little swimmer, but very unadventurous. At no time would she put her face in the water. Breast stroke or a determined back stroke paddle were her favourite modes. She could swim to the deep end

and back again, but always sedately, no crawl, nothing splashy ,
certainly nothing below the surface. She did not jump or dive,
nor did she turn somersaults in the water. On dry land she
turned somersaults, leaped across wide puddles and was a fear-
less climber of rocks and walls, often jumping down from heights
which Annie might have forbidden if her words could have
reached her daughter in time to stop her. And most days Helen
danced like a little dervish for at least an hour. Why was she so
cautious in the water? Annie felt that it was unnatural and such a
pity. She could not be getting her full pleasure from the pool.
What was she thinking about as she pulled herself through the
water, her face completely expressionless? It looked as though
she were involved in a job of work, rather than a recreation.

Annie need not have worried because Helen was busy inside
her head. She would be completely involved in one of her long
inner scenarios. Swimming through the water provided the vital
background for her imagined story, just as music enriched her
dancing stories. She might be a ship in the ocean, heading for the
harbour at the deep end, she might be a whale or a seal or, more
romantically, one of a family of mermaids.

She did not require to do tricks or advance her swimming
techniques, for she was fully occupied and perfectly happy
developing her inner life.

Nevertheless Annie, with the memories of her own wild
swimming youth, persevered.

"Just jump in from the side, Helen. You know you can jump
into the sand from much bigger heights than that in Pittenweem.
Believe me, the water makes it easier. You'd love it. It's great fun.
Look! There's a little girl jumping in and she's laughing."

Helen shook her head and, descending the stairs into the
water, swam off in her dignified way.

There had been great excitement about the new full length
Disney cartoon 'Snow White and the Seven Dwarfs'. All the
papers said it was a miracle of charm and technique. The songs
were played on the radio all the time and both Helen and her
mother were looking forward to seeing it. That week it was
showing at the Ascot, which was a very luxurious cinema and
close to home. It had been decided that they would go to see it.

Annie wondered if she might use the visit to Snow White as a
lever. As usual she had been encouraging Helen to attempt

various little tricks, with no success.

"I'll make a bargain with you. If you can either jump off the side, shallow end or deep end, or if you can turn a somersault in the water, I'll take you to see Snow White this afternoon."

Helen looked at her for a long time and Annie knew that she'd been wrong to take this route.

"If I don't do any of those things, Mummy, will we still go to see Snow White?"

The tears were welling in her eyes, but Annie strengthened her resolve,

"You've got to do one of those things and then we'll go."

"You said we were going to go this week." Helen was crying now, "You promised."

Annie would have given anything to back down, for she wanted to see the film herself that day. She knew that she was not in the right. She had spoken of the intention of going this week and now she had produced a price which must be paid, a price that Helen felt unable to earn. It was a moral dilemma. Helen was sobbing loudly now, probably because of the unfairness as much as the fact of missing the film.

"Stop crying and come out of the pool, then."

They went into the washroom where Helen started to howl unrestrainedly.

"For goodness sake hush, everyone will think I'm murdering you. Be quiet, or I'll give you a smack."

Helen was certainly not calmed by this threat, although there was little likelihood of it happening. The sobs and wails echoed and re-echoed round the hard walls and basins of the washroom. Several old ladies stopped their careful ablutions and looked at Annie disapprovingly. One tut-tutted loudly. Annie was really angry now, with Helen, with the old ladies and most of all with herself. She had no idea how to extricate herself from the quandary and she was cold in her wet bathing suit. It was a nightmare.

There was really only one way out.

"All right then, Helen, we'll go to 'Snow White' this afternoon.

There was no love in the way that she said this but Helen calmed down, though sobbing for twenty minutes. Annie learned the lesson that if you are going to use leverage, you must be morally correct and strongly determined.

They both enjoyed the cartoon immensely, although it was ter-rifying when Snow White was lost in the wood at night. Helen loved the song 'One day my Prince will come'. When the reflec-tion of the handsome prince appeared beside poor over-worked Snow White's own reflection at the bottom of the well, it was just the most romantic moment possible.

Everything about the film had a profound effect on the little girls of that time. Snow White's stand up collar and cape, the little bows on her dress, her dancing grace were admired and copied. The lasting change for Helen was that her imagined stories now centred around caring for seven little men in a hut in the forest. Her thoughts were busy with all the seven sets of clothes, the seven bowls and spoons, seven pairs of slippers and seven sets of pyjamas. Feeding them, sending them off to the mine, welcoming them home. Neither the romantic prince nor the wicked step-mother played much part in these imaginings, although the prince was incorporated into different stories at different times. It seemed rather sad to Helen that the dwarfs should be left alone, while she went off with the prince. What would happen to them then?

These 'pretends' as she herself referred to her imaginings, kept her awake until late at night. She lay in bed perfectly happy, developing the story in her head.

Within months the strange little men would metamorphose in her mind into four children to be looked after, and this lasted for nearly a year. Next she added a lost waif to her group of four and soon she was in charge of a large house, with thirty orphans as well as her own children. In future years she would put to sea in a ship with her orphans, who would be wonderful at climbing rigging. After reading Robinson Crusoe, she and her orphanage were ship-wrecked and had fantastic adventures. Sometimes her stories were romantic Cinderella plots. As she grew older she reduced the number of characters and often found herself alone in adventurous or perhaps penurious circumstances, where she must struggle to survive. She, of course, was the heroine and cen-tre of all the varied secret stories which she continued to weave throughout her childhood. Around the age of ten or eleven, she quite suddenly found that she could not sustain interest from one night to the next. She tried a new story-line, but no, the desire to develop a life in the imaginary world had just faded and disap-peared. It was a sad discovery and she felt the loss, but there was no way back to that complex mental world which had been such a rich part of her childhood.

Her fantasies were now tied to reality and were a mental rehearsal of what might happen or what might be said in some possible everyday situation. Though some of these imagined situations were unlikely, they were nevertheless possible.

◊

Helen was given a large Snow White book with pictures from the film and stories and puzzles in it. It was very nice to read it and remember how much she had enjoyed the cartoon. She would have liked to see the film again but her mother had said not now. Perhaps one day they would, when they had forgotten it a little bit.

One evening, as Helen was looking through this book, she noticed that her father and mother were talking more quietly than usual and glancing over at her as they talked. They looked in a very happy mood. Helen started to listen more carefully to their subdued conversation. She heard her mother say,

"Are you sure, Bruce? It's a long way to drive."

Then later she said,

"I'm sure she'd be thrilled. What an adventure!"

Bruce was smiling broadly and Helen guessd that they were talking about her.

Nothing was said to Helen and she did not ask any questions. Curiosity was not one of her traits.

The following Friday when she returned from school, her mother immediately changed her dress and washed her face.

"Daddy's coming soon to take us a drive. Isn't that nice?"

Helen was noncommittal. She had been planning to make a den behind the couch for Topsy and Teddy.

Bruce arrived and, with Helen in the back seat, they set off. Quite soon Helen had settled into a very satisfactory 'pretend' about the seven dwarves and some animals that they met in the forest. The little green Austin drove on and on and Annie and Bruce chatted in the front of the car.

"The wee yin's not asking where we're going. Did you tell her?"

"No, of course not. You wanted it to be a surprise, didn't you?"

"Yes, well I've often described it to her and she seemed interested so I thought she would like to see it in real life."

"So would I! I'm looking forward to my jaunt tremendously."

"S'funny she's never asked where we're going. We've been driving for a couple of hours now."

"She's a bit of a fatalist. Maybe kids are like that. They just go where they're taken."

"No, no. I was always asking and wanting to know where I was and when we'd get there. My Father used to get angry, for I'd never shut up."

It was dark when Bruce said over his shoulder,

"Are you asleep in the back there? If you look out the window, we're in England now."

The idea of England had a sort of magic for Helen. She imagined beautiful rivers with overhanging trees, but all she could see was darkness. She grunted and returned to the scenario in her head.

"I think she must be sleeping."

"No *I'm not sleeping.*"

This accusation always made Helen indignant.

On and on they drove. Bruce had munched through many sandwiches as he drove. He laughed one of his loud laughs,

"I bet she'll be absolutely knocked sideways when we get there. Great to arrive in the dark. We'll get the full effect. I can just imagine her wee face."

Still they drove through the night. Annie was getting impatient herself, but not a word of complaint or question came from the back of the car.

At last they were obviously approaching a large town. There was a glow in the sky. Suddenly they turned a corner and the blazing illumuminations of Blackpool hung in the air before them. In the distance, the soaring tower glittered in the sky.

"Here we are at last!" Bruce's voice was a mixture of triumph and expectation. "D'ye know where we are, wee Tuppenny?"

"It's Blackpool."

It was said in a matter-of-fact tone and it was all she said.

Poor crestfallen Bruce!

Annie was extra enthusiastic to make up for her daughter's coolness.

If her reaction to the lights was disappointing, Helen was delighted with the hotel room. The twin beds were perfectly appointed with green silk covers and matching quilts. A pale grey carpet covered every inch of floor and everything was new and smart.

"Oh, Mummy, it's like something in a film!"

"Maybe the beds won't be as comfy as your own."

After a short walk and a fish supper, they returned to the hotel As Helen snuggled down in one of the beds, she remarked,

"You were right, Mummy, this bed ... it's a bit like lying on an oatcake."

On the following day, Helen's enthusiasm satisfied even her father.

There were wonderful little rides and trips for young children to take by themselves, magnificent roundabouts and everywhere charming toys and the spun sugar that looked like pink cotton wool and melted in the mouth in a strange delicious way. It was all new and exciting and far beyond anything that she had seen at the Lammas Fair in St Andrews.

Her favourite ride was in a small boat which sailed along past various moving set pieces to the right and left of the stream. One showed Snow White serving food to the seven little men. Another scene had three little gnomes sawing and hammering, making a little house. Then there was a big fat smiling cook, mixing something in a bowl, while two children and a dog jumped up and down in impatience. As the boat swung around a curve in the stream, a waterfall could be seen up ahead. It was pouring down and the boat was heading straight for it. Would everyone get soaked? Of course it switched off at just the last minute. It was very exciting and Helen took that ride several times, never quite sure if the water would go off in time, secretly hoping it might not.

There were things for adults to enjoy as well. Helen watched as her parents stepped into a large revolving tunnel. It was big enough for them to stand up and it was going round slowly, but they must carefully keep their balance and walk through to the other side. She could see it was not easy. Some people even fell down and had to be helped up by others. Helen thought that if she were a grown-up she would not go on that drum. Bruce and Annie were laughing and doing very well. They were almost through to the other side when Annie dropped her handbag. Helen gasped, for it had opened and there, strewn and scattered all over the were all the odds and ends of a lady's bag, purse, comb, wallet, tickets, hankies, keys, matches, cigarettes, loose change! What a mess. The revolving drum had to be stopped to allow them to pick everything up. Annie and Bruce were laughing, but Helen made herself as small as possible. It was very embarrassing.

"Everyone was looking at you, Mummy!"

"Were they? Oh, I don't suppose it's the first time that's happened."

That afternoon they went to the dance hall in the Blackpool Tower and Bruce danced with each of his ladies.

At night, Bruce and Annie went out for an hour by themselves, after arranging that the hotel receptionist would listen in case Helen woke up.

They walked along arm in arm and Annie felt young and carefree.

They went twice on the Big Dipper and ate shrimps from a paper cup. As they laughed about the accident that day, Annie looked in her handbag. They had all had their photos taken in a little booth and suddenly she came across the negative of Helen. The dark face in the picture shocked her just at first. Helen, never far from her mind, seemed distant and unprotected amongst stangers in the hotel. What if there were a fire and Helen was forgotten. That horrible negative looked like a burned child.

"Let's go home now, Bruce."

"Och, there's no hurry. The wee one's fine."

"No, I really want to go back to the hotel."

He grumbled but they returned and of course all was well.

Altogether it was a very successful trip, only slightly marred by Bruce's continuous exclamations,

"Isn't this just great! What a marvellous place! Are ye having a good time? What a wonder this town is! Are ye glad I brought you here? D'ye remember me telling you all about it? Is it the way you thought it would be, wee Tuppenny?"

Helen became bored by the repetition and had to be nudged by her mother to answer politely.

They drove home in the daylight and visited Gretna Green and saw the forge where people could get married.

Annie felt that it was the nearest to a proper family holiday that they had ever had.

Helen would remember it as the only proper family holiday that they ever had.

Empire Exhibition

Remains of a Viking steam bath have been discovered in Caithness.

Glasgow Herald 18th Feb 1938

Annie had very fond memories of the Glasgow exhibitions of her youth. Those had been held in Kelvingrove Park and by the time of the 1911 exhibition, she and her brother could walk there by themselves. She particularly remembered all the free samples of both sweet and savoury things to eat, which meant that one could graze happily all day without spending a penny. Then there were free pamphlets on cookery, crochet and knitting. Annie always brought home a handful of these. Wherever you went in the grounds, you could hear a band playing. If you had lost your way, which was quite easy to do as there were paths going in all directions, you only needed to head towards the music to reach a familiar point. Annie and Willie loved to watch the procession of model ships which sailed down the Kelvin each day. The first one was a strangely shaped little boat with a man in it. They learned that the boat was called a coracle, but they never quite understood why the steersman was wearing so little. You could see a lot of his skin which was painted blue! Very peculiar. The rest of the ships were large models of famous vessels, although they seemed too small to have a man on them. You certainly could not see any person steering them and Willie wondered how they managed to sail in the right direction.

Willie specially enjoyed the Laplander's Arctic village, which was near the grass huts of the West African village. He liked watching the people, but Annie wondered if they really liked to be looked at all day. She knew that she would not like it.

Annie loved the film in the Canadian Pavilion and saw it several times. It showed Canadian scenes, high snow-covered mountains, people skating on an enormous lake, huge trees being cut down then floated down a river with the lumberjacks jumping from log to log. The film showed miles and miles of flat land, where high grass waved and there were no trees and the horizon was just a straight line in the distance. Annie knew that was the prairie that her father's friend, Mr Rosier Morton, had told her about. He had lived there and she had been fascinated by his stories of the deep snow and terrible coldness that could lead to a horrible thing called frostbite. He had assured her that frostbite made your toes, sometimes even your nose, drop off, but she could not believe that was true. He also joked that the way to cure it was to rub snow on your toes or nose.

"D'ye think this exhibition will be as wonderful as the ones I remember from my youth, Maw? Strange to think of that "Flying Across the Kelvin" ride. It was breath-taking. Nothing could seem quite so marvellous nowadays when we see planes in the sky any day and just take it for granted. I must say I'd like to try flying. I wonder if I ever will?"

"It won't have the weather that we had that year we were married. What a summer. The sun shone and shone and I thought it couldn't keep shining until our wedding, but it did. D'you remember, John? And we had that wonderful bicycling holiday!"

John paused before he answered. Lunch was finished and he sat, his elbows supported on the table, his hands clasped and hiding the lower part of his face. Very quietly and tunelessly, he was whistling between his thumbs. He had been looking gloomily at the water jug and scarcely raised his eyes to reply.

"Yes, it certainly was a year of lovely weather. I remember it well."

There was another long silence before Annie spoke.

"I'm determined *not* to be disappointed, but I suppose kids think *everything* is wonderful and so nothing is ever quite as good you remember it."

Her father's dejected face made Annie regret that she had mentioned the exhibition at all. Now she was struggling to make bright conversation. She knew that her Father disapproved of this large expensive exhibition being held at such a bad time, when there was such poverty and all the countries in Europe were threatened with war.

Again there was an awkward silence, then Mary spoke,

"It certainly won't be as handy for us to visit, having to go all the way to Bellahouston."

"I expect they'll put on extra buses and tramcars and ... "

Her father interrupted her in an unusually loud, angry voice,

"I expect a great many of the Glasgow population will be unable to afford the fare or the entry ticket. It's all nonsense and a disgraceful waste of public money when people are dressed in rags and starving. Damned nonsense. And the corporation would be better saving their money to fund the preparations for defence that everyone is talking about. Today's paper is appealing for men above military age to help in air raid precautions. It's *abominable* to think we might be attacked from the air. Attacked in our own homes. What has the world come to?"

His voice trailed away to a whisper as he stood, then left the room.

"I don't know what to do with your father, Annie. He is so depressed by the world situation."

"Well, it's not surprising. Everything is terrible. That Mussolini seems to be a rotter and now he's really friendly with Hitler. Nobody trusts the Bolshevists. Poor Spain has had a terrible time and Abyssinia too. China has been battered by the Japs. How could that happen? I always thought Japan was quite a small nation and China enormous, didn't you? There's always famines and droughts and fevers in Africa, and America can hardly help themselves. The poor farmers have had all their soil blown away and the cities have soup kitchens for the poor, but Roosevelt seems to have good schemes for employment, hydro-electric dams and things like that. That's the thing, there's plenty of money in the world, just a lot of people don't have any of it. I don't know *anything* about South America, but it seem unstable and always having big bloody revolutions. That's terrible to be so ignorant about a part of the world which is so enormous, with millions of folk living there. No doubt there's plenty poverty there too. I must try and read up about it."

"Nobody is buying paintings just now, either. Your father has only sold one so far this year."

"Well, it's only the end of January, early days yet."

"Just listen to that wee soul playing the piano again. Do you think she would like to have lessons, Annie?"

"Don't think the budget would stretch to paying for them, I'm afraid. She's young enough yet and look at what happened with the dancing lessons, she didn't enjoy them and stopped dancing at home altogether. Nowadays I have to switch off the wireless to stop her becoming exhausted."

"Children are so strange."

Elsie was expecting another baby and after a visit to Lambhill, Annie wondered if Helen had noticed Elsie's bump. She had not mentioned it but it was unlikely that she had not noticed it. Helen seldom asked questions and Annie considered Helen a strangely incurious child. Surely children were always asking questions. She remembered that she and Willie were like that although often no answers were forthcoming. Helen liked to work things out for herself with her own peculiar logic. When she would explain her wierd conclusions to her mother, Annie was never sure whether to correct her or allow her the independence which she obviously cherished. She had never asked any searching questions about babies. This could be an opportunity to introduce some facts of life.

"Did you notice Aunty Elsie's tummy, today?"

"Yes, I did. It was *very big*. She was cutting the loaf on it!"

By supreme effort, Annie did not smile.

"Well there's a reason it's so big. Can you guess?"

Helen frowned and shook her head.

"Well, she is going to have a wee baby, a brother or a sister for Maureen. Isn't that nice!"

"And why does that make her tummy big?"

Helen's expression was that of a teacher speaking to a backward child and Annie laughed.

"Now you know where kittens come from and little puppies, their mummies carry them around in their tummies until they're big enough."

"Yes?"

"And monkeys are the same."

"Yes?"

"Well ... human beings are the same too. Aunty Elsie has her wee baby safely in her tummy and next week or the week after, it will be born."

"Oh, I thought people would be different from monkeys."

"No, they're just the same."

Helen returned to her book, leaving Annie with the distinct impression that her daughter simply did not believe her.

Two months later, they were at the cinema watching a dramatic period drama. Annie worried that the historic innaccuracy of those Hollywood tales might be damaging to her daughter's perception of history, but they were usually entertaining.

The aristocratic heroine of this piece was with child. Naturally the Duke and Duchess were deliriously happy and there had been great rejoicings of the peasantry for it was vitally important, at whichever period of history this was, to preserve the bloodline. The fortunate child would inherit vast estates. The pretty Duchess, with her long white ringlets was bowling along in her carriage when disaster struck! A large stone dislodged a wheel, the carriage overturned and the Duchess fell out of the carriage, rolled down an embankment, then lay motionless on the ground.

The audience gasped, but Helen leaned confidentially to her mother and whispered,

"That's the baby gone phut!"

Annie tried to control her laughter, but comforted herself with the knowledge that Helen had at last accepted the strange fact of babies being in tummies.

◊

At her grandmother's flat, when only the family was present, it seemed to Helen that the talk about Willie did not need to be whispered anymore. In fact the voices were loud and furious. Even Drandad was shouting which was very unusual...unheard of! They all seemed unhappy and angry.

Helen was sad to realise from these loud conversations that Uncle Willie *was* going to get married and everyone was really angry about it. Surely it could not be Eileen he was going to marry, because she was nice and everyone would be pleased if it were Eileen.

These loud encounters happened quite often. Sometimes Willie was there, but he did not say much. A phrase unknown to Helen cropped up so repeatedly that she learned it and was able to ask her mother at bedtime what it meant.

"Well, my wee lamb," her mother hesitated for so long, that Helen thought it must be something unsuitable for little girls to know, "It's a bit difficult to explain."

Helen waited expectantly, although she knew that her mother would have liked her to say it did not matter.

"Well, mmm, you know how Grandma Corning goes to church and we don't really go to church much in this family."

"We don't go at all!"

"No, but some people go to church a lot and they think it's very important and they go to a different church from Grandma Corning."

"Doesn't Grandma Corning think church is important."

"Oh, yes of course she does, or she wouldn't go, I suppose, but…"

"What's my other grandma got to do with Uncle Willie?"

"Nothing at all. But you were asking about Roman Catholics and they are people that think their church is very, very important and Willie wants to marry Eileen who is a Catholic. And that raises all sorts of problems."

"What sort?"

"Well, Willie must become a Catholic."

"Can he do that?"

"Well, mmm, he's never been much of a Protestant, so I don't know whether that makes it easier or more difficult for him."

"Where will the Catholic church be, that uncle Willie goes to?"

"Oh, there are lots of Catholic churches all over Glasgow. He'll find one. But my mother and father are very unhappy about it all. My father is very much against the Catholic Church because of its political power and I don't suppose there's a girl on this earth that Grandma would think good enough for her son. And the fact that Eileen's a Catholic just puts the kibosh on it."

"What's the kibosh?"

"It just puts the tin lid on it."

"Oh! Do you like Eileen?"

"Oh, yes. She seems a lovely girl, friendly and funny, though I don't think much of her taste in men and I don't think she'll have her troubles to seek. She's no idea what she's getting herself into … but there you are, marriage is what people do, even though it's a gamble … I expect they will marry. Willie generally gets what he wants. But it's late, so off to bed now. Nighty night!"

◊

Annie was relieved when Helen made a friend at school. Yvonne was also an only child and she shared Helen's timidity and imagination. She lived at the foot of the hill and they played together most days after school. Annie was intrigued to find their favourite game was 'pirates'. Climbing up a step ladder and gazing into an imaginary distance, or hunting for buried treasure in cupboards or below beds, seemed to constitute the main elements of this game.

Helen spoke more of her classmates now.

"There are two girls called Betty in my class. One is awfully pretty and I like her, but I don't like the other one. She is fat and she said her name was Elizabeth and she said she was Princess Elizabeth! Nobody believed her but she kept saying it was true!"

"Och what a shame, poor wee girl." Annie laughed

"No, she's not a nice girl, she pinches people then runs away. There is a nice boy in the class though. He is very handsome. His name is Raymond Hare."

"That's quite a fancy name for a wee boy."

"He's really nice and the class is going to put on a play and he is to be Peter Pan and I'm going to be Wendy."

"That's lovely, my pet."

Annie smiled to herself. Even six-year-olds had romantic feelings! And her daughter had secured the coveted part opposite Raymond Hare, the class heart-throb.

◊

The world was in turmoil and it seemed as though the weather reflected the global disturbance.

Poor Empire Exhibition! From the time that it was opened on the third of May, there was lashing rain almost daily. June, July and August were the wettest in living memory. There were many jokes in the papers, of course. One was that no visitor was allowed entry without umbrella and wellington boots.

In October, gales of wind damaged several buildings. The elegant Treetops restaurant, which was built on a platform and incorporated the upper branches of trees in a way which was much admired, had a large plate glass window blown in. Fortunately no one was injured, but it was bad publicity. One customer was so shocked and frightened by the incident, that she fled from the restaurant and disappeared. There was an intensive search for her for many hours before she was found, still in the exhibition grounds.

In spite of the weather, Annie went several times with Helen, for it was an interesting day out.

The Australian Pavilion appealed to Annie particularly. It seemed to be such a wonderful country. The agriculture, the minerals and the wildlife were fascinating. She longed to buy a toy koala bear for Helen, but it was made of real fur and was just too expensive. And could it be made of Koala fur? Surely not. Besides, she realised that Helen was not as impressed by the furry toy as she herself was.. What Helen liked was a working model of Sidney Harbour Bridge with small cars and trains running over it and ferries sailing underneath it. It was very realistic and the child seemed rooted to the spot as she watched this display. Only with the promise of an ice cream could she be persuaded to leave the fascinating model.

In another part of the grounds, Annie was horrified by the giraffe-necked women, whose tight brass neck bands must never be removed, or their necks would break. What torture and what a terrible mutilation of the human body! What exploitation of women! She found herself thinking about those poor victims for years.

After walking around for an hour or so, Annie would become tired and they would go to Ross's dairy for their favourite snack, a ham roll and a glass of milk. There were also various lectures and demonstrations where they could sit for twenty minutes and allow Annie to recover her strength, although these were not very interesting for Helen. The free samples were mainly soup or health drinks and were disappointing compared to Annie's childhood memories. However there was a wonderful doughnut making machine and mother and daughter enjoyed watching the whole process. Clever machinery formed the doughnuts, then sent them on their journey through the hot fat, turning them at intervals to ensure even cooking, then finishing them off with a dusting of sugar. They were cheap and delicious and Annie advised Helen not to mention to anyone quite how many they had eaten.

Helen hardly noticed the rain, as she enjoyed wearing her yellow oilskin and souwester. She loved walking past the very modern buildings that looked like something in a film. The curving walls, the large windows, the flat roofs and the pale colours seemed so different from any buildings that she had ever seen before.

Then there was water everywhere, waterfalls cascading down stairways, fountains that changed their shape and height as you watched them. One evening she was there after dark and saw the spectacular underwater lighting effects of the Dancing Waters that she would remember all her life.

Another incredible water experience was a model of the Victoria Falls. This was inside a building and the roaring noise of the falling water and the spray in the air was almost too exciting. Sometimes you could see a little rainbow. It slowly became dark and then it would become light again, just like night falling then dawn arriving, only much more quickly of course. There was a model train here too, but it did not seem as realistic to Helen as the other. There was so much rushing water, so very close to you and it was so terribly noisy that Helen felt nervous, it seemed dangerous to her and Annie was able to leave that exhibit quite quickly. She read later that one and a half million gallons of water poured over the model falls each day, but she could scarcely believe that. If it were the case, perhaps the kid was right and it was quite dangerous.

Another Wedding

In September, Helen, in a long pink taffeta dress that her mummy had made, was the flower girl at her uncle's wedding. With a silver mesh Juliet cap trimmed with tiny artificial rosebuds on her specially curled hair, she felt like one of the enchanted princesses in the Yellow Fairy book. It was very exciting.

Annie was fashionable in a navy suit, with grey embroidery around the neck, beautiful soft suede gloves and matching shoes with very high heels. Helen loved to see her mother dressed so stylishly, though, disappointingly for the child, the navy pull-on hat was just the same shape as the ones she always wore. It would be years before Helen realised that her mother preferred the classic style popularised by Garbo.

The service was early in the morning. Annie had hoped that Bruce would come with them, but he had made it plain that it was impossible to leave the business that day. Of course he hated getting dressed up and muttered several uncomplimentary remarks about marriage and fuss. He offered to drive them to the church, which was in a faraway and unknown part of Glasgow, but Annie declined. A journey with Bruce was nearly always fraught, he would be late, he would have little time to spare, the car would be making a strange noise or running out of petrol. Eventually, Bruce always solved the difficulties with many inward mutters and bad language. Annie suspected that he manufactured these problems in order to solve them and impress her.

"Thank you, Bruce. That's kind of you, but we'll just take a taxi. My father gave me some extra cash. I'm sorry you're not coming, though."

She realised that she was not honest as she said this. Bruce hated this sort of event and would have complained throughout the day. It was much easier without him.

At the church, they were welcomed by a young priest in a white lacy pinafore, who took Helen's hand and walked with her to the end of the church where there were lots of shining silver dishes and richly-coloured embroidered tablecloths. There had been nothing like this in Grandma Corning's church. This building was just as large, but it smelled differently from that other cool grey antiseptic space. There was a perfume in the air which reminded her of a favourite drawer in her Grandma's house. The lowest drawer in a chest, it was deep and difficult to open and contained evidence of her Grandmother's relentless bargain-hunting. Forty cakes of soap of all sizes and colours, and thirty little blocks of face-powder in various shades, ranging from pale peach to deep rachel, exuded their delicate but insistent aroma. Whenever Helen opened that drawer in the future, she would be transported back to the church where Uncle Willie was married.

Strangely the people in the seats looked quite poor and shabby, not at all like guests at a wedding.

People arrived late and other people left before it started. It was a bit like being at the pictures, with people constantly coming and going.

"Can you curtsy, my dear?"

The priest had a deep voice and a funny accent.

Helen nodded.

"I'd like you to face the altar and curtsy. And each time you pass the altar, please curtsy again."

After the first curtsy, Helen was taken through a little side door and there were Willie and Eileen having a cup of tea.

Then they all came out into the big church again for the rest of the ceremony and Helen curtsied several times, without being told. She liked it.

From the back of the church, Annie watched her daughter with surprise. What a quaint child she was. Who had told her to curtsy like that?

There was a long time when Helen was left sitting by herself in a pew near to the altar. It was quite interesting. Three boys appeared, wearing white garments like the priest. They were big boys compared to Helen, but it pleased her to see other children. They seemed to go back and forwards a lot and fetch things. They shook hands with the two priests and looked very ashamed of having to shake hands. Helen felt that they had not been trained as well as they might have been in this social grace. Then they carried enormous candles in golden candlesticks across from one side to another. Then they brought them back again. The boys looked very unhappy and Helen wondered if they had made a mistake, but the priest smiled at them and then they all disappeared again and another priest waved a small brass dish on a long chain about. There was smoke streaming from this little dish and the perfume became stronger after that and Helen sniffed it delightedly. Sometimes there was singing and sometimes an organ played. It sounded pretty much the same as at Grandma Corning's church, though it went on for longer. Helen fell into a slight doze and wakened guiltily to find a whole lot of people standing in line in front of the priest. When they reached him, they opened their mouths and he popped something like a small biscuit into each, then they turned and walked away. Should she have been there to get a biscuit, too, she wondered. Perhaps she had been needed to help hand out the biscuits, instead of sleeping. No one had told her exactly what a flower girl was supposed to do. It was worrying. She sat forward on the edge of the bench, very straight and ready if needed. She looked over her shoulder, but her mother was nowhere to be seen in that vast space. She was not afraid, but she did want to be a successful flower girl. What a lot of people were waiting for a biscuit. Some were in very nice clothes and others were shabby and poor looking. Helen found this difficult to understand. Were the poor people at the wedding too? They must be very poor, to be unable to afford a nice outfit for something as special as a wedding.

Suddenly everything stopped. The biscuits were finished! There were still lots of people waiting!. Helen was horrified. What would the priest do? However it was all right, because he went to a very nice little golden cupboard, behind the altar and brought out another packet of biscuits. Helen was relieved.

Sometime later, when it was all over and they were climbing into the taxi, Helen did not feel she had done anything very much, except curtsy.

Helen sat with Willie and Eileen in the taxi to Bath Street, where the reception would be held in the Burlington function rooms. The newly married couple looked terribly happy and Eileen kissed her new husband and her little flower girl alternately. Helen was a little sad to think that she never could marry her uncle now, but she did not feel jealous, only resigned.

Eileen's dress was soft and gorgeous to touch. What luxury it was to ride in two taxis, in one day! No other little girl in Glasgow would be doing that, thought Helen, as well as wearing a long pink dress. It was more like something Shirley Temple would do in America.

Looking down, Helen noticed that lots of confetti had landed in her lap. The people outside the church had been throwing it madly at the happy couple as they climbed into the taxi. What should she do with it all? She could not throw it on the floor of this beautiful clean taxi.

Willie saw her problem and whispered,

"Just hold your dress up like a lady as you get out the car. Then you can throw it away later."

Helen smiled her gratitude to him, and kept her dress held up daintily throughout the boring photographs on the front steps.

When they entered the thickly carpeted reception room, no one seemed to be paying much attention to Helen. She felt tired and hungry and wondered where her Mummy was. As she stood there alone and apart, suddenly someone pointed to her, then said something and started to smile. Others turned round and gazed at her and then at the floor and giggled. Everyone was looking at her and she looked down. She had forgotten the confetti and it now lay in a white and pink pool at her feet!

"It's a little puddle of confetti!" someone said and smiled kindly, but Helen was horrified. What a mess she had made on the carpet in this important place. Everyone was thinking what a fool she was. And that person saying 'puddle' was almost as if she had wet her pants, something she had not done for years, but she was young enough to remember the ignominy of it.

Fortunately Uncle Willie, with his usual sensitivity to children, spotted how upset she was and quickly lifted her up. As he walked into another room, where there were lots of tables with flowers, he whispered in her ear,

"I hope that the prettiest girl in the room is going to sit near me for lunch."

At that moment, how very much Helen regretted that he had married someone else! And married a Roman Catholic, too, whatever that was.

When they returned to the first room after lunch, the confetti had magically disappeared.

The Butler

One morning at the Renfrew Street flat, Annie and her father were talking. She was resting on the couch with her feet up, for after doing one or two household chores for her mother, she had suddenly felt tired and faint.

"You'll need to see a doctor, my dear, and find out why you tire so easily. It might even be the same problem as your mother had."

The tears came into Annie's eyes. It was seldom that anyone showed her sympathy or even acknowledged her tiredness. Bruce always talked of the curative powers of hard work and the golf course. Her mother seemed to think she just made excuses to justify her apparent laziness. She hated the idea of her father being worried, so she smiled brightly,

"Oh I don't think it's anything like pernicious anaemia, for I soon recover after I've had a wee rest and I'm just fine sometimes. Full of oomph, in fact. Don't worry, Paw."

"Well I've been wondering how I could help you ... "

"That's very kind, but don't worry! I can jog along. Sometimes things are a bit difficult for me, but I'm getting stronger all the time."

It was dishonest, but she was unwilling to admit to her father or to herself just how worried she was.

"Annie, I've been approached by an old friend who wants me to do him a favour. You remember Major Morrison that I painted last year?"

"Oh yes, you had difficulty painting his enormous moustache. What sort of favour?"

"He was telling me that one of his men in the last war had got in touch with him. He'd been pretty shaken up, shell shock I expect. He didn't say exactly what. Anyway this man, Lyndsay, a very decent chap he assures me, is looking for work. Desperate for any sort of work that he can get. I think he has a widowed sister with a family to support. He's strong enough physically, just rather nervous and unwilling to take an office job, although that's the sort of thing he did before the war, accountancy or insurance or something. Anyway I've offered to help him for the next four months. Your mother doesn't know yet. He'll come here and do heavy housework a couple of times a week. That'll help you too. And he can give me a hand as well, lifting heavy frames downstairs and that sort of thing. Getting a bit frail and doddery in my old age, I'm afraid."

"You haven't told my mother yet?"

One of Annie's eyebrows was raised.

"No, hm, I haven't ... just found the right time, but what I thought was that this fellow could also give *you* a hand in Hyndland, one day a week. Heavy lifting y'know or cleaning windows, brasses, all those things that are hard work. You could take it a bit more easily until you're back to yourself again. Having the baby, then your mother's illness, it was all too much for you, I think."

"Something like my own private butler, you mean? Sounds very posh. Would he be prepared to do these things, d'ye think? Might he not feel it was beneath him?"

"Oh I think he'd do practically anything to get a regular income. That's what the major said anyway, and his moustache bristled very self righteously as he said it."

As they spoke in this light-hearted way, she realised with a pang that her father was not facing up to her deteriorating condition any more realistically than anyone else in the family, including herself. Why could it not be faced that there was something the matter with her health? She should certainly have returned to normal fitness in six years. She must consult a doctor soon. It was up to her to act, for everyone else was *pretending!*

◊

The following week, Mr Lyndsay reported for duties at nine o'clock one morning ...

He was a tall man in his late forties, with a gaunt, sensitive face and dark thinning hair. His posture was military with a ramrod straight back.

"Good morning, Mrs Corning. Your father said you would be at home today so I took the liberty of coming out to see if there were any household tasks for me to deal with."

Just at first his manner was nervous and hesitant. His voice was educated and it was obvious to Annie that he had been used to being in a position of authority, a position which he was now struggling to relinquish. Annie felt very sorry for him and extremely awkward. How could she give this man orders and expect him to act like her charlady?

However Mr Lyndsay, which is what she would always call him, was determined to give satisfaction in his new job. He suggested that if he might bring out the step ladder, he would do all high-reaching tasks today, windows, light fixtures and high shelves. Annie was very happy to agree to this.

He worked hard and Annie spent the morning at her sewing machine.

When Helen came in for lunch, he was friendly with the child without being effusive. She liked that cool approach and whispered to her mother that the tall man was very nice.

He accepted a cheese sandwich and coffee at lunchtime, but wanted to continue working and would eat later, by himself.

By two o'clock, he had accomplished a lot. Annie felt that the upper part of the house had been spring-cleaned.

She wondered how much she should pay him when he left and hoped desperately that she would have enough in the house. However as he put on his coat and saw the purse in her hand, he said,

"Mr Mackay is dealing with my remuneration in the meantime, Mrs Corning. I should like to thank you for this opportunity. I'm so very grateful to you and to your father for employment. Thank you. My life has been very difficult for some time and I am grateful."

Annie was almost sure that there were tears in his eyes as he spoke.

After arranging to come at the same time the following week, he tipped his hat politely and left.

Annie smiled to herself as she shut the door. She was intrigued. What a man of mystery! How hard he had worked! And what a thorough job he had made of everything! How polite, yet dignified he had been. Not at all servile, yet always ready to please her. What was the word she wanted? Deferential! That was what he had been. Perhaps that was what real butlers were like?

Could he possibly have been a real butler in a stately home? No, she certainly could not believe that, but how exciting to have her own manservant. She felt like someone in a Noel Coward play.

' Having a butler added a whole new aspect to her life. A protective and caring person had arrived to make her existence easier. She felt better already.

She wondered how her mother was dealing with having a butler.

Mr Lyndsay rang the bell punctually each week at nine o'clock. Although he always asked Annie if there were any special jobs that she required, he had his own agenda prepared and she mostly followed his suggestion. The suite, the leather seated dining room chairs, the large brass coal scuttle, the silver teapot and many other bits and pieces would be gleaming by the time that he left the flat at two thirty. Or it might be a day for floors, rug-beating, vacuuming, washing, polishing. One day he cleared, washed and organised the kitchen cupboards. Annie had never seen anyone work in such a focussed way. In her experience of hired help, cups of tea at regular intervals, with accompanying chit-chat, had been a necessity. One of their maids had filled the house with the savoury smell of frying bacon two or three times daily. Mr Lyndsay only stopped for a sandwich and coffee at one thirty and was at work again by one forty-five. He was a treasure.

He became less nervous and strained as the weeks passed, although familiarity never developed between him and his employer. He made mild jokes about the weather and started to refer to himself as 'your butler' sometimes 'your esteemed butler'. Occasionally if she asked him to do something which he had not himself suggested, he would reply,

"Certainly m'lady."

At first she wondered if he were being ironic or even cheeky, but she realised that it was part of the butler joke.

He made a great difference to Annie's life. The house was sparkling and he was able to bring in heavier shopping and that also saved Annie's energies. Each Thursday, she tried to be extra organised and tidy ready for her butler's visit. She usually baked that morning, as she found that he enjoyed a scone or a piece of shortbread after his sandwich. She started to feel much stronger again and very positive.

Her neighbour on the ground floor, Mrs Walton, commented on how well she was looking. Mrs Walton was a kind, motherly lady who was always ready to make a pot of tea for Annie and have a blether. She had a son and a daughter of roughly Annie's age but she bewailed the fact that they seemed unlikely ever to marry and make her a grandma.

"Wee Helen is my wee adopted grand daughter, I think." She would laugh and cuddle Helen., who liked her and was in fact more relaxed with Mrs Walton than she was with Mary.

One day Mrs Walton said teasingly,

"Annie, you're looking absolutely blooming. Maybe it's that handsome man that comes here every Thursday that's cheering you up!"

But Annie was quite sharp with her,

"I know you're only teasing, but you shouldn't say things like that. It's absolute nonsense, but someone might take you seriously. Mr Lyndsay is my employee, if that doesn't sound too grand. I mean that he is paid to work for me and we're not even terribly talkative together. He is a very nice man and he has been a great help to me. That's why I'm looking better, I've had a real rest. But it's unkind to *suggest* even that there is anything else between us. Our relationship is entirely business-like and please remember that, Mrs Walton."

Although the older lady apologised, Annie felt cross with her for weeks.

Mrs Walton wondered if perhaps "the lady doth protest too much." But she did not share this thought with anyone else.

In fact, Annie often dreamed of her butler, although in the dreams he was as small as a ten-year-old boy. As in real life, he worked continuously, sweeping, polishing and often carrying enormous loads which Annie worried were too heavy for such a little man. Sometimes she begged him to put them down in case he hurt his back, but he would just smile and shake his head. The dreams were always much the same and Annie would awaken smiling, with a feeling of optimism for the day ahead.

◊

Because of her mother's constant nagging, Annie was sure that Helen was dangerously underweight. She dreaded the wrath of the examining doctor at the school medical inspection in October. There seemed to be nothing that she could do to help her daughter eat more food. Helen was full of energy but Annie feared to expose that slender little form to criticism. Would they judge her mothering capabilities to be inadequate?

As she drew the vest over Helen's head she said apologetically to the doctor,

"I'm afraid she is terribly, terribly thin."

"Oh, not at all. She's a very well-nourished child and look how brown she is! She's a healthy wee girl."

No comment could have been more surprising or sweeter to Annie's ears. From then on she was armed against her mother's carping and learned to disregard that particular complaint. She noticed that her mother made a practice of accusing other people's children, even their dogs and cats, of 'being starved' when this was patently not the case. Why had she never noticed that before, she wondered?

Mothers and daughters were such a close and strange relationship. Annie realised that she was in many ways a disappointment to her mother. She was honest enough to admit that there were aspects of Helen which disappointed her. Of course Annie adored Helen, but she would have liked her to have a bit more courage, a bit more sense of adventure. There was the incident of the tricycle last spring. In spite of the fiasco of the Triang trike and the toy car of several years ago, Bruce had bought a large splendid tricycle for Helen. It had solid rubber wheels, a leather saddle and an even louder bell. Helen was entirely indifferent to it and Annie felt responsible.

"Let's take your new trike to the park today and see how well it goes on the smooth paths. Will we?"

Helen did not say no, but her grimace showed that she was averse to the idea. However, Annie believed that eventually the child would find out how much fun it was, if she just gave it a chance.

It was not to be.

Annie had wheeled the trike all the way to the park, cajoling, urging and at last losing her temper, before wheeling it all the way home again, unridden. A weeping Helen trailed disconsolately behind her mother, ashamed but determined. The atmosphere between mother and daughter was very unhappy. This strife-torn day only served to convince Annie that she must push her child to grow up and have more gumption. Bruce was perhaps right, she had mollycoddled their daughter. She and her brother had certainly been more dare-devil. What was she to do? Helen could be like a little mule if she did not want to do something.

Helen had enjoyed the tricycle on one occasion only. At the end of term, the school playground had been divided up into 'streets', with traffic lights and flashing Belisha beacons at pedestrians crossings. The children were told to bring their bikes, trikes or pedal-cars to school. Any girls who did not have a vehicle might bring their doll's pram, boys could bring a barrow. Two policemen came and talked about the rules of the road, then everyone went out to the playground and pedalled or walked about just like a real city. All the vehicles stopped at the red lights and also at the Belisha beacon when a pedestrian was there. One policeman stood at the big crossing in the middle of the playground and directed the traffic. The other strolled around and offered advice to the nervous and warnings to the speed fiends. It was a beautiful sunny day and Helen loved it. She could have pedalled her trike up and down forever. The main thing was that she was safe. If she rode her trike on the pavement, those careering buses and noisy trams on the road always seemed too close to her. What if she went off the pavement and under a bus? It seemed far too big a risk to take. Here in the playground there were no buses or trams, everyone was obeying the rules and no one could go very quickly. She thought it delightful.

Anne watched through the railings, pleased and astonished as her daughter, showing every sign of enjoyment, cycled briskly along with the other traffic, skilfully turned corners, stopped at lights and waved gaily to other children in their vehicles.

After the day in the playground, Helen hardly ever rode her trike again and then only inside the house.

Annie sold it the following year to a friend in Pittenweem.

For a long time Helen had wanted to grow a coaliflower. Annie thought them unnatural and obscene, but they were a great fashion and she finally agreed. A piece of coal was placed in a bowl and a mixture of various chemicals poured over it. Red ink was added, if a pink coaliflower were wanted and blue ink for a blue one. After a few days crystals formed over the coal. As they grew and spread, the black coal disappeared and an amorphous shape of pink or blue, somewhat reminiscent of a cauliflower, sat in the bowl. They were to be seen as decoration in the empty windows of fish and chip shops and also in private homes of course, though Annie could never understand why. Helen found the spreading crystals fascinating. She was really delighted with the strange object, often standing beside it, smiling.

Helen had settled into school more comfortably now, although Yvonne remained her only real friend. The two little girls were well matched and Annie stopped worrying that her daughter might be a social misfit, although Helen often seemed just as happy to play by herself. When she was alone, she was obviously immersed in some complicated game of imagination, but she did not discuss these games with her mother. Annie was intrigued by these long hours of dedication and sometimes asked leading questions. Helen would just smile and give no inkling of her invisible scenario. It was the only area of her life which she did not share with her mother, but it was obviously important and Annie felt excluded, as well as curious.

Storm Clouds Gathering

Annie felt there was a breathless unreality about life. Political chaos engulfed Europe. Militaristic madmen were in power. America was suffering terrible poverty and hardship. The Chinese were battered by the Japanese and counted their dead in millions, even more were homeless and starving. Africa, as always, suffered drought, famine and disease. Hurricanes and earthquakes were causing destruction in various parts of the world. Could things get any worse? Her own poverty-stricken country hovered on the brink of war. Would that war really happen? Might Bruce be called up into the Navy, as he was a trained marine engineer? Had there ever been such a bad time? Perhaps life was always difficult. Her own health was unpredictable, although she felt particularly well just now, hardly tired at all.

In spite of all this world horror, people lived their lives as they always had done. She shopped and cooked, met Helen from school and joined her friends at the baths to chat, laugh and swim. Her father painted pictures. Her mother played bridge and golfed and had just bought a hat for seven pounds, which seemed exorbitant when so many poor people were in such misery, but Mary could always justify a stylish hat.

Just like Helen, people were in a state of pretence, acting as though no war shadow existed.

What could they do, anyway?

Fatalism seemed the only option

On the first of April, the war was brought very close, when one read in the *Glasgow Herald*,

> ... the scheme for administrative staffing of the Air Raid Precautions may cost £30,000. Further proposals are ... an architectural and engineering staff, a doctor and four organising officers to be charged with supervision and training in first aid and casualty services ...

Where was all that money to come from? And surely more than one doctor would be needed in a city of a million people.

The next page described a barrage balloon demonstration at

Ibrox. Annie looked at the date and wondered if this could possibly be a joke, but as she read on, it seemed serious enough

> **Many people in Glasgow today had their first view of the type of balloon to be used in large cities, as defence against aerial attack. Filled with 16,000 cubic feet of gas and anchored by a thick steel cable, it floats 600 feet above ground level, with the silver envelope glinting in the sunlight.**

How astonishing and even poetic it sounded, but surely a couple of well placed bullets from a reconnaissance plane would soon puncture a balloon, or more dramatically set all that gas on fire. What sort of gas would it be? It was only two years since the conflagration of the Hindenburg airship and the horrifying newsreel was still vivid in her mind. Besides, what use would one balloon be over a city the size of Glasgow? A plane could easily avoid it. They would need *hundreds* all over the city *and* all over the many other cities. It hardly seemed feasible. Annie felt her world become even more unreal.

On the following photo page was a large picture of Herr Hitler in evening dress with Frau Wagner, attending a performance of the Flying Dutchman in Bayreuth.

How very British to publish this polite society gossip about the warmonger who was the *raison d'être* for all these expensive and terrifying preparations.

Annie was surprised that such a man would have been interested in opera. Her father hated the music of Wagner, but whether for political or aesthetic reasons she did not know.

On the Woman's Page, under the heading 'Latest in Bustles' an illustration and text described a dinner gown,

> **"... of black crepe, with new square shoulder line and all drapery at the back, showing the new bustle effect. Collar and sleeves edged with gold embroidery."**

She thought it a particularly ugly dress and wondered how many Herald readers dressed for dinner. Would those who did dress continue to do so when war started?

What guarantee was there that we could win the war, if it ever really did start?

Reading the newspaper had not helped her, she felt angry and more confused than ever.

◊

The previous summer, John had spoken of painting another portrait of Helen and had taken some preparatory photos. Unfortunately a nasty summer cold had brought on his bronchitis and he painted very little in July and August

This year, John again expressed his determination to paint his granddaughter as soon as they were settled at the coast.

"I'm not going to let all this talk of war hold me back. I'm not sure that it will come to anything, anyway. Hitler is posturing and brow-beating, but surely he wouldn't be mad enough to fight us."

Annie was less sure than her father. The news in the papers made war seem inevitable, but she said nothing.

"How will you paint the wee soul this time, John? In a pretty summer dress? I sincerely hope so anyway. And with a nice, bright ribbon in her hair?"

Mary had never forgiven him for the boyish outfit which he had chosen for the previous portrait.

"I thought I might have her knitting, with the sea in the background. She seems to be knitting every time I see her and she looks so intent and purposeful. And it might make it easier for her to have something to do."

Mary only murmured 'hmm'. She was obviously not enthusiastic, but could not yet summon up the arguments against the proposal.

Annie thought it was a good idea.

"She'll be delighted to have her knitting in the picture, Paw. She's very keen just now and she's just started a scarf."

Helen was used to climbing up the outside stone stairs to the studio, she had climbed them all her life. Now that she was to be painted there, she felt that everything was changed. On the day of her first sitting, she noticed things very clearly, the bed of marigolds at the foot of the steps, the bright yellow stonecrop which nestled in the corner of several of the stairs and the hollyhocks that grew almost as tall as the top step. Even the sound of the door opening and shutting was special. It was so different from the Glasgow studio, where the first portrait had been painted. And she too, was different, for now she was a schoolgirl and could read and write and knit and swim. She would not need to be bribed with stories and she would be able to sit still for hours and hours.

The best bit was that she was able to take a lot of interest in the way that the painting progressed.

She felt that the first few pale strokes and lines on the pure white canvas were filled with danger.

"What would happen if you used a wrong colour just now, Drandad?"

"Oh that's of no consequence with oil paints, you can always paint over your mistakes, y'know. It's not like life."

Helen could not always follow exactly what her grandfather meant.

As he spoke, he held his brush out at arm's length, sometimes horizontally, sometimes vertically. As he did this, he would shut one eye, then make one small mark on the canvas, before stretching out his arm and brush again.

It was a very strange way to paint a picture, she thought, but did not like to ask. Perhaps her face showed her puzzlement, for quite soon he explained,

"I am measuring. I have to get all the measurements just right, or it won't look like a little girl. And it certainly won't look like you. Would you like to come and learn how to measure with the brush?"

She enjoyed the lesson and felt even more grown-up. How very different from that other time when she was little and Topsy was in the picture. Topsy was still a an important part of her private imaginary life, but she knew that a doll would be out of place in this painting ...

Quite often John would call her over to watch the big puddles of paint being mixed up. It was surprising how many different colours went into one mixture. The smell of linseed oil was an integral part of her earliest memories and she sniffed it like a little dog.

July is not the warmest summer month in Pittenweem and if it were cold, John would say,

"Let's have a wee fire today. I sawed up some logs specially for you.

He showed her his method of laying the fire, using rolled up newspapers with just a few pieces of coal. Then when the logs were added and started to crackle and blaze, she felt that she and her drandad were in their own little home. The fact that he had sawed them specially for her made it extra nice. One day when it was raining hard, he had brought a few potatoes upstairs to roast. The crackle of the fire, the rain pattering on the window in the roof and the smell of the hot potatoes mingled with the linseed oil and created a safe and delicious environment to share with her grandfather.

The painting of the picture, 'Girl Knitting', would always remain a memory of perfect happiness for the child and the old man.

◊

BIG MANOEUVRES IN GERMANY

German armed forces are about to start what may prove to be their biggest manoeuvres.

A large area of North West Germany, 13,000 square miles, is closed to air traffic.

Foreign attaches have not been invited to observe these exercises.

Motorised troops are assembled in various districts of South East Germany, extending to the Polish border.

In many areas, private cars have been requisitioned and civilians are also faced with petrol shortages.

Glasgow Herald 1st August 1939

"What d'ye think will happen next, Maw? The news is fearful today."

Mary was baking bread and kneaded the dough with a vicious energy.

"Oh, I never thought we would have to go through another war. I can hardly face it. And your father's terribly depressed by it all. That beast, Hitler ... what a brute."

As her mother bashed the dough, Annie smiled,

"I think you're imagining him there on the kitchen table in front of you!"

"Aye, I'd just love to get him under my *fist*. In fact, I'd take a rolling pin to him, it would be quicker."

"Oh well, I'm glad it's the dough you're knocking about, for I'm looking forward to a nice crunchy crust with thick fresh butter."

"Yes, ye'd better eat good stuff while you can. You never know what shortages we'll have to put up with if a war comes.

You know what that fruiterer that comes round with the barrow is always saying to his fussy customers, *"Aye, if the war comes, thur'll be nae pickan, NAE PICKAN AT A'."'* and it's only too true, I'm afraid."

They both laughed for it was now a family saying when there was hesitation about choosing anything such as a cake or a piece of fruit.

Annie watched as Mary divided the dough into the tins and set it near the fire to rise again.

"Another thing in the papers today that's not really funny, but it made me smile, for I always thought it was a daft idea in the first place. It was down south somewhere, one of those barrage balloons was struck by lightning and went up in flames."

"Damn silly things anyway."

"Not only that! It was the sixth balloon struck by lightning in the last two weeks!"

"What a hell of a waste of money! The worst thing is that there's been no gasmasks given out for babies yet. Imagine if you had a wee one and had no way of protecting it in a gas attack"

"Och Maw, I honestly cannot think that they would ever drop gas on us."

But Mary could not bear to be gainsaid and, her anxiety developing quickly into fury, she cried,

"Well all the rest of the population have gasmasks, so someone must think that gas is a possibility. And the poor soldiers in the last war certainly had to deal with it."

"Yes I suppose it does seem rotten that they've done nothing about the babies."

That evening after listening to the dismal news on the wireless, John said,

"Your mother and I have been thinking that Glasgow is a pretty dangerous place to be, what with the shipyards and the steelworks and all the rest of the industry. That's where bombing would most likely start. Why don't you and Helen stay on here, that is if the war comes, which I suppose it must. I never thought it was possible before but now ... I'm afraid I do."

He wiped away a tear.

"That's very good of you to offer me the house, Paw."

"Stay as long as you like, Annie, I agree with your father. I don't think it would be right to bring the child back into danger."

"Would you not want to stay here, too?"

"Oh no, we have to get back for your father's work."

Annie looked at her father. He wore a thick woollen muffler about his throat, in spite of the summer evening. His health was poor, he was over seventy and looked older. She had little idea of her parents' financial situation, but it seemed unfair that he must still keep working. Was it really necessary? She knew that he had never paid into the government's old age pension scheme. He must surely have other arrangements, she supposed.

She suspected that her mother would not care to live in Pittenweem, but perhaps that was unfair.

"I'll write to Bruce and see what he thinks."

"Yes, do that," her father had composed himself again. "I'm sure he'll agree."

And Mary added,

"He'll surely not make any fuss about it. If he has any sense at all, he'll realise that it's for the best."

Annie looked around at the house. It was a summer holiday house with no electricity, no hot water, no bath. It was draughty and chilly in a cool summer. What would it be like in the winter? She would be far away from family and friends and the luxury of the Arlington Baths.

However the idea of bombs was terrifying and there would certainly be no bombs here in Pittenweem.

"I'd need to go back home and collect a few things if we were going to stay, winter clothes and our gasmasks."

"Well do consider it seriously, my dear."

"I think there's no question about it, Annie. You owe it to the child to keep her safe."

PART TWO

A New Era

Annie was surprised at how little emotion she felt as she sat in the railway carriage, watching the countryside fly past. It all looked calm and very like many another day in late summer that she had viewed from a train. Some fields had a few workers in them and sometimes a cart or bus would trundle along a country road. A gypsy family was gathering something from a hedge. Surely it was too early for brambles?

Annie always meant to gather brambles for a tart, but somehow the season was often past before she remembered.

As usual, the train stopped at all the small stations of Fife, each one vying with the other in its floral displays. Although the nasturtiums and geraniums would not last for much longer, they were still bright cheered Annie up. She marvelled to think of the care and application that had gone into the formal planting, the hanging baskets, the names of each station spelled out in white shells. Meanwhile political leaders in the large cities of Europe talked of death and destruction and ordinary people planned how to defend themselves against attack. It was wonderful that folk still had enough faith in the future to plant alyssum and lobelia seeds in April.

As it seemed that war was now inevitable, she had decided that it was best to move to Pittenweem with Helen. If there were to be air attacks, an industrial city like Glasgow was certain to be a prime target.

Her parents would return to Glasgow, as they must be in the city to sell John's paintings and find new commissions. Annie wondered privately whether many folk would buy paintings in this national crisis, but said nothing. How much longer would he be able to paint and sell pictures? Other people were allowed to retire when much younger than he was.

The distribution of gas masks earlier that year had laid a cold chill of horror on Annie's heart, so much so that she had put her own and her daughter's masks on the top shelf of a cupboard and tried to forget their implication and their very existence. Now she was returning to collect those obscene rubber objects which conjured up such hellish visions.

Would the situation really arise that they were needed?

Annie felt curiously empty and relaxed. She had not made a train journey alone for seven years, not since Helen was born. She had forgotten that feeling of freedom, the feeling of a time that was apart and completely her own. There was nothing that she must or could do until the train arrived at Queen Street.

The other occupants of the carriage, a young couple, were smoking. Annie wondered if she wanted a cigarette. Although she had smoked from an early age, she seldom smoked alone. For her, it was a shared social skill and she enjoyed it most when she was one of a laughing, smoking crowd. She firmly believed that smoking could not be very good for you. If your lungs were purifying your blood, it was probably pretty stupid to pump poisonous smoke into them. But then most people smoked and you read everywhere about how relaxing and beneficial it was. There were even some doctors who recommended it. Or was it only in advertisements that she had seen that? Annie could not be sure. She certainly had little time for advertisements. They would say anything to sell a product. Perhaps, as she still had those spells of tiredness, she should think about stopping. But then Bruce smoked like a chimney, sixty or more a day, and no one had as much energy as he had. Perhaps moving to Pittenweem and living in the fresh sea air would help her health. Glasgow was so fearfully filthy. Who could worry about a cigarette or two, when those November fogs enveloped the city and filled your lungs with solid yellow gas for days on end, sometimes weeks. These thoughts brought her uncomfortably back to the gas masks and the fearful circumstances which might make their use necessary.

Her thoughts were interrupted by the man in the opposite corner.

"Here, can I offer you a fag?"

"Oh, thank you very much, but I have my own here."

Annie smiled and quickly produced a packet of Player's from her handbag.

"Have ye a match all right, hen?"

"Yes, yes, thank you."

She shook the box to prove it. They all smiled at each other.

"Terrible worrying times, these."

Annie replied that they certainly were and they all shook their heads sadly.

"But what can you do?"

"Just hope for the best." The woman spoke for the first time.

"Yes, just hope for the best." Annie agreed.

There was no more conversation, but Annie felt cheered by the human contact and kindliness.

She did not immediately take out a cigarette, but looked at the packet with its picture of a bearded sea salt framed by a lifebuoy. The small box was neatly and attractively made with its fresh colours. It was a nice little object to hold and the protective silver paper inside gave it a sense of luxury. She smiled to herself, as she remembered the Pittenweem fisherman who grew a large beard and was immediately dubbed Players Please, in honour of that firm's well known slogan which adorned every hoarding and every newsagent's shop. They were clever with nicknames in Pittenweem and the poor man would be stuck with it for his lifetime.

Just then the train pulled into Falkirk.

As Annie finally withdrew a cigarette from the box, the door was flung open and a pale-faced and breathless young porter leaned into the carriage,

"That's it been declared, just there the now, on the wireless. The WAR's on an' the train'll no' be movin' fur a while."

The door was slammed shut and the three people sat silently, the man frowning and the women biting their lips. What was there to say?

The only sound to be heard was of carriage-doors opening and shutting noisily, as other passengers were informed of the dreaded but expected news. To Annie, there seemed to be a relentless rhythm in the repeating bangs, like some cacophonous modern music whose theme was lonely and tragic.

She replaced her unlighted cigarette in the packet and decided that she would not smoke again until the war was over.

◊

Meanwhile in Pittenweem, Mary had heard the horrible news on the wireless and was not taking it as calmly as her daughter, in fact she was on the verge of hysteria. Her state of mind was not improved by the shriek of the Pittenweem air raid siren, which screamed out as soon as the declaration of war was made.

To Helen's consternation, her confident, all-powerful grand-mother had been crying real tears and even sobbing. Helen had never seen a grown-up weep with the abandon of a child.

As no one had talked directly to Helen about what the war might mean, she felt very puzzled and stupid, a state which always angered her. In fact she found herself quite forgotten.

Through her tears, Mary kept repeating

"What can I do for the child? What can I do for Helen? If I only had her gas mask!"

She said it to John, who was unobtrusively wiping away his own tears.

"We've known this was coming for a long time, my dear. Try and calm yourself. Nothing is going to happen immediately, I'm sure. Some fool has set off that warning. There will be no enemy planes coming to this wee corner anyway. I'm positive about that. Sit down and have a cigarette and I'll put on the kettle."

But his words had no effect. She opened the front door and spoke to some of the distraught passers-by in the High Street, each one of whom had a different, terrifying rumour to report. The imaginative east coaster can manufacture blood-freezing rumours at the drop of a hat. It was all very cold comfort to Mary and she stood there trembling, as though she were icy cold.

"London's flettened, ye ken! Jist flettened."

"Aye, an' thur sayin' Glesca and Manchester an' a! Jist boambed tae bits."

"Aye, an' the Germans have landed at Fifeness, fifty tanks an' a hunner big guns!"

"Ma aunty seen German planes ower Kirkcaldy. An' a bomb wis drappit at Cowdenbeath."

"Ah believe there's been mustard gas drappit a' ower Edinburgh and hauf the gas masks divenae wark when ye pit them oan.! They re sayin' that thur leakin' like sieves, an' they jist *divnae wark!*"

Mary shut the front door and poured herself a Martini.

"John, do you think any of that can be true? How could they know about it so quickly?"

"I wouldn't believe a word of it just now. It's far too soon for all that to be happening. You know how wild exaggerations get about. Just try and calm yourself, for the child's sake as well as your own."

John tried to add a dash of angry authority to his voice, but Mary was beyond noticing.

"Oh, John, the child! If I only had her gasmask with me I would feel better. And Annie in Glasgow too, what danger she may be in. And Willie and Eileen, too. Everyone we know is in Glasgow."

"I'm going to put the kettle on. I think a cup of tea would do us good."

Mary's imagination and sense of the dramatic needed no encouragement from village rumours and John was not sure that a Martini was the best calming agent either. He himself felt sad and leaden at the news and had no energy left for worry or anger. It was part of getting older he supposed. For him, there was a feeling of relief with the actual declaration. John had never been sure whether war would come or not and the suspense of the long waiting period had seemed unbearable. Of course it was what that madman Hitler wanted. John only hoped that Britain had prepared herself sufficiently. He had little faith in the government.

Helen listened to all the excited conversation with wide eyes. She certainly hoped her Mummy was not in danger. She tried to hold back tears at such a horrible thought. She was surprised that Grandma had never looked at her once, or cuddled her since the announcement on the wireless. She just kept on talking in a strange, loud, high voice about how worried she was. Helen slipped away to her bedroom and brought Topsy into the sitting room and was rewarded with a smile from her Grandma at the sight of the cheerful little doll.

After her cup of tea, Mary seemed more in control and went into the garden and started to talk over the wall with the Browns, the elderly couple who lived next door.

Mr Brown had been an engineer in the merchant navy and had travelled all over the world. Now in his seventies, he was all-knowing and philosophic about the war and its outcome. He was inclined to believe that there had been planes over Kirkaldy, less than twenty miles away. He was less sure about the bomb at Cowdenbeath.

"I'll say this, Mistress Mackay, they Germans are awfy cliver, awfy awfy cliver, but they're no' cruel. They're no' a' that diffrent frae you an' me, ye ken. Ah'm thinkin' they widnae herm ye, they widnae mean tae herm ye, onywey."

"Mr Brown, they'd surely mean it if they were dropping bombs on us!"

"Na, na ma lass, they're jist like you an' me. But cliver, awfy cliver. Ah've kent many a German in ma time an' they wur a' awfy cliver, ivry wan o' them."

"Mr Brown, I think you're forgetting the first world war!"

Ignoring his reply, Mary started to tell her tale of woe to Mrs Brown, again bemoaning her responsibility for Helen and how she had no gasmask to fit the child and how Annie had gone away into possible danger and finishing once more in extravagant tears. Petite Mrs Brown peeped over the five foot high stone wall and was as comforting as possible.

Helen, clasping Topsy, stood beside her grandmother and listened to it all again for the sixth or seventh time. She was now bored with the drama and repetition and not pleased at being constantly referred to as 'the child'. She no longer believed that her Mummy was in danger,

But she was still shocked each time that Mary once again burst into tears.

The word 'invincible' was not in Helen's vocabulary, but had it been, she would certainly have used it to describe her grandmother. But from the day that war was declared, those tears and sobs transformed Helen's perception of Mary. From that time onwards, she could even feel a little sorry for her bossy, determined Grandma.

Settling In

Helen was enrolled in the village school and found it much the same as the Glasgow one, although the teacher was not given a name. One just said "Please Miss." They wrote their sums on slates in Pittenweem and the belt was used more often.

She often thought of Yvonne, missing her company and the games they had played together. She was not welcomed by the other children and it was some time before she realised how alien and unacceptable she appeared to them, with her careful middle-class accent, long blonde plaits and lovingly hand-made clothing. In Glasgow, she had become used to being considered 'different' by other children, something of an outsider in the class. Now, in this narrow fishing community she was even more different and it was hurtful to find that she was disliked and mistrusted. With a wider general knowledge and a larger vocabulary than the unso-phisticated local children, Helen was branded a 'teacher's pet' and a 'swot' and hassled and shouted at in the street. She had never enjoyed any popularity, so school seemed just the neces-sary evil that it had always been, although this reception was harsher than the city. She learned the new skill of chanting her lessons with the rest of the class. Tables, poems and the books of the Old Testament, were shouted in unison for much of each day. It seemed a little strange to her, but it was not difficult and made the time pass until she could return to her mother and the pleas-ant life at home, where she could read, knit and listen to the radio. At bedtime she would return to her rich imaginary world with its ongoing adventures.

Annie had tried every argument to persuade her parents to stay in Fife with her, but Mary and John had returned to Glasgow and whatever dangers might be waiting there for them.

The trip to Glasgow had tired Annie and she wondered if the fact that she had stopped smoking could be the reason, but that seemed silly.

It was the first time that she had been in sole charge of the lit-tle house since Helen was an infant. She had to admit that it was very pleasant to arrange her day to her own satisfaction. In spite of the worry of the war, the increasing shortages and the inconveniences of the holiday house, she found that she was happy and relaxed. She seemed to work less and yet accomplish a great deal more than she did when in thrall to her mother's erratic managing skills. She was able to spend more time with Helen than she usually did in Fife They had long walks and pleasant picnics in that particularly warm Autumn. Annie could choose her own pace, rest when she felt a little tired and she was positive that her health would eventually improve completely in the fresh sea air.

As usual she looked on the positive side and wondered if, for her, this upheaval might be the best thing that could have happened. Then she would smile bitterly and scold herself. All those poor soldiers away from home and the terrible things that were going on in Poland and other places. How could she be so self-centred!

The radio was a great source of entertainment. The mother and daughter sat and knitted while listening to the surreal humour of Claude Dampier, Arthur Askey and Tommy Handley. There were plays and concerts and talks with interesting advice to help people adapt to the new restrictions and shortages. Annie jotted down cookery hints and found many of them useful. The messages of 'save' and 'make do and mend' were constantly reiterated and inspired Annie to cut the sleeves off an old lambswool cardigan and make it into a little bolero for Helen, decorating it with a colourful crochet edging. Normally, she hated mending of any sort and would always prefer to make something entirely new. The bolero would be her first and last attempt at make-do-and-mend. Helen loved it and Annie felt quite virtuous and patriotic.

The propaganda affected Helen too and she tried to be saving in any way that she could. She decided to fold and tear each sheet of toilet paper into four pieces and, for the rest of the war, she kept a little stock of these miniature sheets, in a corner of the bathroom for her own use. It was a secret and her mother probably never knew of this personal sacrifice.

The only drawback to the wireless was the accumulator. This was also called a wet battery and it must be taken each week to the garage, where it was re-charged. It was a large glass box about ten inches high, square in plan and filled with liquid and other mysterious material. It had a wire handle to carry it, but as it was heavy, the wire cut into your hand uncomfortably. Helen was warned that the liquid was acid and although it did not appear to leak out, there was always the fear that it might. Acid was a familiar subject in films and there was terror attached to the word for it was often used for evil purposes. Helen always carried the accumulator very steadily, well away from her legs and skirt and was tremendously relieved when she returned home and deposited the replacement beside the wireless. Each week, when the sound from the wireless started to fade, she knew that it was nearly time for that horrid trip to the garage again.

The little local cinema changed its programme three times a week and although the films it showed were old ones and not always in the best of condition, it made a pleasant evening out for it was inexpensive and the hall was cosy. Anstruther was only a mile away and it had two cinemas, one of them almost luxurious. Altogether there were eight different shows each week, almost as good as the choice in Hyndland. The walk home from Anstruther was one mile. They took it slowly and enjoyed looking at the stars, which seemed so much more brilliant than those in the smoky, overcast Glasgow sky. The first winter was extremely cold and sometimes, as they sauntered home, the aurora borealis lit up the Northern sky. Annie had read of the glories of this phenomenon in the gripping stories of Jack London. To be honest, the flickering lights on the Anstruther road were not as magnificent as she had imagined. Probably one had to travel to the frozen vastness of Canada to see it in all its glory. However Annie and Helen always looked for it on their walk home and felt specially lucky when they saw it.

On Sunday night, a large zinc wash-tub was set in front of the fire in the sitting room and filled with several kettles of boiling water from the gas cooker and from the large black kettle which always sat warming on the fireside hob. It was a lot of hard work for an unsatisfactory result, but it was the best that could be done. Each week, as Annie sat squashed uncomfortably in the second-hand, cooling water, she planned that if they really must stay here for any length of time, she would find a bath of a proper size and put it into the wash-house. There need not be any expensive plumbing, for a fire could be lit below the boiler to produce a decent amount of hot water. The water could be scooped by hand from the boiler and the bath could empty into the drain in the floor. The idea of a more permanent arrangement did not occur to her, as she considered the house as belonging to her parents. They had owned it now for nearly thirty years without seeing any necessity for a bath. The house had always been used as a summer home and all members of the family had been keen swimmers. Annie had always joked that in Pittenweem, it was a case of 'stink or swim', but swimming in the sea was out of the question in winter. However, she was sure that the war would finish quickly and there would be no need for any improvements to the house.

In November, the weather worsened. It would be a severe winter and the house was colder than Annie had thought possible.

They slept together in the small bedroom downstairs, which had shutters and heavy black-out curtains. With several blankets, two eiderdowns and two stone hot water bottles, Annie tried to combat the bitter cold of a house which was damp and draughty, geared only for summer weather.

She bought a paraffin heater for the bedroom, which warmed the little room quickly, though Annie never quite trusted its safety. She remembered the day nearly twenty years ago, when the family was staying in Iona. A paraffin heater had flared out of control and Mary, with great presence of mind and one of her famous high kicks, had sent the whole contraption flying out of the open back-door and into the garden. So Annie always put the heater out before getting into bed. However, once it was extinguished, the cold poured back immediately and in her imagination, filled the room up like an icy, grey liquid.

The paraffin was heavy to carry home too, and lifting was a task which brought home to Annie that her health was not improving, as she had hoped it would. Sometimes she experienced sharp shooting pains in her wrists and shoulders, though they would pass quite quickly. She was also aware that she was not as deft as previously, when sewing with a needle. The feeling in her finger-tips was certainly not as sensitive as it should be and she was liable to drop china in a way that she would not have done some years before. She was relieved that her mother was not there to fuss about the breakages.

One day in November, quite a large parcel arrived from

Glasgow. In it, a shoe-box was filled with delicious gingerbread buns. Grandma had been thinking and worrying about them. All was fine in Glasgow and really she thought they should come back home. She was missing her little granddaughter very much and she had something exciting to show her, for she now had *another* little grand-daughter. Wee Eileen, daughter of Big Eileen, was the most beautiful baby ever, and Willie was absolutely besotted with her and working very hard at his new job. Grandma was sure that Helen would adore her new wee cousin for she was just like a little doll.

Helen was unenthusiastic about the baby, but thought it a very good idea to go home to Glasgow, for her days at school were becoming increasingly difficult and lonely, although she said nothing to her mother of her problems.

"Wouldn't it be lovely to go to the Arlington and have a swim!" Helen said wistfully.

"Yes and a big, hot, really deep bath. And you'd love to see the wee new baby too, and Grandma and Grandad and Daddy."

"Mmhm."

"I think we'd better wait until the Christmas holidays."

"Oh."

The labour of up-rooting herself, then perhaps having to return to Pittenweem once more, if danger did threaten the city, seemed more than Annie could contemplate. Pittenweem was certainly not ideal, but she was settled here now and Helen seemed tolerably content at school, if not enthusiastic. Because of petrol restrictions, Bruce had been unable to get through to visit them. She realised that she felt emotionally more stable when her husband and parents were not part of her daily life. It seemed a sad fact. She loved them all and wrote to them regularly, but there was no doubt that she was more able to cope with her problems when they were not present. She wondered wryly if everyone felt this way about their nearest and dearest, or was she unnatural?

"Here's another parcel to open, Mummy!"

"Oh, look at that, what a lovely bed jacket! Look, there's a PS that says it's called a nightingale. Well, I've heard of a farthingale, but I thought a nightingale was a sort of bird, but isn't this pretty, try it on!"

"Oh, it's so warm, I think I'd like to sleep in this."

"Why not? Anything to keep you cosy. I think I'll make myself one too."

The 'nightingale' was of fine wool, knitted in two layers of blending pinks. The layers trapped the heat and made it extremely warm, as well as delicate and feminine. Helen adored it. Within a week, Annie had made one for herself and it seemed to be the perfect answer to those cold nights. She knitted, in a different colour scheme, one for her friend Georgina, who was a great knitter herself, but appreciated the pretty present. She made another for Mrs Hill, the eccentric but generous old lady from Glasgow, who had also decided to stay in her Pittenweem holiday house until the war was over.

> *Dear Maw,*
>
> *Thank you for that wonderful parcel, I don't know which was the biggest success, the cakes or the jacket, but the gingerbread did not last long, I can tell you. It's the sweetest bed-jacket I have ever seen and so simple and quick to make on the big pins. Where did you find the pattern? I'm half way through making one for myself to try and keep warm in this arctic weather. Needless to say, Topsy must have one too. Is it as cold in Glasgow? I cannot believe it could be. I have never felt cold like this before, the wind is like a knife and no one cares how they dress, anything to protect themselves from the fierce bite of the atmosphere. Can Canada be any colder, I wonder? I suppose it must be, but I can't imagine it.*
>
> *I'm glad that Eileen is recovering so quickly and I've no doubt the baby is a wee beauty with such handsome parents. I'm dying to see the baby, but I do not think I will come back to Glasgow just yet. We will wait and see what Adolf gets up to next. I think we might come home for a holiday at Christmas. I have decided to see a doctor when I get back, because that tiredness does not seem to go away. Perhaps he could give me a tonic or something, but don't worry, I'm doing fine here, apart from the icy cold.*
>
> *Mrs Hill sends you her love and I am quite excited, because she tells me that her daughter is going to put on a concert in Pittenweem, so we will see the mysterious actress at last!*
>
> *Georgina also sends her regards, what a scream she is, she keeps me in fits of laughter. I suppose we make each other laugh*

and a visit to her always cheers me up, not that I'm needing cheering so very much. Just a wee bit lonely sometimes I suppose. You know how it is, but don't worry about me, I am fine, really. I wonder if Bruce has visited you, at all. He seems to be terribly busy at work and he's joined the Home Guard at the golf club. He hasn't managed to get through here yet.

I hope you and my father are keeping well and rationing does not make life too hard for you. That gingerbread was truly delicious.

Your loving daughter, Annie

All things considered, Annie thought it was quite a pleasant life that they lived, although they both missed the swimming baths a lot. In a house which had no hot water supply and no bath, the extravagant showers and deep hot tubs of the Arlington club seemed like a wonderful, distant dream.

◊

On the day before the concert, they met Rena Hill briefly in her mother's house. She had a deep, rich, loud voice and a warm, friendly smile and was terribly, amazingly tall, nearly six feet. Helen had never seen such a tall lady. She was especially surprised, because Mrs Hill was very small and rather fat and shapeless. Helen had always thought that the old lady looked very like a witch, a good, kind witch in a fairy story. She wore baggy dark clothes and had the big sharp nose, pointy chin and untidy white hair that all witches seemed to have in llustrations. Such an oversized daughter added to her magic. Annie thought Rena extremely handsome and was devoured with curiosity as to what she would do at the concert. She had no idea and did not like to ask, but she thought the tall beauty would make a magnificent Lady Macbeth, though Shakespeare might be unlikely to attract a big audience for a Pittenweem Saturday night.

Annie took Helen along to the pretty little Georgian town hall, which was absolutely crammed. As they had not arrived early enough to get a good seat, they chose to stand, squeezing along the wall to get as close to the small, makeshift stage as possible There were no wings for a proper entrance and Annie felt sorry for professional entertainers who must appear under such amateur conditions.

Helen found it very exciting. The room was full of an electric anticipation, with everyone speaking hurriedly, but with unnaturally quiet voices.

It was very different from the cinema, where screeching laughter rang out and loud conversations were shouted back and forth until the film started. Many would be eating chips which filled the air with their special aroma. The town hall was obviously a more special and elegant outing.

First on the programme were two ladies singing old Scottish songs in uncertain harmony. They sang with great facial athleticism and Annie suspected that Helen would mimic them for her later that evening. The accompanying piano was untuned and more of a hindrance than anything. After the ladies, a boy of sixteen, with the usual skin problems of that age, sang some favourites from the First World War and encouraged the audience to join in, which they did with great gusto. Annie disliked mass singing and the unbearable sadness of those songs always upset her. That turn seemed interminable. Helen was fidgeting and Annie felt her left foot become quite numb and wished that she had chosen to take a seat at the back. Then a very old man told a few pawky stories in a weak, wheezy voice, which tended to fade on the punch line, as he broke into giggles at his own wit. The audience sat coldly and hardly clapped as he left the stage.

"How embarrassing," Annie thought to herself, "to be such an out and out failure in a town hall. I bet I could have done better myself. I wonder *when* Rena is going to come on. I can't stand here much longer, or Helen either. I hope it's worth waiting for."

Just then bagpipes could be heard in the distance.

"What's that noise, Mummy?"

Helen had never heard her national instrument played before.

As the sound grew nearer, the audience turned around in their seats with renewed interest. Louder and louder grew the wild music, until Helen became quite afraid. Then at the back of the hall, the door flew open and the fantastic noise enveloped everyone like a magic spell. Resonating and beating back from the walls and the high ceiling, the immense sound was paralysing, as Rena, all six feet of her, in magnificent Highland dress and playing a fine set of pipes, advanced through the crowded room to the stage. Behind her, also clad in full Highland dress, followed her retinue of six little men, hardly bigger than Helen herself. The first five each beat a small drum with fast flicking sticks. The sixth and last little follower had a an enormous drum which practically hid him. He attacked it with such great vigour that Helen put her hands over her ears as he passed close to her.

Rena mounted the platform and the drummers ranged themselves on either side of her before they stopped playing. Then after she acknowledged the loud applause, which forced Helen to cover her ears again, laments, reels and marches echoed and re-echoed around the hall for the next half hour without a pause.

More thunderous applause.

It seemed like a contest of loudness, in which the audience did not want to be beaten.

Then, not at all breathless, Rena declaimed 'The Charge of the Light Brigade', 'Tam o' Shanter' and 'The Ballad of Sir Patrick Spens'. Helen enjoyed the resounding words at first but became bored before the recital finished. She guessed that the six little men were bored too, because they were fidgeting and gazing around the hall like naughty children.

However, Annie and Helen forgot their weariness in the colour and drama before them.

After long and appreciative applause, Rena started her pipes awailing again. The miniature highlanders twirled their sticks and, beating their drums enthusiastically, followed Rena out as she marched from the hall to the strains of 'We're No' Awa tae Bide Awa'.

Back home, they discussed the show over a cup of Horlicks.

"That was quite a night out, wasn't it, my wee pet! Very exciting when they all marched in playing, I thought. Although I was really convinced that Rena was going to play Lady Macbeth."

"Why do you think she only had six little men? If she had seven she would be like Snow White."

"I suppose so. Perhaps it was neater to have three on each side of her on the stage."

"Were those dwarfs? They were awful wee."

"No, those are what are called midgets. They have smaller heads than dwarfs and are just like an ordinary person, only proportionately smaller. A dwarf usually has little legs and arms and a normal sized head and they are often very clever."

"Why d'ye think she had those little men there?"

"To play the drums, I suppose and maybe make her look even taller."

"I think she is very pretty."

"Do you? So do I."

"But I don't think she looks so nice when she plays that pipe thing."

"No I don't suppose it improves her beauty. But you enjoyed your night out at the theatre did you?"

"Yes. My ears are still ringing! Do you think Rena is sort of magical?"

"Magical? What d'ye mean?"

"Well, she is different from anyone else I know."

"I suppose anyone on the stage is rather magical."

"I don't think those two singing ladies with the big mouths or the boy with the pimples were magical."

"No I suppose not, my darling. They were pretty third-rate."

"What does that mean?"

"Oh I'll explain another time, darling. I'm tired. Aren't you? Let's get those hot water bottles filled."

"I think I would like to be on the stage sometime when I grow up."

"Would you, my wee jewel?"

"Yes, but not playing the bagpipes."

"What would you do?"

"Dancing, I expect."

◊

They returned to Glasgow for the Christmas holidays in a slow, cold train and stayed with Annie's parents rather than open up the Hyndland flat. Annie went there once but it looked forlorn and dusty and made her sad. She did not see any of her neighbours and the tenement seemed deserted.

Santa Claus had brought fewer toys and a larger proportion of useful things this year, a sweater and mittens, two pretty all-in-one sleeping suits and a Fair Isle tammy. She knew that her mother had knitted the last but allowed Santa to parcel it up and give it to her.

They visited the Arlington four times and steeped themselves in hot water up to their ears, then had a much longer swim than they had ever had before. Helen swam forty lengths one day and the bathsmaster said that was more than half a mile. She would not swim that sort of distance again for many years, because truthfully it was quite boring going up and down, up and down.

The next day she was terribly tired, but it was worth it. Forty lengths was an achievement to be proud of and made up for the months ahead, when there would be no swimming at all.

They were invited for New Year's dinner to the Cornings' house and had the usual meagre, over-cooked meal.

Bruce teased his mother and daughter all evening, laughing heartily at his own jokes. His father and brother scarcely smiled. Helen ate little and Annie felt cross with her and sorry for her mother-in-law, who had recently had all her teeth removed and could not yet wear her false teeth with any comfort. It seemed like the ultimate horror to Annie, but Jane Corning smiled a brave and toothless smile throughout the meal.

Helen found it strange to be in that house again. She hardly remembered it or her grandparents. It smelled dusty and every-thing was very, very unfamiliar. She was relieved when it was time to return to the Charing Cross flat. She would play the piano there for a little while before going to bed and that always made her happy.

IN THE COMMONS YESTERDAY

Mr Kirkwood, (Lab); "Is the minister aware that Dixon's and Colville's have eternally blazing furnaces which light the heavens every night?"

Sir John Anderson Home secretary; "Yes that is recognised as a great disadvantage, however the structural changes required will take time."

Kirkwood; "I can see it when I am miles outside Glasgow!"

Mr McGovern (ILP); "We welcome the Glasgow light. It shows us how to work in our gardens!"

Glasgow Herald 15th March 1940

Annie and Helen slept in a small bedroom upstairs which over-looked all the buildings round about. Helen noticed that there was often quite a bright light in the sky and also that the tram cars nearly always gave a big flash as they rounded the several corners at Charing Cross.

"Mummy, does the blackout not matter here so much in the town?"

"What d'ye mean, darling?"

"Well you know how fussy the wardens are in Pittenweem if only a little chink of light is showing. They're hammering at the door and shouting, but look out the window there, it's really bright and the trams are flashing all the time. No one would notice if your curtain wasn't pulled across properly."

"Yes, you're absolutely right. I know what that light in the sky is, it's Dixon's blazes. That's a big steel works. It's always made a big glow in the sky. And I don't know what you could do about the trams. They'll be flashing like that on corners all over the city. It does seem to make a nonsense of the blackout."

Annie also made time in the fortnight to visit the two old aunts, Beatrice and Gerty, in Kelvindale. They were Bob Corning's elderly sisters and the only members of the Corning family for whom she felt any affection, apart from Bruce. They were patronised and somewhat neglected by their brother and his wife. Perhaps that was one reason that Annie enjoyed visiting them.

Although in their seventies, Annie found them much more modern in their outlook than their dour brother. They loved to discuss the latest screen musicals and had records of Al Bowly and Bing Crosby. They always admired Annie's smart clothes and, although they had never swum in their lives, they delighted to hear about the baths. When Helen's recent marathon swim was mentioned, a sixpence was produced to reward such a strong, clever little girl.

As usual, the fragile old ladies made a great fuss of Helen and her mother, making tea and bringing out the crystal biscuit barrel. Helen was encouraged to help herself to the narrow chocolate fingers and iced biscuits. She pleased her mother by taking only one of each and eating so daintily that not a crumb dropped on the carpet. What a model child she could be when she wanted, Annie thought. Helen answered questions politely, loudly and clearly because the two old souls were both quite deaf.

The flat that they lived in was an exact replica of Annie's first house in Kingspark and she marvelled again at how small, cosy and convenient it was, with the sitting room fire effortlessly producing constant hot water. How great to have a wee house like this in Pittenweem! She did enjoy visiting these kind folk, although she knew that later on that night the good and bad memories of those first months of marriage, in a similar house, would come flooding back uncomfortably. Once more she would question just how much she had been to blame for the way that things had gone wrong.

It was a 'visiting day' and when they left the old aunties, they popped in to see Eileen and her new baby, who lived practically next door in a flat which was a mirror image of the Kingspark flat.

Eileen looked thin but happy and the baby was certainly beautiful with large enquiring eyes and dark hair.

"How grown up she looks for such a wee bit thing!" Annie laughed, for she loved babies. Her daughter was more interested in the view from the window than the baby.

"*What* is that great big grey thing up there in the sky?"

"Oh, that's a barrage balloon, Helen. That's supposed to protect us from enemy planes. It's like a big elephant tethered up in the sky, isn't it!"

Eileen laughed as she spoke,

"You know that is exactly what I felt like, when I was expecting the baby! Just a great big elephant."

They all laughed, but Annie felt embarrassed that Helen was ignoring the infant. Surely it should be the centre of attention and she hurried to keep it as the main subject.

"You wouldn't be thinking of bathing wee Eileen soon, would you? That would be a treat for us, wouldn't it, Helen."

"Of course, Annie, I was just going to bath her anyway."

Helen stiffened. She had no desire to see another baby in its bath. It might have some disability like Audrey's little cousin. Why did people want to watch a baby being bathed? What was the attraction? If this one had any funny lumps on it, she would just go and look out of the window at the balloon.

Fortunately, apart from wrinkles of fat, this baby seemed entirely normal and Helen dutifully watched the whole process. Her mother and big Eileen laughed and exclaimed throughout the bath-time and the baby kicked and chortled happily.

As Helen sat expressionless, a horrible thought suddenly occurred to her. If everyone thought a baby's bathtime was so fascinating, perhaps she too had provided this spectacle as a baby! With dismay, she wondered just how many times her naked body had been displayed at bathtime *to total strangers*.

Enemy Action

It was February and Annie stood in the garden and watched the convoy heading up river towards Leith. The ships were only a few miles from her and it was a wonderful sight on the bright, fresh day. Mr and Mrs Brown next door were also in their garden, gazing out to sea.

It struck Annie that the escorting warships were like small anxious dogs as they hurried their charges towards the safety of port. Planes were circling above the pageant of slow-moving craft, when suddenly a few puffs of smoke appeared above one of the ships, adding a picturesque touch to the scene. There was nothing to be heard.

"It's an awfy grand day again, Annie! Awfy grand tae get rid o' that icy cauld. Ah niver remember a winter sae bad afore." Mrs Brown's old voice drifted over the wall.

"Yes, it's just lovely isn't it. So mild for February, it could easily be May. Oh, look at that!"

Another few clouds of smoke bloomed over the first ship of the line. One plane had separated from the others and was leaving the convoy and heading back out to the North Sea.

"Aye, it's jist practice, ye ken. Thur aye at thur practice oot there."

Mr Brown had removed his pipe from his mouth for this statement and immediately replaced it.

"Aye, it's jist practice." echoed his wife, smiling and nodding her shimmering white curls.

But Annie could see three planes chasing the one that was headed seawards. Before they were out of sight, the single plane spurted a plume of smoke and flame, lost height and plunged into the water.

"No" said Annie grimly, "that's the real thing out there. That's a battle! And I'm going inside, where it's safe and you two should go in as well!"

"But we haven'y even heard the sireen gan aff. It cannae be real, shairly. D'ye think it's real, Annie? Dae you think it's real, Wullie?" Mrs Brown appealed to her husband, who, though unwilling to retract his previous assertions, could see the obvious violence that had been enacted on that sparkling sea.

"*That's the real thing* and I'm away inside." Annie turned on her heel.

"Right, cheerio Annie. C'mon Jessie, we better gan in, an' a'."

Annie poured a spoonful of sticky coffee essence into a cup and added water from the fireside kettle. From the sitting-room window, she could still see the ships heading upriver. It was incredible. Her hands trembled as she thought that, only a few miles from her, there were young men killing each other. War had been only a frightening word until now, but there, in front of her, was the reality. It was happening in this exquisite, familiar, yet ever-changing Firth of Forth. She had feasted her eyes on this scene throughout every summer of her life. She had always loved the sea, with its typical days of breezy white-tipped waves and mirror calm evenings. She enjoyed the excitement of the occasional wild storms, when waves would lash the harbour wall and throw foamy spray forty feet into the air. Then there was such romance and mystery when the haar blew in and the world disappeared in a white silence. She had delighted in the night-time twinkling lights of the small towns of East Lothian on the opposite shore, with the Bass Rock at sunset looking like a crouched cat licking cream from its saucer. Further west, the miniature mountain of North Berwick Law as it floated in a morning mist might almost be a tiny Scottish Fujiyama.

Now it was desecrated by bloodshed.

She had brought her child here to be safe and this had happened only miles away.

She had watched the violence from their garden.

She could hardly believe it. How could this picturesque cottage ever feel the same again? She felt physically sick. This was just the beginning, too. What beastliness might yet take place out there in front of the sheltered garden which, even in February, had several flowers blooming in it. What right had flowers to bloom when men were murdering each other?

She knew that because of her health, her emotions were near the surface. How could she deal with the horrible thing which was happening so close to this village where she had thought they would be secure?

Much of the time, nowadays, she felt angry as well as ill.

Angry because she was ill and angry at all the small vague symptoms which tormented her, symptoms which would come and go until she wondered if she were imagining them.

She was pretty sure that her mother and her husband did not take them seriously.

"Aye, if I could just get you out on the golf course regularly, Annie, you'd soon be feeling better. It's just exercise you're needing, Honeybun. Nothing like exercise."

She was tired listening to this repeated formula. Her husband's tone would be jokey and of course golf was his panacea for all ills, but surely he must notice her physical difficulties. Did he think she was imagining her problems? A hypochondriac? She had not told him how bad things sometimes were, but surely he must be aware of her frightening lack of deftness and the small unexpected, stabbing pains, which made her exclaim sometimes.

Her impatient, energetic mother seemed to suggest that a lack of work was part of the problem. Annie was expected to wash floors and windows in her mother's house as usual. Her mother would 'Tut-tut' irritably if Annie stumbled or dropped something, which seemed to be happening more and more often. The refusal to recognise her condition hurt her, but she wondered if they were covering up their own fears. She would give them the benefit of the doubt. Annie often did give people the benefit of the doubt.

No one knew how tired she often felt, or how hard she pushed herself to finish tasks when she longed to rest. In the last five months her left foot had started to drag at times, and she often just saved herself from overbalancing. She wondered how noticeable this was to other people. If she were cold, her fingers became rather numb and at night they tingled, as though she had just come in from an icy walk.

She knew that she should see a doctor and she had meant to visit one at Christmas, but had not. However, she had a lot of faith in the health and strength of her own body, and because those stupid little troubles would often disappear for days at a time, her optimism was renewed. Perhaps rest and fresh air were all that she needed. She hoped so.

Her thoughts were interrupted when Helen returned from school. She hugged her daughter protectively. It was horrifying to learn that the children had all crowded round the classroom windows to watch as much of the 'air display' as possible. What an irresponsible teacher! People seemed to have as much difficulty believing in the reality of the war as her family had in recognising her illness.

She did not talk to Helen about the battle. She found it too distressing even to think of it.

That night in bed Annie slept very little. They had been here on the east coast for seven months now, ever since war had been declared. So far, no bombs had fallen in the west and today something very terrible had happened practically in her own garden. She felt like packing and rushing home immediately. She also worried about Helen's education. The child would have been enrolled at Glasgow High School for Girls by this time. She wanted Helen to work harder at school than she had done herself. She wanted Helen to achieve something, become a professional woman and not just a wife whose talents found their outlet in knitting and embroidery.

Next day Annie spoke to Helen and broached the subject of returning to Glasgow with some trepidation. In many ways there was more freedom for a child in a small fishing village than in a Glasgow tenement. Perhaps Helen was just settling down and would resent changing again. She need not have worried. Helen was delighted to return to Glasgow and could talk of nothing else.

Her life at the village school had been much more difficult than her mother would ever know. Not that school life in Glasgow had been particularly easy for Helen, timid and introverted child that she was. The Glasgow school had brought her little joy. She was a competent scholar but she felt herself different and separate from the other children. She did not understand them and she hated to be teased. However her trials in Glasgow were nothing compared to the uncouth behaviour in the Pittenweem playground. The classroom with its many inexplicable rules, and the belt which was wielded with such regularity, was also a nightmare. The fact that she was often the only one to raise her hand with the correct answer to a question made her unpopular and the butt of cruelty in the playground. There had also been a very embarrassing experience, which she could not forget. Each morning as she entered the classroom the whole shameful situation would replay itself in her mind distressingly.

If only she could go back to Glasgow and never see that room again the humiliation might fade away.

The disgrace had come about through fear, which made it worse for Helen was a proud child.

Miss Don, Helen's fiery-tempered teacher, had rules that might well have been engraved on tablets of stone. Perhaps she required this severity to bolster her strength against forty-five energetic and noisy eight year-olds who had learned few of the finer graces from their over-worked parents. One of Miss Don's absolute rules was that a visit must be made to the toilet at play-time. If this visit were neglected and 'leave of absence' was requested before lunchtime, the child would be allowed to go out and make itself comfortable, but on return to the classroom it would be belted. At first, Helen was a little hazy about this rule. It seemed so very severe that she could not believe that Miss Don would act like that. Miss Don, in spite of her occasional extravagant crossness, seemed such a very nice lady. Eventually Helen realised that this belting was the accepted practice, horrifying as it seemed. As the weeks went on, Helen observed that there was a way to avoid physical punishment. Sometimes a child would accidentally wet itself in class and then that unfortunate must go to the janitor for pail and mop and clean up the puddle. In that instance the child would not be belted. Perhaps Miss Don considered the shame was punishment enough.

When the day at last arrived that Helen's bladder informed her that she must visit the noisome brick building in the playground before the lunchtime bell sounded, she sat in terror for some time. Her choice lay between the pain and degradation of the leather strap and the equally horrifying thought of wetting her pants. Helen considered and debated in her own mind which she should choose. Perhaps if she were careful and sat very firmly in her seat, it would not drip on to the floor and no one would notice it. Perhaps then she could race to the cloakroom and hide her damp skirt under her coat. The thought of the belt was too much for her and she made the coward's decision, knowing it to be cowardly and despising herself.

The bell rang for lunch and they started to file out.

"Please, Miss! Edward Bowman's peed the floor!"

"No, no, it wasn't me." the poor embarrassed boy mumbled.

Helen felt very bad about that. Edward, who sat beside her,

was one of the cleverest and best behaved boys in the class.

"It was me." said Helen in a small voice and burst into tears.

After mopping the floor, she had a very cold walk home, but that was nothing to the feelings of shame and failure which had burdened her ever since. Her mother had not been cross, only slightly puzzled, but it was a continuing nightmare for Helen. She imagined that every child that entered the classroom each morning would still remember the puddle under her chair and think of how she had wept. She could not meet the eye of any of her classmates. Still less could she apologise to Edward for the mistake, although she thought of a hundred ways to say it. None of them was possible.

To Helen the thought of returning to Glasgow seemed like a dream come true.

BRITAIN'S FOOD PRODUCTION
Nearly 2,000,000 new acres ploughed up!

Glasgow Herald, 18th April 1940

Annie wrote to Bruce and told him of the sea battle. It had all happened so quickly and silently that it was quite difficult to convey the horror she had felt. The description of a few puffs of smoke and a plane diving into the water seemed less dramatic when written down. No doubt he would grumble about their return. He generally did grumble, however he also took great pleasure in showing that he could solve any difficult problem.

It was the end of April before they were finally settled back in the Glasgow flat and Helen was enrolled at the High School. Helen was inordinately delighted to have a navy blue blazer for the first time. The top pocket was entirely overlaid by an embroidered badge in different shades of pale blue with the Latin words, *Non scolae sed vitae, discimus.* Helen was not a curious child and did not try to find out what the words meant, but she was proud of them. Helen had to wear a shirt and school tie and found the latter terribly uncomfortable. Although she knew that schoolgirls in books always wore this uniform, she was sure the tie made her look too much like a boy.

As the weather became warm very early that year, Annie sewed a uniform summer dress for Helen. It was white with a small navy spot and it was bound around the collar and sleeves with navy bias binding. It was a very smart dress indeed. Helen loved it and felt much prettier in it than the shirt and tie.

Annie enjoyed making the dress so much that she made three other summer dresses for Helen, who was allowed to choose the fabrics. One dress had stripes of bright multi-coloured flowers, another was a pretty forget-me-not blue and the third was of green and purple flowered voile, a type of diaphanous fabric which Helen had never seen before and which she thought was very glamourous. She was specially delighted when her mother made a pair of knickers to match each dress, though not from the flimsy voile of course. That would have been rude.

Annie felt happy and relaxed at her sewing machine and she convinced herself that all her health problems would soon pass away.

Because of the wartime restrictions, some of the High School primary classes had been moved from the main building, which was in the centre of town. Helen's age group was re-located in a church hall about a mile from her home. This was very convenient, as she could travel there on the tram by herself and, as the days grew warmer, she often chose to walk home.

From the beginning she found it tremendously different from the two previous schools she had experienced.

Delightfully, the terror of the belt was removed, for the belt was not in use at all in the Girls High School. Helen, a retiring and well-behaved child, had experienced the pain and indignity of such punishment only four times, but the threat of it had always hovered over her. She could not but be relieved that she would never again have to feel that sharp sting and worry if she were going to weep. Those who wept for the belt were deeply despised and reviled in the playground.

The classes in the church hall had a great deal of hymn-singing, mainly of a martial character suitable to the times they were living in. 'Onward Christian Soldiers' was the out and out favourite and was seldom missing from the morning service. Unfortunately Helen had a sad handicap at those services. Her paternal grandmother, the only church-going relative in the family, had given her a little hymn-book. Helen was very pleased with the soft leather covers and the fine silky leaves, which could be turned in a delicious fluttery way. Unfortunately, for some reason, the hymns were differently numbered from all other hymn books. Helen could never be ready when they started to sing. She must refer to the first line in her neighbour's book, then scrabble through her index of first lines to find which number of hymn was the correct one in her unique book. By the time that she had feverishly turned the onion skin pages and located the correct hymn, the two or three chosen verses were usually finished. If it were a psalm, she must hurriedly exchange her hymnary for her bible as there were no psalms in her hymnary. Besides, she did not know any of the tunes which all seemed to have very high bits as well as very low bits. Morning service generally left Helen with a feeling of stress and failure. Again she was aware of being terribly different from the other girls who managed so well.

The classroom was a small vestry and very crowded with desks and chairs. In order to reach the teacher or the door, the pupils had to crawl below tables or squirm between chairs and walls, often asking others to stand. There was a blazing fire near the teacher's table and Helen felt it was not properly guarded. The informality was quite good fun, but it all seemed a bit dangerous to the thoughtful child and not at all like a proper classroom. As well as this, there was a much higher standard of etiquette. 'Excuse me' or 'I beg your pardon' were phrases with which Helen was hardly familiar and they seemed to be as necessary as 'Please' and 'Thank you'. Also, the teacher's name must be used when you spoke to her, while in Pittenweem the children had addressed the teacher simply as 'Miss' and more usually "Please, Miss". Helen had spent seven months in Pittenweem un-learning the use of the teacher's name. Now she must change back again to 'Miss Brown'. Once more she was often in the wrong and constantly corrected. When she forgot and used only the title, it seemed that everyone looked at her reproachfully.

Although Helen thought the girls all spoke in a very nice way and with perfect grammar, so very different from the village children, the teacher seemed dissatisfied and constantly corrected the way that they pronounced things. There were little poems which they must learn and say each day. Helen found them particularly stupid and embarrassing. The one which she hated most was about,

Mother McRoon, in your wooden shoon.
How many miles to get to the moon.

The girls were encouraged to open their mouths wide and then make very round lips for the 'oo' sounds. Another poem about a mermaid and her green glass beads, was more fun, if it had not been ruined by the teacher's insistence on the 'a' in glass being long and in the back of your throat somewhere, like an announcer on the wireless. Helen was possessive about her own accent and she had struggled hard in Fife to retain it. Now, she was certainly not about to start speaking like a hoity-toity BBC person.

At home, when she thought of the ridiculous faces that the teacher made she giggled. That teacher would have had such awful problems with the Pittenweem children, who would have pronounced glass harshly to rhyme with mess.

"And even Miss Brown could never change them!" she thought to herself with satisfaction, as she repeated the mermaid poem and pronounced glass just as she liked to say it.

Otherwise, the school in the church hall was pretty good and she had a really nice reading book, with coloured pictures and good stories and it was her very own book. She need never give it back and she liked that.

One of the special experiences at that time was a film which she saw at school. It was a documentary about Africa and opened a door into another world for Helen. Although she had seen the model of an African village in the Empire Exhibition of 1938, Helen had been a very little girl then and had viewed it as almost unreal, like a piece of theatre. The sad black ladies with lots of brass rings round their necks had looked like actors who were dressed up. Even when her mother had told her that they must never remove the rings, or their necks would break, she enjoyed the scary thought, but did not quite believe it. Neither the women nor their huts, had any reality for her, especially with the perpetual Glasgow showers which drenched the scene. Nor had any picture book ever given her an idea of how different life in that dark continent would be.

Now this film inspired her with interest, terror and amazement. Fierce lions bounded through trees and grassy fields, which did not seem so very different from Scottish trees and fields. Surely this was not what the jungle looked like? Small children very like herself, though black and unclothed of course, lived dangerously close to those trees and fields, in unsafe grass huts. While still young, they learned the grown-up skills of pottery, weaving, carving and cooking. Helen envied them.

Tall stately black men drove terribly thin cows in small herds, in just the same way that farmers in Fife drove their cows, shouting and whacking them with sticks. But then the big difference was that the Africans took blood from their cows and mixed it with the milk to drink. That made Helen feel rather sick. She wondered if it was really true. She thought that she had once heard her father, who hated milk, say milk tasted like blood to him, but her mother had said 'Shush' very loudly. Helen was not sure if he had said that or not.

The most fascinating bit for Helen, was the part filmed in the interior of Africa, where the film makers had discovered a tribe of pygmies. The little men had beards and smoked little pipes and the women had tiny babies. They were almost like children playing at being grown up, but when the camera came close to their faces some were old and wrinkled. Helen watched with her mouth a little open and held her breath while the camera followed the tribe as it crossed a precarious rope bridge spanning a deep chasm. Far below, a wild river thundered over rocks. How brave of them to trust themselves to that slender bouncing ropeway. How clever of these little people, hardly higher than the white man's elbow, to make such a bridge in the first place. Helen was to wonder for years how one even started to make a bridge like that. It was a puzzle she could never solve.

◊

Annie still felt distressed by the sea battle that she had witnessed and it was decided that, rather than return to Pittenweem in the summer, they would take a holiday on the west coast. Millport on the Isle of Cumbrae seemed an attractive and a safe place and Helen was quietly curious and excited. The name conjured up various scenes in her imagination. Apart from several days in Blackpool and the disastrous rainy week in Arran, she had spent all her holidays in Pittenweem. Now she was going to a *real island, just like a storybook.*

And for many reasons it *was* going to be a very special summer.

It would be the summer that she learned to ride a bike, although as the fiasco of the tricycles had suggested, she would never completely master or enjoy the skills of bicycling and would always prefer to walk.

It would be the summer that she learned to make chocolate last a little longer, by melting it over hot water and eating it with a spoon.

It would be the summer that she inadvertently walked into the bedroom where her elderly grandfather was changing his trousers and learned that bottoms are not always round and fat, but can be thin and wrinkled.

It would be the summer that she felt her first maternal stirrings, when she helped a little girl at the beach one day. As she held the small, soft, plump foot in her hand, before slipping on its pristine white sock, she became aware of its vulnerability and perfection, compared with her own bony brown feet in their scuffed sandals. She had a sudden perception of herself as a large, strong creature, totally responsible for the care of someone who was small, weak and helpless. The recognition of these feelings was almost painful and that self- identity would become an integral part of her personality.

Most importantly, it would be the summer which, after having spent her eight years as a rather lonely little girl surrounded by adults, she met and became friends with children of her own age, became part of a 'gang' and for the first time found herself admired by the opposite sex.

While it was a short flash of social success, which was to disappear with autumn and not return for nearly nine years, it gave her hopes, ambitions and possibilities for her future. It was to be a very important summer.

Millport

One bright fresh Saturday in May, Annie, who was feeling strong and able, set off early with Helen to catch the train to Wemyss Bay where they would then board a boat for the Isle of Cumbrae.

Helen adored the boat journey, with the sea just rough enough to make the deck a little unsteady for walking. The seagulls soared beside the ship in the friendliest way and the beautiful Clyde spread its deep blue water around them. Helen felt she was entering another country as she walked down the gangplank at Millport. It looked so different from Pittenweem, it even smelled different. The houses were not so pretty, but the air was pungent and wonderful. Perhaps it was the pinewoods, perhaps it was the seaweed on the beach or perhaps just the milder climate of the west. Whatever it was, it was an overpowering and unforgettable aroma for the little girl and her spine tingled with excitement. It was a perfume that she could conjure up in her imagination, for the rest of her life.

A newsagent at the pier had postcards in his window, advertising various apartments to let. While Annie took a note of several, Helen gazed at the shop next door. In large golden letters it proclaimed itself,

THE TOY EMPORIUM

This was a word which Helen had never come across . It obviously meant a very superior type of shop, because this one was *crammed* with toys. And not just seaside toys, spades and pails, blow-up beach balls and swimming rings, fishing nets, although there were plenty of those hanging outside the door, but in the window there was every sort of toy that she had ever seen. Elaborately-dressed dolls, teddy bears, tricycles and scooters, wooden soldiers to knock down with a wooden ball, spinning tops, hoops, tin train sets, farmyard sets, toy yachts, wind-up monkeys and motor cars, multi-coloured rubber bouncing balls, a doll's house filled with wonderful miniscule furniture, a castle with a draw-bridge, china teasets, net bags with marbles, jigsaws and board-games all jostled with each other for space. It was like heaven. Perhaps emporium meant heaven? She decided to keep the word locked away for just now and not trouble her mother with it. Helen preferred to find out the meaning of unusual words for herself. Then she could drop them casually and unexpectedly into the conversation at some future time. It always made her mother smile.

They set off along the sea front, with Helen taking deep sniffs of the air.

"You're like a wee dog there. What are you smelling?"

But Helen just smiled.

It was much more like a seaside resort than Pittenweem, with brightly painted rowing boats for hire and several cafes. Stretches of grass had seats for visitors to sit and admire the sea view and though it was May, quite a few visitors were strolling, or sitting reading newspapers.

"Come over here and see this, Helen. I've heard about this rock."

At the edge of the beach was a strangely shaped rock. It was long and rugged and, to the imaginative eye, it had something of the form of a crocodile. In case of a lack of imagination, two fierce eyes and a set of crocodile teeth had been painted on the appropriate parts of the rock but, in Helen's opinion, in very inappropriate colours. The eyes were patriotically, but unrealistically, red, white and blue, like two little targets. Helen felt that it was an interesting idea, but she was repelled by its crudity and even at her mother's urging, refused to sit on its back.

Quite soon they reached the first address. It was in a side street and was an extension at the back of an old shabby house. A glass door led into a large bed-sitter with many windows. A certain artistry was shown in the draping of pleasantly coloured fabrics over the ad hoc furniture. It overlooked a wild little garden. A screen, which had hundreds of postcards pasted all over it, hid a tiny cooking area with a bright green wooden cupboard holding an exciting assortment of different coloured china. It was Bohemian! Helen adored it and had no doubt her mother would too. How lucky to find this place at the very first address. It was like a room in a story. Within moments, Helen was imagining their first meal at the rickety card table. How lovely it would be to run into the garden. Which of the thinly disguised beds would be hers?

Incredulously, she awoke from her daydream to hear her mother say,

"I'm so sorry to have troubled you. It's not quite what I was wanting. I do hope to invite my parents some time ..."

"It can easily sleep four people you know ..."

Even Helen thought that was unlikely.

"No, really it's not quite ... big enough.. I'm sorry. Thank you."

Helen grabbed her mother's hand and squeezed it hard. Was this marvellous place to slip from their grasp so easily? Just because it was too small?

"I could always let you have another room, if your parents came to visit. It would cost a little extra, pro rata you know. It would be quite comfortable for elderly people. Would you like to see it now?"

"No, really. Thank you so much for your trouble. Not just what I'm looking for, today, thank you. Thank you. Goodbye."

They walked in silence back to the sea front.

"I liked that place." said Helen in a small voice.

"It was hellish! What a dump! It was like some old stage set, done on the cheap ... and it smelled. All that ancient broken-down furniture with dauds of old ragged cloth to tart it up. And it was damp. It certainly smelled damp. And what a price she was wanting! And I certainly wouldn't like to get on the wrong side of that old harridan either, greedy old bitch."

Helen filed the word 'harridan' away for future use and wondered why her mother was so angry.

"Was she old, Mummy? She was wearing lipstick."

"Humph, she was no chicken, I'll bet. Humph, elderly parents indeed. What a hell-hole that was."

But Helen kept her romantic vision of the bed-sitting room and it would be the setting for many of her imaginings.

They viewed five other apartments before Annie found one that she considered suitable. They were all terribly ordinary, with none of the bizarrre charm of the first one. Helen was not a moody child and she did not sulk, but she lost interest in the day's work and followed her mother from house to house with dutiful politeness, but no excitement.

The fifth flat that they visited was in a tenement at the far end of the seafront, close to the bay, where a curved terrace of affluent villas clustered in middle-class propriety.

The flat had three rooms and a large kitchen. By locking the door which led to the sitting room and a small bedroom it became a 'room and kitchen' and could be rented more cheaply. Then when Helen's grandparents arrived, the door could be unlocked and the house enlarged for them. The lady was only willing to do this as it was to be a let for the whole summer.

The kitchen was large and had a bed in the recess. Helen was interested to see what this looked like. The kitchen at home had a recess for a bed and Helen knew that it was for a maid to sleep in, long ago when maids were cheap. Nowadays there was no bed in the recess at home and generally her mother did the ironing there, while Helen kept her toys in a big box in the corner.

This bed was exactly the same size as the recess and was very high, so high that Helen knew that they must step on a chair to climb into it. It had a patchwork bedspread. Helen began to feel really interested again. She had only seen pictures of patchwork and now she might be going to sleep under a real one. There was a mixture of some pretty materials in the bedspread, and some horrible ones as well, she noticed as she inspected it carefully. Somehow it all looked fine in spite of the ugly colours. What a lot of work it must be to make such a big lump of patchwork. She knew she would be able to look at that patchwork spread every night for a long time and always find something interesting to think about.

Annie seemed to be getting on really well with Mrs Tait. Helen was pleased and relieved to hear her mother's voice friendly and soft for the first time that day.

"Oh, that will be fine. Yes, good. Very convenient. It's beautifully clean too. Thank you. I like it very much. And I can have it for two months at that price? Great. Well I think I'll take it. Oh but where is the bathroom ... in here?"

Annie opened a door in the hall which proved to be a cupboard.

"The toilet's along the landing ... in the close there. Come an' I'll show you."

Helen noticed her mother's face had changed.

They followed Mrs Tait out of the front door and along the landing to the head of the stairs where there was a door, which Helen had not noticed before. Inside it was similar to a restaurant toilet, with a tiny WC and wash basin. It was very clean and

smelled strongly of Izal disinfectant. There was a window looking down on the large garden at the rear of the tenement.

After inspecting it, Annie said nothing, but walked back into
the flat. Helen noticed the signs that her mother was getting tired.
Her left foot was starting to drag and also her expression was different, as though she were trying to hide something. Annie stumbled very slightly on the thick coconut mat at the door and as
soon as she reached the kitchen, she sat down.

"That toilet does make a difference, Mrs Tait. There's no bath
and I'm not happy about a shared outside toilet." Annie bit her
lip as she looked up at Mrs Tait.

"Och, but you wouldn't be sharing it, Mrs Corning, the house
next door will be empty all summer, they're away to the Isles.
They're teuchters."

Annie could not help herself from smiling at that word, but
immediately she looked stern again and hesitant.

"Mmhm."

She had a very particular way of saying 'mmhm' which could
mean any one of a dozen different things.

Helen could hardly bear the suspense. She liked the idea of
running along the close in her pyjamas to brush her teeth at night
and what did it matter if there was no bath? They had got used to
the big tin bath in front of the fire in Pittenweem. Helen thought
it was fun. Besides she adored the patchwork bedspread and the
beach was just across the road.

As well as all these childish enthusiasms, the practical part of
Helen's mind knew that her mother had run out of energy. There
was no more strength to look at other apartments. This was their
last chance to arrange something on this particular day. Until
they had seen the outside lavatory, her Mother had seemed to
think that this was by far the best place and she willed her
mother to smile and say that it was settled, but her mother still
bit her lip and would not look at Helen.

After an unconscionable time, Annie opened her little
crocodile handbag and brought out a five-pound note.

"I'll take it, Mrs Tait, is this enough for a deposit?"

Mrs Tait and Helen both smiled broadly in relief and Annie
gave her daughter the special little grimace that Helen loved.

"Come away downstairs and I'll give you a receipt and maybe
you would like a cup of tea and a pancake. I've been baking today."

Helen thought that an excellent suggestion.

"No thank you, Mrs Tait, that's very good of you but not today. We've got friends to visit."

Helen turned sharply to her mother. What friends? She knew of no friends in Millport. Was this a special surprise? She caught her mother's eye, but a faintly raised eyebrow and an imperceptible shake of the head warned her to say nothing.

"That's very nice, Mrs Corning. That's nice when you've got someone you know. It will be company for you in the summer. Do they live close by?"

"Oh no," Annie hesitated slightly, "they're at the other end of town, I'm afraid."

That was when Helen knew absolutely that her mother was lying.

They walked back along the front towards the pier.

"I thought you weren't going to take that place, Mummy, you were so long making up your mind."

"I was kind of hoping she might knock a bit off the price, but she didn't."

"And why did you say we had friends to visit? That wasn't true, was it? That's terrible, to tell lies! Why did you say that?"

Annie laughed.

"Och, I don't know. We might have had friends here. She was just a bit too sweet to be wholesome and I didn't want to get stuck eating her stodgy pancakes. Would you have liked a pancake, my wee pet? Anyway it's time for something more solid. Here's a cafe. Let's have a ham roll with mustard on it and a glass of milk. Would you like that? I know I would."

Helen grinned and nodded and squeezed her mother's hand. Her mother could be quite naughty sometimes and she liked that.

The cafe had marble-topped tables and green glass walls and the rolls were filled with lots of thinly sliced cold ham and too much butter. Annie asked for French mustard but they only had the ordinary kind so Helen did without. They were able to buy a big bar of chocolate, which was a nice surprise, for chocolate had become very scarce in Glasgow.

Lord Woolton, Minister for Food, yesterday warned that consumers must be prepared at an early date for a reduction in the butter ration, in view of the cessation of Danish supplies. He

intimated that sugar may also be cut. He emphasized that the problem of sugar was a difficult one because, for the poorer sections of the community, it was an essential food. He asked people in a better position to save on their sugar ration and use it only for preserves.

Glasgow Herald 7th May 1940

When they left the café, the weather had changed, black clouds hung low overhead and large drops of rain were falling. Mist had appeared over the sea and the hills. The afternoon boat was just about to leave for the mainland.

"Will we get away back home now, jewel? It's going to pelt and we've done what we came to do ... for better or worse. I hope that place is all right. It's much more expensive than I thought it would be. Can you run?"

Of course Helen could run! Annie was less able and they were amongst the last to board.

The rain had stopped again and they stood on deck as the ship pulled away. Helen gazed down at the clear dark water roiling against the wooden supports of the jetty where masses of blue mussel shells clung and rich seaweed flowed and danced gracefully, making her think of the mermaid poem and her green glass beads. Inside her head she tried out the several different pronunciations of glass and laughed to herself.

Sticking her hands deep in her blazer pockets, she watched the gold letters above the toy emporium disappear into the mist. In a few weeks she would return to this magical place and stay in the flat with the patchwork bedspread.

GREAT BATTLE ON FRENCH COAST

Allies fall back under German pressure on flanks.

Navy's valiant part in evacuation.

Three destroyers lost in operations

Fierce rearguard action still in progress.

Glasgow Herald 31st May 1940

On the first of July, Helen and her mother sailed back to Millport. Annie was quiet and sad. The news had been so bad for weeks. The war had certainly started in earnest now. She felt a sense of guilt, as if she were running away to this quiet island and allowing other people to risk danger, so that she might be safe. What could she do? She was not particularly well just now and she had no idea how she could contribute to the war. She supposed that, like many others, she must just live her normal life, put up with the scarcities and not grumble. The government constantly exhorted people to save and she would certainly try to do that. She had saved all her life, so that should not be difficult! Perhaps coming to Millport was extravagant? She laughed quietly to herself at the thought of her meagre housekeeping allowance. No, surely she could never be accused of extravagance.

Helen, unaware of the sad developments of the war, enjoyed her journey to Millport. She was anxious to settle into their flat. It was such an adventure. The weather was sunny and warm and she hoped that the patchwork bedspread would be just as exciting to sleep under, as she imagined.

They explored the town and bought crisp rolls, fresh Millport butter and locally grown lettuce and tomatoes, which tasted sweeter than any other tomatoes had ever seemed.

"Those tomatoes are *so delicious*! Can I have another one?"

"Certainly my darling. They are very, very good for you. They are picked straight from the plant and that's why they're so good. I'd just love to grow tomatoes myself. Maybe I will, one day."

Annie was relieved to have arrived safely. Physically she was feeling relaxed and strong and she tried to rid herself of the sadness of war. Soon her natural optimism reasserted itself.

While shopping, they had visited the wonderful emporium, but Annie explained that she was very short of cash these days and besides, who needed toys when you were in such an interesting place with so many things to see? Helen saw the common sense of this

"Perhaps we'll buy something at the end of our holidays?"

"That's a good idea, my little jewel. And you always have Topsy."

They explored the pine woods behind the town which smelled resinous and delicious. The carpet of needles was soft and silent to walk on and Helen felt she was in some foreign land where they spoke a strange language. It was all so different from Pittenweem. Further away there was a small deciduous forest where the path passed underneath a large tree, growing at a terrifyingly acute angle to the ground. Helen was very unwilling to walk under this dangerous tree.

"What if it falls down when we are underneath it?"

"It's probably been standing there for about a hundred years and it hasn't fallen yet, you silly billy."

Annie walked forward herself, but the child held back and obviously wanted to return home.

Annie was quite tired and the kid obviously felt strongly about this tree, so she said,

"All right, you wee dafty, we'll come back again another day."

Helen held her breath and clenched her hands until the nails bit her palms as her mother walked back towards her and passed under the dangerous tree a second time.

They took a slightly different route home and came to a farm, where an unfriendly hen tried to peck Helen, but even the hen and the frightening tree could not spoil the magic of the day, With its glorious smells and dangerous experiences, it would always remain clear in Helen's mind. It was a walk taken for sheer pleasure and it was a longer walk than they would ever take together again.

One evening, that first week, they visited the Pierrots at the other end of town. This was a variety show held in a large hut. Helen was more familiar with the open-air shows which were performed in the Glasgow parks throughout the summer. Indeed these brave entertainers worked in city parks and seaside resorts all over the country. For a few hard-working months, each small band of dedicated performers would present to the public a selection of songs, jokes, dances and dramatic sketches of greater or lesser merit. The show would change from week to week, sometimes more often. The actors, in spite of small wages and shabby costumes, seemed able to present professional and merry faces, night after night. Sometimes the audience would be minimal or hardly appreciative, but the Pierrots soldiered on and must be saluted as contributing much to the morale of the British public in those difficult times.

The hall was quite chilly and the seats were hard, but Helen was entranced from the moment that the stage lit up with brilliant colour and the seven members of the troupe danced on from the wings, singing,

"All the World is waiting for the Sunrise."

The jokes were simple and sometimes smutty, sometimes too

much so for Helen to understand, the songs were loud and had oft-repeated choruses for the audience to sing. The dancing was energetic but poor, even Helen could see that, but the dresses were bright and freshly-ironed. The little plays were patriotic and philosophic and had happy endings which appealed to Annie in their innocent poignancy.

"I think we'll come here every week."

"I'd love that, Mummy. The programme says the show changes twice a week. Could we not come twice a week?"

"Oh, well you never know. It really was marvellous. We'll wear warmer clothes next time, though."

Another evening they visited the cinema and watched a terribly good but unbearably sad picture called 'Good-bye Mr Chips.' They had only one handkerchief and it was passed back and forwards between them until it was sodden and useless.

One day they walked to the other side of the bay and visited the Aquarium, where lobsters and crabs crawled slowly around immense tanks. Annie had gathered a few long blades of grass and she used one to tickle a lobster, but she dropped it hurriedly when the lobster immediately grabbed it and tried to climb up and out of the tank.

Behind glass windows there was an amazing variety of different fish which lived in the local waters, fish which Annie had never seen in a fish shop. Why? She wondered. Were they difficult to catch? Or perhaps unpleasant to eat? Some looked tropically colourful. Helen liked the giant sea anemones best as they swayed languorously in the large sinks. They were as brilliantly colourful as something from a Robinson Crusoe island, yet the attendant assured Annie that they were all to be found in the waters of the Clyde. Some anemones were pink and soft and fluffy and looked very like the marabou that Aunt Vida had sewn around her bed jacket. Others were delicately lacy and dark purple. Others had tentacles and looked like several small scarlet octopuses crowded together. Helen was completely fascinated by their graceful movements and would have stood gazing at them for much longer, but the attendant borrowed one of Annie's long grasses and started to touch each anemone gently with it. Immediately, with a smooth speed, each amazing creature withdrew its waving tentacles neatly into an unbelievably small jelly-like sphere, which was attached to the side of the tank. Helen was open-mouthed with surprise. What a disappearing trick! Apart from their colour, the small jellies were completely uninteresting. The attendant told Helen to look in the rock pools at the shore and she would see tiny anemones clinging to the rocks.

"We'll come here again soon won't we?" pleaded Helen. But other horizons opened out for her and it was the end of the summer before they returned for a last look at the exotic sea creatures.

Annie had noticed a shop which hired out bicycles and, as there was practically no traffic on the island, she thought it would be a good idea to teach Helen to ride a bike. Annie had such happy memories of her own bicycle. She had adored the independence it gave her throughout her teens and early twenties.

When she broached the subject to Helen, she was surprised to find that it was greeted with little enthusiasm.

"Don't you remember the tricycle, Mummy?"

That day, forever terrible in Helen's memory when she and her mother had quarrelled in the street over Helen's extreme timidity. It had ended with her mother furiously dragging the trike home and Helen following on foot, weeping and feeling a fool.

"Yes, pet, but remember you enjoyed the traffic day at school when the playground was laid out in little streets."

Yes, Helen had enjoyed that. It was all so safe and disciplined, with miniature traffic lights and the kindly policemen. Best of all was the fact that the tall school railings shut out the real traffic, the frightening trams, buses and motors that rushed along the road. She had never been able to explain to her mother the terror she felt about those fast heavy vehicles, which were only a few feet away from her as they hurtled down the hill. What if she lost control of her tricycle and it veered off the pavement and under a bus or lorry? That would be the end of her. Did her mother not think of that? Even thinking about it now made her tremble.

"I suppose it might be nice to go on a bike when there's no cars about."

"It would be great! We could go picnics and adventures all over the island. You'd like that, wouldn't you? You'd be absolutely safe, if that's what worrying you. There's hardly anything driving on the roads here."

The next day they hired a child's bike. As soon as Helen wheeled it away from the shop, she knew this was something she was doing to please her mother, rather than herself. Just wheeling it was difficult, it was unwieldy and threatened to topple away from her. When she straightened it up, the pedals knocked painfully against her legs.

Dutifully she allowed her mother to balance her on the seat and then walk along beside her holding the bike steady. Helen was positive that she would never reach the stage that it would be safe for her mother to let go. Annie was too kind a mother to force her child into anything, but because of Helen's polite stoicism, she had no idea of the unhappiness she was inflicting. The hour seemed like ten to Helen and Annie certainly realised that her child was not a natural born cyclist.

The following day, the lesson was repeated with no improvement in the child's skill. Annie noticed how happy and lively Helen became as soon as the bike was safely returned to the shop.

By the fifth day, Helen could wobble along by herself, though she could not, or would not, mount or dismount without help from Annie.

"You're doing just fine my darling." Annie said heartily and untruthfully. "Perhaps tomorrow, I'll hire a bike too and we can go for a little journey together."

She thought that if she were not so available, Helen might develop a little more independence. Increasingly she found the supporting role too much for her strength..

The two bikes were hired and they travelled gingerly through the main street.

Quite suddenly a young woman stepped off the pavement, just in front of Helen. There was no time for Helen to ring her bell or take avoiding action. They collided and both shouted out at the same time. Fortunately neither fell to the ground and the young woman grabbed the bike. There were a few scratches on their legs but Annie and the woman parted with joint apologies and polite smiles, while Helen stood thinking that it was quite exciting to be in an accident. It appealed to her sense of humour that a bicyclist should be knocked down by a pedestrian. It seemed, in a strange way, to help Helen dispel her fears and she thought how she would be able to make people laugh with that story!

The next day they again hired bikes and this time set off towards the Aquarium. It was a lovely day and there was not a car to be seen. They sniffed the dank smell of the Aquarium as they passed it.

"Just round the corner there is a big rock called the Lion Rock, I believe. Let's go as far as that and then turn round for home, shall we?"

Helen smiled back over her shoulder to her mother. Like all beginners, she found it easier to go a little fast rather than slowly and had pulled ahead of her mother. Annie was delighted to see that her daughter was at last sampling the pleasures of bicycling and she was enjoying it very much, herself.

They passed the Lion Rock, which was disappointing, and as Helen was bowling along, Annie did not stop her or suggest turning around.

As they travelled along, the distance between them started to increase. Helen struggled slowly up the hills and Annie would start to overtake her, but once over the hill, Helen would shoot downhill at high speed and gain another few yards. Each hill that they came to increased the distance between them. Annie had no idea how far they had come, nor what was the distance around the island. Eventually Annie became worried about the widening gap and shouted for Helen to stop. Unfortunately, Helen's dismounting skill was still far from perfect and Annie was dismayed to see the child fall off her bike.

It was quite a nasty fall because of the gravelled road surface. Annie did her best to comfort the little girl and clean her bleeding knees with a handkerchief. Fortunately Annie had half a tube of Horlicks tablets in her pocket and they sucked these and chatted until Helen was quite cheerful again.

"Now what do you want to do? We could turn round and go home the way we came or we could go on and right around the island. We've come so far, I think it would be quickest to go on, but I don't really know. Anyway, try not to get so far ahead of me this time!"

Helen promised to try and, having complete faith in her mother's judgement, agreed that it would be best to go on. Unfortunately her mother was wrong in her calculations. They had scarcely covered one quarter of the circumference of the island.

Annie helped Helen on to her bike and shouted.

"Not too fast now!"

Then she hauled up her own bike. She felt a bit tired. What a nuisance this tiredness was! As she pushed off with her right foot, something unexpected happened and the next thing she had fallen and she too, had two scraped and bleeding knees.

She shouted for Helen but she was far in the distance, manfully pedalling up a steep hill. Annie mounted her bike and set off as well as she could. Her knees were stinging but she expected she could ignore it.

It was almost laughable.

What a pair of wounded soldiers after a short bicycle run!

On and on they travelled and it became very hot. Uphill and downhill, with Helen always ahead and always gaining at every hill.

It was lunchtime and Annie cursed herself for not bringing a snack with them. No sign of the town.

How many miles was it around this damned island?

Annie was exhausted and she was worried about Helen, who had so recently learned to ride the bike. She had been foolish to take her on this marathon ride. She was a bad mother.

Just then, astonishingly, she saw a little shop perched beside the road. Could it be a mirage?

GINGER BEER AND SNACKS

Proclaimed a large roughly-lettered sign on the gable-end of the hut.

Helen was far ahead whizzing down a hill. Surely the wee thing had seen that sign and longed for some of those promised delicacies. Was she afraid to stop? As Annie watched, her daughter reached the foot of the hill. Then, looking back over her shoulder, she wobbled slowly across the road to a grassy embankment where she bumped into a large boulder, and once more fell off her bike.

Annie reached her and was relieved to see her smiling.

"Can we *please* have some ginger beer, Mummy? I'm so hot and tired and thirsty! What a long long way! Are we not nearly there yet?"

Then her brave face crumpled and she cried bitterly for a few moments.

"Now, now, I'll go back and get us something at that wee shop and I'll ask how far it is into town. I might even be able to phone for a taxi to take us home."

This was something Annie could not realy afford and she sincerely hoped that there would be no telephone available.

"That would be lovely, Mummy. I would like that. I don't think I can pedal another inch."

"Or maybe there's a bus we can catch. Or perhaps we are nearly there now."

The ginger beer in the cold stoneware bottle tasted like the most wonderful drink in the world to Helen and the tea biscuits were delicious.

Annie broke the news gently that there was no taxi or bus coming to save them. However it was only two and a half miles to town now, which was nothing because they had come nearly fourteen.

"What a clever girl you are to make such a long trip when you have just newly learned to go a bike. If we just take it easy and *you stay right beside me*, we'll soon be home."

They returned the bikes to the shop and walked slowly back to their flat. Annie's leg was dragging badly and her knees were painful, but she d a feeling of satisfaction. Life in the old girl yet! She had circumnavigated the island on a bike.

Helen was very quiet and limping.

There was bacon and an egg, some cold potatoes and half an onion in the larder and soon the two of them, with neatly bandaged knees, were sitting up in bed and eating a tasty meal.

"I don't know about you, my jewel, but I'm going to lie down and sleep now."

"I thought we were maybe going to the Pierrots tonight?"

"Well, we'll see how we feel when we waken up. It's only three thirty now, though I can scarcely believe it."

Three hours later, they awakened refreshed though painful and hobbled off up the hill to the Pierrots.

It was a week before they felt like hiring bicycles again. Annie stayed quietly in the house, knitting. Helen crossed the road to the beach each morning and there she made friends with a pretty little girl called Flora, who was to awaken her maternal instincts.

Flora said that she was three. Helen could never understand why such a young child was allowed to stay alone on the beach for hours. She knew she had never been without an adult to look after her at that age. In fact she knew that even now, when she was eight and a half, her mother often peeped from the window to check that she was all right. Helen hoped that perhaps some other window had a Mummy watching Flora. The child was beautifully dressed and very sweet, but helpless. Helen would remove the child's cardigan when it got hot, help her to build and decorate castles, take off her shoes to paddle and put them on again afterwards.

Annie had arranged to hang a hankie in the window as a signal that lunch was ready and Flora must be left alone on the beach when Helen went back home. Helen hated to leave her like that.

"Will you be all right by yourself?"

"Yeth."

"Would you like me to take you home to your Mummy?"

"No, tanku."

"Will your Mummy come and collect you soon?"

"Yeth."

No adult ever came to collect her while Helen was there, but when she climbed the stairs and rushed to look down from the front window, Flora was no longer on the beach.

It was a terrible puzzle and Helen was always relieved to find Flora on the beach the next morning, dressed in another pretty Shirley Temple style dress.

After a week, Flora disappeared. Helen never saw again and the mystery was never solved.

Towards the end of that week, Annie had recovered her strength and suggested an evening walk along the front. The weather was perfect, the sea calm and glassy and the fading daylight changed the way that everything looked and even sounded.

"Would you like to go out in a rowing boat?"

Helen looked at her mother. She was always surprised by Annie's adventurous suggestions.

"Do you feel strong enough?"

"Sure thing, baby!"

Helen laughed, she liked it when her mummy talked American.

They found a nice little green boat called 'Nancy' for hire and, though getting into it was scary, Helen soon saw that her mother knew how to use the oars very well.

"You've done this before."

"Oh, often and often, my love. Willie and I spent half our lives on Bingham's Pond."

They rowed round the little island in the bay and looked at the fish deep in the water.

"How about fishing tomorrow night? We could catch our own tasty tea!"

Helen was not sure if her mother were serious or not, but by next evening they had bought two simple fishing lines at the Emporium, dug up some worms on the beach and were out in the bay on the 'Nancy'. Helen was glad that her mother did all the gruesome work of sticking the worms on the hook and removing the fish when they caught them, but she really enjoyed catching the flat flounders. Her mother bashed them hard on the head when they were pulled on board. Helen was astonished at how violent her kind mother could be, and also surprised that she herself rather enjoyed watching the violence.

Later, back in the flat, dressed in their pyjamas, they ate the fried flounders with slices of brown bread and butter. Helen learned how to separate the fish from the bones and she thought it the most delicious meal she had ever tasted *and she had caught it herself!*

Annie and her daughter would only fish together for five or six nights, but Helen often remembered and enjoyed in retrospect, those calm evenings, when the sky faded from green to purple, and when the slight noise of the water against the side of the 'Nancy' and the calling seabirds seemed to be the only sounds in the world-until suddenly, another fish would be pulled on board and noisily bludgeoned.

When they did venture out on wheels again, Annie took a picnic with brown bread and butter, tomatoes and two little sponge cakes. There was ginger beer, too.

They cycled inland and the scenery was quite different. The pungent aroma that hovered around the coastline and that Helen loved so much, slowly disappeared as they approached the centre of the island.

"It doesn't seem like Millport here, Mummy"

"Millport is just the town. The island is called Cumbrae, but I know what you mean. Where d'ye think it seems like, my wee love?"

"Somewhere else, I suppose."

As they ate their picnic, they agreed that ginger beer, though always refreshing, could never taste so specially wonderful as it had that day of their long bicycle ride around the island.

"Mrs Tait told me that there is a very nice bay for bathing just beside that wee shop. Perhaps we will go there tomorrow."

"Oh, no, no, no!"

"We would go the short way of course, the other way out of town, dafty."

"I don't know if I ever want to see that place again."

They did go, several times, and Helen loved it. The bay was incredibly close when approached from the other end of town and it was a wonderful beach. Helen and Annie both swam in the clear sandy water which was so much warmer than the chilly waves of Fife. Annie felt that it did her a lot of good.

Helen discovered a small hot spring bubbling out of the sand, which seemed specially magical.

"That's amazing, Helen, I thought you had to go to far away places like New Zealand to find hot springs."

"No. This is definitely a very hot spring."

Annie felt that it was an ideal life that they were leading. There was a simplicity about this holiday which would have been impossible in her parent's house in Fife. The war seemed terribly remote. Letters came from Bruce and her parents, but she felt curiously detached from her relatives and their problems. It was wonderful to feel so calm and unemotional. Although as usual she was pretty hard up, expenses were few. The fresh locally grown food was cheap and delicious, and there was just enough extra cash for bike hire and nights at the Pierrots. She felt well, although she could get strangely tired sometimes. It was so unpredictable. It was damnable.

But it was specially good to be away from Pittenweem, with the multitude of prying eyes that watched her if she stumbled. They were probably counting the weeks since her husband last visited. Privacy did not exist in a small town. The anonymity of Millport, the freedom to please herself and, most important of all, the companionship and happiness of her little girl, gave Annie the sense of having arrived at a goal in her life, a happy and undemanding place.

Quite suddenly, the holiday changed for both of them.

They were returning, tired but not exhausted, after the fourth bike run to the bay outside town.

To Helen's utter astonishment, her mother suddenly shouted to a tall man on the other side of the road.

"Derek! Hey! Derek Dickson!"

At almost the same time the man, whose face was very red, shouted,

"Annie!"

"How are you?"

"It's absolutely *years*! How've you been?"

The man had quickly crossed the street and he was dragging two boys behind him. They were about Helen's age and they were sun-burned, very dirty and looked terribly tired. They had obviously just had a pink milky drink, for a bright sticky circle marked each brow where the rim of a large glass had rested. They hung back behind their father and looked at the ground.

"Fancy you being here!"

"Oh, we come to Millport every year, take the same house. Practically natives."

"How lovely! And how's Nan? It's been such ages. I don't know how long it's been since ..."

"Great! Same old Nan. She'll be over the moon to know you're here."

"It's really wonderful. I'm dying to see her again. We're here for the whole summer."

Helen thought how vivacious and terribly young her mother suddenly appeared. Not like a Mummy at all.

"Well we're just over there at number fourteen."

He pointed to the elegant villas on the bay.

"And we're up a close, just along here. By the way, this is my wee girl, Helen. She's my only one and I see you've beaten me."

"Yes, these are our twins, Matthew and James." The boys glowered at their father. "Better known as Matt and Jimmy, though. And I have a little girl as well, Norma. But I'm afraid these two are a bit wabbit. We've just walked round the island. And they're filthy!. Better get them home to bath and bed."

"Poor boys! *Right round* the island! They must be *exhausted*! Righto, on you go and give Nan my love and we'll see each other tomorrow maybe. Fancy you both being here. It's a lovely surprise! Cheerio just now, Derek! Tata boys!"

What a vast amount of things that short meeting had given

Helen to think about, but first of all she asked how her mother knew Derek.

"Well, long ago, when Nan and Derek got married, I was the bridesmaid!"

"But I've never met them before or even heard of them. Were they good friends?"

"Yes, very good friends, I suppose, but they went to live in Greenock and we just lost touch. Silly. I was always fond of Nan, too. Never knew Derek very well."

"Do you think those boys had really walked all round the island? That same road that we cycled?"

"I suppose they did, if their Daddy says so."

"They must be awfully strong."

"Boys are strong, I think. I expect they had food with them to help them along."

"It seems like an awful long walk to me."

And although the boys had not been much to look at, certainly not as handsome as Raymond Hare for instance, Helen was impressed by their ability to walk such a distance. There was a fascination about this family which had suddenly materialised. It fell neatly into the category of a storybook family with a mother and father, twin boys and a little girl who came here every year and stayed in one of those swell villas. What possibilities for adventure that conjured up!

Then that suggestion of going home to 'bath and bed'. It would be a proper big bath in a bathroom and it was a long time since Helen had been in a bath like that. The tin tub in Pittenweem and the baby bath here in Millport were not the sort of bath that children in books ever had. And no doubt Matt and Jimmy (even their names were straight from a book) had a proper set bedtime to keep, possibly eight o'clock or even seven-thirty. Annie was not at all severe about bedtime, she enjoyed her daughter's company and as Helen needed little sleep, she could go to bed pretty much when she pleased. Although Helen enjoyed and took full advantage of this freedom, deep down she worried that this was not quite right for a properly reared child. Sometimes she would make a deliberate effort to get more sleep and go to bed earlier, but it made no difference. It just meant that she spent longer on her nightly prologue to sleep, when she acted out the heroine's role in her latest imaginary scenario.

That summer, for the first time, Helen's nightly imaginings ceased. It was only a temporary cessation, but her day-to-day life became so interesting and exciting that she slept as soon as her head touched the pillow and had no need of pretending.

On the first visit to the villa, the children had been awkward, full of silences and embarrassed giggles, while the mothers chatted happily. Helen went home feeling rather despondent. Next day, however, Matt came to the door about nine-thirty and asked Helen to join them on the beach.

That was the beginning of Helen's marvellous summer. For the next six weeks, Annie could only be sure of seeing her daughter at mealtimes and by eight o'clock each evening, which was bedtime at the villa, as Helen had correctly surmised.

Helen turned her back on bicycles with no regrets. She would always prefer to walk. Twice weekly, she did tear herself away from the Dickson family early enough to accompany her mother to the Pierrots. Then there was the hour or two spent together before Helen's bedtime each night, when they played cards or knitted. Annie was pleased to see her little girl so happy, but the loss of her company was a bit of a blow. She admitted to herself that sometimes she felt very lonely, although she and Nan met for a coffee each week. Nan had relatives staying with her and was too busy with her domestic duties to spend much time chatting. She had changed from the jolly giggling person of ten years ago. Without disclosing the full story, she hinted that her marriage had a lot of difficulties and Annie believed that Derek's red cheeks explained some of the problems. Annie confided that her married life, too, was less than perfect and they shook their heads over those distant years of their carefree girlhood.

Annie sometimes smiled cynically to think that the Dicksons were not the happy storybook family that her little girl imagined them to be.

Matt and Jimmy were not identical twins. Matt was taller and quieter and Jimmy was sturdy and restless. Their personalities were very different, but they were agreed in thinking that Helen was marvellous.

While their middle-class conventionality attracted Helen, her relaxed attitude to accepted rules fascinated them. She could go to bed whenever she wanted to and get up when she wanted. She did not wear socks or vest or sweater and hardly seemed to feel the cold when the wind blew. She prided herself on her toughness. She was different from the girls they knew. She could climb and run as well as they could and she swam every day, whatever the weather. She did not fuss about little things like sand in her shoe or a scraped knee. As well as being so tomboyish, she had such wonderful long fair hair. They had never met a girl who wore her hair in two plaits and to Matthew it seemed delightfully old-fashioned, like a fairy story princess, while Jimmy thought she was very glamorous and it was just the way that every girl should wear her hair. Neither of them was able to speak to her or to each other about the waist length plaits and how they felt about them, but Helen soon realised that they both liked her very much, whatever the reason was.

After all those miserable years of teasing and unpleasantness that she had suffered at the hands of schoolboys, it seemed a miracle to Helen that these two terribly nice, well-spoken and well-behaved boys should so obviously think she was a very special girl!

Their admiration astonished her and gave her a delightful sense of satisfaction.

She awakened each morning, full of the unfamiliar joy of being attractive and popular.

Perhaps she would marry one of them one day and if so, which one?

They were clever, too. Each evening at seven, the three Dickson children and their little cousin Jean would settle down at the table with drawing books and pencils and paints. The pictures that they produced seemed marvellous to Helen, far beyond anything that she could do. Although she had grown up in an artistic background, Helen was not very keen on drawing. Her grandfather was so good that it was scarcely worth her while. She preferred to dance.

What excellent paintings those children produced! The whole discipline of the nightly artwork appealed to Helen.

It was hard for Helen to criticise her mother in the slightest degree, but why had she not insisted that her daughter did some drawing each night? Then Helen might have been as good as the Dicksons.

Another wonderful thing that the Dickson parents had done was to dig a play area on the beach. They had used garden spades and, working all one morning, had produced a deep complex of trenches and ramparts, quite beyond what children could have achieved in execution or design. It was like something from World War 1.

The Dicksons were friendly with other holiday-making children and Helen was introduced and immediately accepted into a little gang of nine or ten. She could hardly believe it.

It was so *very like* a storybook

Because the trenches belonged to the Dicksons, Matt and Jimmy assumed command and at once placed Helen as second in command. She was sensitive enough to see that others thought this unfair, but the twins were all-powerful.

They expected an attack that morning from a rival gang of local children and Helen, always anxious to avoid violence, felt some dismay. Would she be expected to fight? Some of the troops were ordered to make tightly packed sand-balls for ammunition and Helen joined in with some enthusiasm for making the balls, but horror at the thought of throwing them at anyone.

Matthew soon removed her from this menial task and said they should inspect the defences. The raised walls of sand were collapsing slightly and Helen with her practical streak started to build them up and press them firmly into place with the flat of her hand. She enjoyed this occupation much more than the ammunition and she made a solid and decorative wall.

When the twins saw what she had done, their enthusiasm was unbounded.

"That's simply terrific. Look how strong those defences are, Jimmy."

"They're a lot better than when Mum and Dad did it. That's great Helen. How did you know what to do?"

"I think we'd better give you a special title for this work."

"What could we call her?"

Helen felt they were making a fuss over nothing, but it was pleasant to be such a success.

Her designation was never fixed because the rival gang came running along the beach, waving towels and sticks.

It was *terrifying*"

Luckily Derek Dickson came running from the house at the same time and the local children ran right past the trenches, along the beach and into town still shouting. Whether they would have fought or not, Helen never knew.

In the afternoon, to Helen's great relief, the local children had not reappeared. In order to make something exciting happen, the gang was split in two, with a twin in command of each section. Matt cleverly arranged for Helen to be in his section. Jimmy was to station his troops at a farm which was nearly half a mile away. They all went to reconnoitre the farm and the farmer's wife was welcoming and seemingly delighted to have fourteen children invade her premises. Just before Matt led his men back to the beach, Jimmy asked Helen if she would be a secret agent and bring information of Matt's plans to him. She immediately agreed. However she told Matt of this strategy and he decided that she could be a double agent. When the duties of a double agent were explained to her, she thought it a great idea and she spent the rest of that day rushing between the beach and the farm, hiding behind tractors and passing information, some of which was true and some false. It was one of the best games she had ever played and, though she had never told lies before, Helen enjoyed it and found she was very good at it.

There was no violence of any kind and the two sets of troops hardly did anything except lurk about the farm or get too hot in the sandy trenches. In fact it seemed to Helen that she was the only one having fun, for she was the one who made up the secret messages and rushed from one place to another to deliver them. It was as though she were the power which manipulated the whole game.

It was a superb day for Helen.

There were five weeks of days like this ahead.

Other days were spent in the woods where they would slide downhill on the pine-needles and Helen was so pleased to have knickers that matched her dress, as it was impossible to hide them in the wild slither.

In August Annie's parents arrived for a fortnight's holiday. Mrs Tait unlocked the extra rooms and the flat changed its character and became quite a spacious house.

Helen was delighted to find a piano in the newly revealed sitting room and brought her friends home to see it just as her grandparents were arriving. Helen played her three little pieces on the piano and Jean, the Dickson's cousin who was only six and wonderfully musical, played several jolly little tunes very fast. Helen was in awe of her skill and asked her to play repeatedly. Then the twins and Norma, who were all taking piano lessons, played various simple melodies. No one was as good as wee Jean. Then Annie came through to the sitting room,

"I think you kids could go out to play now. Grandma has a bit of a headache after the journey."

Helen felt ashamed. She had spent so much time in the Dickson house and had been made so welcome. Now, when she had something of interest to offer in return, they were all pushed out into the street! She knew it was her grandmother's fault. She had seen that she was in one of her moods as soon as she had arrived. She made up her mind to stay out of her grandma's way as much as possible.

The visit to Millport was not a success for the Mackays. Mary made continual disparaging remarks about the flat, the ugly town, the boredom and the weather, which was much wetter than the previous few weeks.

"I find it so clammy and miserable here, I don't know how you've stood it for the whole summer. What on earth possessed you to come here in the first place? It's got none of the beauty of Pittenweem. Even the people are plain-looking. And there's absolutely nothing to do! How I miss my garden too."

Her husband was more content and thought the Isle of Cumbrae delightful. John loved the Aquarium and went there several times. He also took long walks all over the island, sometimes sketching and often returning soaked by a sudden shower. It was on one of those times that Helen had walked in on him while he was changing and was shocked by the wrinkled and *empty* looking cheeks of a seventy-year-old male bottom. She was sad to realise that her beloved Drandad was such an old man.

However Helen immersed herself in her new storybook life and saw little of her grandparents.

After the Mackays had been there a few days, Annie received a wire from Bruce to say he was coming down the following Saturday and bringing a surprise for Helen.

Annie wished that he had not chosen to come when her parents were there. It was typical of Bruce to do the awkward thing. Poor Bruce, she thought, he was so often in the wrong. She had a good idea what the surprise would be. It would be a bicycle and she was almost positive that Helen would not be enthusiastic.

There was also the practical problem that she and Helen were nearing the end of their holiday and would be returning to Glasgow in less than two weeks. How would she manage the bike on the boat with all the luggage? Oh Bruce, Bruce, she thought, what problems you make for us all. And yet she felt kindly towards him. He had given her a few pounds extra for this holiday and here he was bringing a present. He really did mean well.

When Helen saw the telegram from her father, she made a face.

"Aren't you excited about the surprise, darling?"

"I wish that it was just you and me again. The house is different and too full and Daddy will make it fuller."

"Well, you know when it was just you and me, I didn't see much of you. You were always away with your friends and I was here by myself. Maybe it's nice for me to have my mother and father visiting. And Bruce, too."

Helen looked at her mother and felt a twinge of conscience. However, her common sense suggested that surely it could not be nice to work so hard and listen to Grandma complaining all the time. She thought her mother looked tired and she knew her father's noisy visits were not generally successful.

She wondered what her mother really thought, and she was sad because she knew she had neglected her mother that summer.

Annie wondered if she should mention that Bruce might bring a bike and prepare Helen to show some proper enthusiasm, but perhaps it wasn't a bike.

Bruce arrived on the Saturday, pushing a girl's bike. His cheeks were coloured bright by the windy voyage and he was in a happy mood, which as Helen had dreaded was also a noisy mood. What with his loud, sharp voice and his recurrent laugh and the awkward bike in the narrow hallway, it seemed as though five people had invaded the house.

Annie was proud of Helen because she appeared delighted to receive the bike and thanked her father, giving him a spontaneous hug. She looked at the bike and tried the bell and polished the leather seat with her hand and repeated her thanks several times. Then she went off to the Dickson house.

"Oh, the wee yin's pleased with her bike, isn't she!" Bruce asked rhetorically. His face was alive with delight as he looked around at the three others.

"Oh, she's over the moon, Bruce, that was very generous of you." Mary smiled graciously.

"Yes, a very nice present for a little girl. D'ye remember when I gave you the bike, my dear?" John was referring to the incident long ago when he had give the young Mary her first bicycle and caused a furore in her family. In those far-off days, a young woman's morals were in question if she received such an extravagant gift from a sweetheart.

"I think it's a lovely present and I know she's delighted, Bruce. I'm just a bit worried about getting it back to Glasgow on the boat and the train."

"Oh, it was nae bother at all! I just lifted it in and out the guard's van in the train and I just wheeled it on and off the boat too. Nae bother. It won't be any trouble, I promise you."

"I'll have quite a lot of other luggage ..."

"Oh, I found it very easy, Annie. Helen will be a good help to you. I'm a wee bit surprised that she didn't want to take it out for a run first thing. If I'd got a bike when I was that age, you wouldn't have prised me off the saddle till midnight!" and he laughed uproariously. "Where is Helen anyway?"

"She's off to see the Dickson children. They've practically adopted her, but she'll go for a ride on her new bike after supper, I expect."

Helen did have a short ride after supper. She was very wobbly again after four weeks away from a bicycle and she was relieved when her father offered to take her for a glass of lemonade in the café.

That night, Helen slept in the newly unlocked bedroom. It smelled strange and she cuddled Topsy to get warm. Poor Topsy had also been neglected that summer, but her dark little face smiled cheerfully. Helen determined to knit her a nice striped jumper as soon as she got back to Glasgow.

Annie and Bruce conducted an angry but whispered argument under the patchwork quilt in the recessed bed in the kitchen. Annie had again expressed doubts about her ability to bring the bicycle and the luggage home on boat and train. Bruce's mood had changed with the usual bewildering speed.

"I don't know why you brought so bloody much stuff down with you, if you can't manage to take it back again."

"I had to provide sheets and towels, Bruce. They're heavy and bulky. And warm clothes, too, in case it was a poor summer. I don't know why I have to justify myself. And you know that some days I'm not as strong as I would like to be. I didn't bring a bicycle down and I didn't think I'd have to take one back."

"It was hardly worth my while bringing the damned machine all this way if I've just to take it back again tomorrow. What a bloody carry-on. I don't believe the kid cares two hoots about the bike anyway. Any other kid would have been miles away on it as soon as she got it. Any other kid would have been as excited as all get out. She said she was pleased, but I can't understand a kid that doesn't jump on a new bike right away."

"I know I loved my bike, but Helen is her own wee person. A bike doesn't mean as much to her as it meant to you and me. You're not saying that you're disappointed in your child are you? She's a very imaginative kid."

"Don't know that that sort of thing should be too much encouraged. It can lead to problems."

"What on earth sort of problems do you mean? Are you suggesting that I should curtail her imaginative games? Perhaps a really good mother would force her to ride her bike around the streets all night. I taught the child to ride a bike, for heaven's sake, and it wasn't easy for me. I can't make her *enjoy* riding it!"

"Keep your voice down for God's sake. You're always telling me to be quiet. Your folk will think we're always rowing."

"And aren't we?" Then Annie wept, for she had hoped that their night under the patchwork quilt might have been romantic and loving.

Bruce left the next day with the bicycle and Helen felt enormous relief.

In the last week of their holidays, there was the concert which the gang put on at the farm. There was little rehearsal and it all seemed like great fun, until the problem arose about the landlady and the white dress. It was all because of the twins' determination that Helen must have first position in everything they did.

The lady who rented the villa to the Dicksons lived in a caravan in the back garden. She had a daughter, Julia, who was a little bit older than the twins and who sometimes joined their game. When the concert was being planned, Julia offered to sing, and the next day Julia's mother produced a long white satin frock that Julia would wear for her performance. The children all gasped when the dress was unfolded, as it was very splendid, with lace at the neck and a full swirling skirt. Julia looked quietly triumphant, Helen thought, at her obvious future success. Julia would be the star of the show!

Helen felt regretful, for she would have liked to dance and be the star of the show. She had not performed in public since her teddy bear dance when she was little. She knew she could do a spectacular dance in that dress, but philosophically she accepted that it was impossible. It was not her dress and of course Julia must wear it. The twins were not so accepting.

"Helen, I think you would look better in that dress than Julia. It's a dress for dancing and not for singing, I think." Said Jimmy.

"I agree. Anyone would look silly singing a song in that dress." Matt nodded his head like an old man.

"I don't mind really. It's her mummy's dress."

"Yes, but it's our concert. We can say who is wearing what in our concert."

"I think we'll ask if it's all right for Helen to wear the dress for a dance."

"We'll just go and ask now."

They came back in five minutes looking glum.

"She said the dress was for Julia and for no one else. She said it would be too big for you. I don't think so. Do you?"

Helen was worried to see how seriously the boys were taking this.

"It might be too big, I don't know. Just let Julia wear it. I don't mind."

The boys ignored Helen. Her status had now become the issue and their pride was at stake.

"Well, Matt, I don't know about you, but if she's not going to let Helen wear the dress, I don't think we should let Julia be in our concert."

"No, and it's probably some stupid song she's going to sing anyway."

They grumbled about it for an hour, until Helen was thoroughly bored and went home early for lunch. She was feeling guilty about it all, though not quite sure why.

That afternoon the boys told Julia that she could not be in

their concert unless Helen could wear the white dress. Poor Julia ran home in hysterics.

It made for a lot of unpleasantness with the landlady in the caravan. Derek and Nan were really angry and spoke sternly to the twins and to Helen about property and politeness and sharing. Helen felt ashamed at the reproaches and yet cross that she should be blamed for the twins' determination.

In spite of the preliminary problems, the concert was a success. It was held in the farmhouse garden and it was beautifully sunny.

Norma recited a long poem and her cousin Jean played the piano terribly well for such a little girl. The piano was inside the house of course and sounded faint and far away, but Jean played as loudly as she could.

The twins did cartwheels and somersaults and told some jokes.

Helen danced to the almost inaudible strains of a Strauss waltz played on a gramophone in the same room as the piano. She wore her voile dress which fluttered prettily and she danced in and out and around a weeping willow tree, using its graceful greenery and mysterious depths to disappear and appear again in a way that she felt was magical and romantic. She found the applause delightful.

Lastly, Julia appeared, dressed in a tartan skirt and white blouse, for her mother had diplomatically folded the dress away. Julia sang her song and was thunderously applauded. Jimmy muttered that was because lots of her friends were there. The song was rather silly and Julia was not a very good singer, but Helen did not mind because she could not sing well herself and she knew she was a good dancer.

Matt and Jimmy thought she was the best dancer in the world and told her so several times. They were very keen for her to dance again to a different record, but as no grown up seemed keen to put on the gramophone again, the concert ended. Helen would have danced again if there had been more music, but she suspected that her dance with the weeping willow was just about as good as she could have done in that particular garden.

Helen was on a constant seesaw about which of the twins she preferred. They each complimented, spoiled and petted her, and she could not make up her mind.

Matt was wonderful at drawing and wanted to be an architect when he grew up.

Jimmy wanted to be an analytical chemist like his dad and he had lots of potions and experiments on the shelves in the garden shed.

One day Jimmy shyly gave Helen a badly wrapped little parcel. Before she could open it, he told her that it was perfume that he had made himself, from rose petals.

She discarded the crushed brown paper and saw a small Bovril jar. When she removed the lid and sniffed deeply, there was certainly a smell of roses, rather old ones, with just a slight undertone of the original meaty contents of the jar.

It was delicious and she loved it and it swung the balance of her affections. How nice to have perfume specially made for her. No one else was likely to have such a present. Jimmy was really the twin she preferred, although she did like Matt very much too.

Forever after, the perfume of fading roses, or the sight of a brown glass Bovril jar or its savoury aroma, would immediately recreate that first successful and romantic summer of Helen's life.

It was the summer when Helen reigned supreme.

◊

The holiday ended and they sailed from Millport pier with the waving seaweed and the mussels glowing in the deep clear water, looking just as it had looked in June. The little town where Helen had been so happy seemed to rush away into the distance and, for the first time in her life, she experienced a real sense of loss of environment. Those two months in Millport had been an idyll which would always stand alone and special in Helen's childhood memories.

Momentarily, she thought of Topsy, tightly packed away in the suitcase. It would be a comfort to cuddle her just now, but she had hardly played with her all summer. Poor ignored Topsy had just sat in a chair for months. That made Helen feel sad and guilty. Was she too grown-up for toys now? And would she soon become too grown up for those long pretend thoughts at bedtime? Quite often this summer, she had chosen just to go to sleep. That was very sad. There was nothing, nothing, *nothing* nice to look forward to. She felt enveloped in sadness as though weighted down by a heavy cloak. It had been such a special summer, a summer that could never be repeated. Now she must return to that hot stuffy little room in the church hall and she knew that she did not want to. She hated the idea. She did not want to forgo her freedom to play in farmyards or forest or beach. She did not want to wear her despised gym tunic instead of her pretty dresses and matching knickers. She shuddered as she remembered black stockings and rubber suspenders attached to a liberty bodice. She loved her bare feet in the canvas shoes that she could whiten so easily, so sparkling snowy white that they made her brown feet look almost as dark as Topsy's feet. And she could run faster than most of the kids in her brown Clarks sandals though, because her feet had grown so much, Grandad had cut a piece of leather out at the toes, like a ladies' peep-toe shoe though not so neat. He had done that with his sharp penknife and, though she knew it was necessary, she had felt a pang as she watched him. Sad, sad, sad! The thought of her wasted sandals brought tears to her eyes. Now there would be a visit to Coplands and she would stand up on the X-ray machine to have her feet measured and feel stupid and conspicuous. It had all happened before and she hated it. The shoes would be black and stiff with overlong laces and thick leather soles. After the money was handed over, the saleslady would take a pair of scissors and make some deep scratches on the soles, smiling a horrible saleslady smile as she did so.

"That will stop you slipping, dear! The leather is so slippy when they're new, Madam."

How she loathed to see a new pair of shoes scratched and wasted like that before she had even worn them! Why did her mother allow it? They would not be slippy anyway, because they would have Philips' rubber soles put on them at the cobbler's. And she hated to be called 'dear' and she hated those black school shoes anyway and she hated everything.

She felt very like crying, but holding the wooden rail tightly and watching the water rush past the boat had a soothing effect. She cheered herself up by thinking hard about the friends that she had made that summer. What a nice family they were, with two parents and cousins and aunts and going to bed at the same time every night.

What adventures they had had. She had loved every minute. Perhaps she would see them quite soon again. She had listened to the two mothers talking over a last coffee together.

"Now, Annie, we mustn't lose touch again. It's just ridiculous that we've not seen each other all these years."

"Och, I know. It's daft isn't it?. Not as if Greenock is at the other end of the country. And the children get on so well, too. Helen's had a wonderful summer. I've hardly seen her. I suppose I could get a train down quite easily. Or why don't you come up to Glasgow, Nan? We could have lunch and go to the pictures afterwards."

"Not so easy for me to get away, really. There's the kids and there's ... mmm ... Derek's not always ... well he has problems at work you know ... I won't go into it just now, but ... nothing is ever as simple as it seems, is it. But you're not going back to Fife to stay, d'ye think?"

"I suppose we've moved back home permanently now, though I don't really know. Who knows? Need to see what Hitler's plans are. Just have to wait and see what happens."

"Yes, just have to wait and see, Annie. And I hope you start to feel better, soon."

"Aye, I hope so. I suppose I'm just a bit under the weather."

Helen was sure that they would visit Greenock very soon. She wondered if Greenock looked like Edinburgh, which was the only other city that she knew.

The breeze had an autumn coolness as it blew Helen's short fringe about. She watched the seagulls as they skimmed the waves or soared above her head. Though constantly changing height, the birds matched their speed perfectly to the boat's speed. She started to daydream of future visits to the unknown city of Greenock, where the Dicksons inhabited a house exactly like their Millport house, and Nan and her mother were best friends.

She imagined welcoming the twins and their little sister and cousin to her Glasgow flat and producing favourite books and games that they might share, then taking them for a walk around the streets and lanes of Hyndland. Then she became more ambitious and visualised the twins chasing up and down the steep wynds of Pittenweem. What amazing games they might all play there. Would they appreciate the wonderful swimming pool as much as she did? Swimming had not been a favourite occupation with the Dicksons, but Helen was happy to swim by herself. Pittenweem was so different from Millport, but with the companionship of the Dicksons, it would be great fun. With her very own friends, it would seem a fantastic place, she was sure.

Then when they were grown up, she and Jimmy might both go to the University up on the hill in order to follow in Mr Dickson's footsteps and become analytical chemists, though she was not absolutely sure what such a career entailed. Obviously one wore a white coat and worked in a laboratory. She felt quite familiar with the layout and paraphernalia of laboratories, having seen so many of them depicted in films. Laboratories had a mysterious fascination for her. All those differently shaped bottles and flasks with unknown, perhaps dangerous, dark liquids inside them. Often in films there was something sinister happening that she did not quite understand, not even by the time that the film was finished. Occasionally, they were all obviously good young men in white coats and they were very excited and happy at what was discovered in one of their little glass dishes. Then they laughed and slapped each other on the back. Sinister or jubilant, Helen was just as much in the dark. However she thought that she would enjoy working in a place like that, carefully measuring out powders, anxiously checking temperatures of bubbling mixtures or squinting upwards at a test tube filled with something important. It was a little bit like cooking, only more exciting. Helen certainly thought that she would like to work in a laboratory, it seemed so interesting and special and it must be well-paid, too. Money, or the lack of it, was not such an ever-present problem in the Dickson house as it was with her mother.

Helen thought of the years ahead and wondered if perhaps she would marry Jimmy or Matthew. The two little girls, Jean and Norma, would be bridesmaids and there would be no confetti at the wedding. She liked both boys very much and she knew they liked her. Jimmy was so funny and energetic, but Matthew was taller and such a terrific artist. It would be really difficult, almost impossible, for her to choose between the two boys.

But Helen never needed to make that choice, as she was never to meet any of the Dickson family again.

Unsettled Times

When they walked out of Central station, the Glasgow streets seemed gloomy and dirty after Millport and the city smelled bad after the long hot summer. By the time they reached Hyndland, it was bright and fresh and they felt quite cheerful. Annie and Helen appreciated the high ceilings and space of the flat. It was nice to be home amongst their own possessions, and the trundle and groanings of trams and other traffic in Clarence Drive seemed friendly and familiar. Annie was glad to be living on the ground floor again and to have her own bathroom and not to have the worry of the damned gas meter. That meter had been a constant, though unconscious strain on Annie. She did not trust it. She could smell a faint smell of gas each time it was fed another shilling. She was sure that halfway through cooking a meal sometime, she would find herself without a shilling for that hungry meter. Once or twice, she had a nightmare about it exploding. She knew it was irrational, but especially after the visits from Bruce and her parents, when she was so exhausted, she found her mind dwelling on the meter and imagining how much damage an explosion would create and wondering whether she and Helen would live through it.

Even physically, Annie felt better in Glasgow. The very relaxing climate of the Clyde had sapped her energy. At times she had been aware of being very low mentally and she worried about that. For the first time, she had seen Helen making a life away from her and, especially after the first few idyllic shared weeks, she had felt hurt and lonely that the only person who seemed to care about her deeply had become so involved with others. She admitted to herself that she was jealous of the paragon family that made Helen so happy. She was realist enough to know that in less than twenty years Helen would have grown up and married. The twins were no doubt just the first in a long line of young men who would absorb her daughter's interest. It was only natural, but it saddened her. She hoped that she would never be a selfish possessive mother, but perhaps these things happened without your knowledge. Her mother had always called her a very jealous child and perhaps she had been right.

Back in her own home Annie felt more positive, more creative. Helen became her own little girl again and the buzz of the city cheered her up. Annie got in touch with old friends, went to the Arlington Baths regularly and ordered another Readicut rug. She decided that she would see the doctor sometime, though not just yet, as she was obviously improving all the time.

One of the most positive people in her life at this time was her neighbour across the landing, Mrs. Walton. She had lived in the block almost as long as Annie. She was a widow of sixty, with a son and daughter in their thirties, who both still lived at home. The cheerful, kindly older woman was very fond of Annie, who was a similar age to her own unmarried daughter. She always made a great fuss of Helen.

"I don't think I'm ever going to get any grandchildren." Mrs Walton would joke, "But I've adopted wee Helen and she'll do just fine for me."

Then she would cuddle Helen and bring out the biscuit box and some small thing of interest, perhaps a box of shells, or a pack of cigarette cards or the miniature tea set which Helen adored. Then, most importantly, she would leave the child alone to play with them. Mrs Walton made no demands on Helen, except to enjoy herself. There were no requests to perform and no expectations of good behaviour. Helen appreciated this, without quite realising what it was that made Mrs Walton so different from other old ladies that she knew. Then this energetic little body would bustle about to make a cup of coffee for Annie and they would sit and chat for an hour. It seemed to Helen that Mrs Walton was much older than her own grandmother and more like a real grandma, with her white hair and flowered apron. She also noticed that her Mummy was much more talkative and laughing with Mrs Walton, than she was with Mary, her own mother. They would sometimes talk of the doctor and Helen could hear Mrs Walton encouraging Annie to 'find out what was wrong' because 'they could do so much for you these days'. And Annie always agreed and did come away from the house feeling more cheerful and with every intention of seeking medical advice. If Harry and Peggy, the younger Waltons, were around they too made a fuss of the child and were friendly to her mother. They were a very pleasant and happy family. Harry was tall and good-looking and when Helen had been younger, he would take her on his knee and compliment her on her dress or her pretty hair. She had always thought he was wonderful. While Harry petted the little girl, he usually managed to speak to her handsome mother and perhaps flirt a little too. It was the only time that Mrs Walton showed discomfort in Annie's presence. The older woman would break up the party by requiring some small chore from Harry or claiming that she must go out shopping immediately. For, although there was not much sign of him around, she knew that Annie did have a husband, and she did not want her son involved in any messy divorce proceedings.

After the idyllic summer with the Dicksons, Helen found Harry slightly less attractive. She realised for the first time that he was quite old, more than thirty. He was now in the army and when he took her on his knee as usual, his rough khaki uniform scratched the back of her legs and she decided that she was too old to be treated like a small child and politely jumped down and avoided sitting on his knee again. She still liked him, but she found herself shy and self-conscious when he complimented her.

Although there had been no real air attack so far, the sirens were regularly tested and occasionally they howled a warning of possible or imagined danger. In Pittenweem the siren had hardly seemed threatening. It had been located quite far away from their house and if the radio were playing or even if the fireside kettle were singing over a crackling fire, it was easy to miss hearing the siren completely. In Glasgow the siren was on the roof of the school, just across the road, and the incredibly loud and ear-splitting noise was terrifying and panic-striking. The overpowering shriek seemed to last for many minutes and almost paralysed Annie and Helen. Immediate attack from overhead planes seemed the only justification for such extremes of decibels.

The first time that they heard it they flew into each others' arms.

"Is that the siren, Mummy?" whispered Helen when the turbulent atmosphere had returned to normal.

"A bit louder than Pittenweem, isn't it!"

"It's horrible. Isn't it just as well that Grandma's not here!"

Mary had been in Pittenweem several times when the faint whine of the siren sounded and, to Annie's astonishment, her mother had been badly affected by it. Although Mary was a dom-

inating and assertive woman and had been known to show great
courage in moments of crisis, (like the time that she had kicked
the flaming paraffin heater out of the back door), the distant
scream had turned her to a cringing jelly. She had started to tremble at the first ominous note and although there seemed little
likelihood of an attack on Pittenweem, her trembling had not
stopped, until the all-clear sounded. It was quite irrational and
uncontrollable. One night, when Annie and Helen had gone early
to bed, she had joined them in her terror when the siren sounded.
She sat on the end of their bed and caused it to shake for nearly
an hour. At first Helen had been inclined to giggle, as the large
double bed shuddered continuously, but her mother had given
her a small secret pinch and a look full of meaning. Annie was
sorry for her mother and yet it was not unpleasant to find herself
morally stronger than this dominating woman. Which vassal is
not delighted to discover the chinks in their overlord's armour?

Helen, who liked to find reasons for everything, thought that
first day of the war must have made her grandmother extra
frightened and she had never recovered. Mary's uncharacteristic
tears and fears that day had made an indelible impression on her
granddaughter.

The Glasgow siren was not only more terrifying in itself, but
Annie knew that there was more real danger of attack and she
worried about what she should do for the best.

Mrs Walton also worried about the young woman next door.

"Now if the siren goes, Annie, you be sure and come through
to our house. It will be company for you and for us too. Don't
stay by yourself through an air raid. It's not good for your peace
of mind."

"You won't have a sing-song, will you?"

They both laughed. Neither of them could stand the tuneless
renderings of sentimental First World War songs that seemed to
be so popular in the public shelters.

"No, no, Annie. No long, long roads to Tipperary or only girls
in the world. Just a cup of coffee and a few baurs."

"That's very good of you. We'll be there if it's not too late."

"Doesn't matter what time it is, three in the morning or any
time. Gerry won't choose a convenient time. You just chap at the
door any time at all. I'll be listening for you."

This sounded like fun to Helen. Fancy visiting the Waltons in the middle of the night! What would they do? Would they all sleep in the same bed? Or would they just stay in the kitchen and chat as usual. She hoped that the siren would go off that very night!

Suddenly a horrible thought struck Helen. Her all-in-one sleeping suit had a split at the back for hygienic convenience and the unfastened split gaped in a very immodest way. This had never worried her in her own home, but it was a disastrous garment for visiting. *Especially if Harry was there.* She had three of these sleeping suits, all indecent, and no other night attire. They were a family who dressed immediately on rising and Helen did not possess a dressing gown. She blushed deeply as she imagined the humiliating scene. Would she be able to hold the fabric together? Or perhaps keep her back hidden from Harry at all times. That would be awkward and impossible. It was a constant worry for the child and obsessed her when she went to bed each night. The old embarrassing dreams returned. Now, as well as Coplands lift, she found herself in various other places, the school, the swimming baths, the cinema and always trying, unsuccessfully, to pull the inadequate vest down over her bare bum.

Helen learned that it is silly to worry too much, for things seldom turn out the way that you expect. The siren always screamed before bedtime in the next few weeks and visits to the Waltons were fully clothed.

Then, surprisingly, the dreaded shopping for shoes turned out to be a very happy occasion The X-ray machine was out of order, and because of wartime restrictions there were no school shoes available. Instead, some very elegant wedge-heeled shoes, in finest tan leather were produced. Helen could not believe her eyes. They were like ladies' shoes! She could tell that her mother was not enthusiastic but she must have shoes for school. They were paid for and she wore them straight away, although her incongruous white rayon socks meant the effect was not perfect.

School was not as expected either, because High School no longer held classes in the church hall. Helen must now travel into the city to the complex and dilapidated building in Garnethill which her mother had attended as a child. Before the war had started, there had been talk of building a new school. Indeed there had been talk of a new school when Annie was a pupil thirty years previously, but nothing had materialised. Strangely, parents from all over the city and its environs, were willing to pay fees and send their daughters to this inadequate and dangerous building for their education.

To Helen it seemed like the most enormous rambling building that she had ever seen, with long flights of stairs that crisscrossed confusingly and a layout that she felt she would never comprehend. As a junior she saw only glimpses of the gloomy building when they were marched through everlasting corridors to the Assembly Hall for prayers. Sometimes they were taken through the playground and reached the hall by some other route that bamboozled her completely. She almost felt that the stuffy room in the church hall would have been better after all.

The walls of the big chilly classroom were hung with ragged old maps which looked interesting, but which were never used. The only thing that Helen enjoyed and remembered about that school in later years was the knitting class, which was held downstairs in a room that, as well as other strange chemical aromas, had the same slight gassy smell as the Millport kitchen. It was the science laboratory and was situated at the foot of a long flight of stairs, near one of the many doors leading to the playground. Just outside this door, a brick air raid shelter had been hurriedly built, when war was declared. This unlit shelter was a dark and fearsome cavern with a dank smell. It was never used for its purpose while Helen attended the school. At break-time, some of the braver girls would venture a few yards into the shelter, clutching each other's arms and giggling, then come rushing out with screams and laughter.

In the laboratory were glass-fronted cupboards with shelves crowded with vari-coloured bottles and jars. Dainty golden scales were housed in glass boxes. It all looked rather like a shop. The girls sat on wobbly wooden stools around large wooden tables which were fixed to the floor. In the middle of each table four tiny taps exerted a mysterious fascination. Every week, the teacher spent the first ten minutes of the lesson reminding them that *they must never touch* the taps.

Helen added the subtle importance of smell to her mental recreation of a laboratory and she thought of knitting class as quite an adventure.

The girls were given a choice of what they would like to knit. A book of patterns and various kinds of wool were produced and poured over. Helen, taking her usual delight in the large multi-coloured hanks and feeling quite an expert, chose a pattern for slippers and some very soft camel hair wool. She did not know whether it was really wool from a camel or not and she did not want to seem foolish by asking. She could still remember riding on a camel in Edinburgh Zoo, when she was four. When she had touched the hump, it had been hard and rough, feeling very much like a coconut. It seemed unlikely that a camel would produce such soft wool as this.

The teacher had red hair and spoke in a clipped, affected voice that Helen immediately disliked.

"Oh, slippers! Did you learn knitting in your last school, dear?"

"Yes."

"Do you think you will be able to follow this pattern, Helen? It is quite complicated."

"I knitted myself a cardigan last year."

To Helen, this was just a simple statement of fact. Shyness muffled her voice and the teacher asked her to repeat what she had said. Then the red-haired teacher smiled broadly,

"A *cardigan*, dear? When you were *seven*?"

"Yes. Mummy helped me to sew it up."

"Oh well, you'll have no trouble with slippers then ... dear."

The teacher's smile had faded and Helen realised that she *did not believe her*. Helen gritted her teeth and determined to wear her cardigan next week.

The following week, however, a different teacher took the knitting class and Helen never saw the doubting lady again. She was glad about that.

As they were not allowed to take their knitting home with them, Helen worked hard in school every Tuesday and finished her first slipper in six weeks. She fantasised about wearing her beautiful soft slippers, though truthfully it looked terribly big.. By the ninth week, Helen was slowing down and only one third of the second slipper was completed.

On Friday of that week, Annie broke the news to Helen that they were returning to Pittenweem the following day. It seemed very sudden and everything was packed in a great rush. Helen did not quite understand why they were going back, whether the long-threatened bombing was about to start, or perhaps her parents were angry with each other again. She was quite happy to leave the High School for the last nine weeks had been a strain and she had forgotten much of the unpleasant side of Pittenweem school, in the months since she had left.

Packing up was exciting and she looked forward to seeing the sea again, although it was now November and getting cold. She thought of last winter when the fierce waves were beating against the harbour wall and the spray had leapt as high into the air as a house. She had never seen anything like it in her life before, so beautiful and yet so terrifying. She shuddered as she remembered the scene, and the horrible urge she had felt to throw her darling Topsy into the wild boiling water, which was such a terrible, terrible thought!

For Years to Come

The train arrived in Pittenweem at four-thirty and it was a dark and freezing walk from the station. Annie walked slowly and though it was less than half a mile, it seemed interminable because it was so cold. The wind blew in their faces and Helen had never felt so miserable in all her life. It was a great relief when they opened the stiff front door and stepped into the house and out of the blasting wind. But the house was icy and draughts were blowing through every crack and crevice. Annie groped her way along the lobby and into the sitting room, carefully pulling the curtains before lighting the gas lamp on the mantelpiece. She was thankful not to worry about feeding a meter. Then she knelt and put a match to the fire, which was already set. The flame soon disappeared and only smoke curled slowly from the piled sticks. It was too optimistic to expect it to burn immediately. The whole house felt damp as well as cold and the fire did not kindle until Annie's fourth attempt. Helen had forgotten how difficult it was to live without electricity. In Glasgow they could have had the radiator glowing immediately and would soon be cosy and eating tartan toast.

The gas jet made quite a loud hissing and Helen had forgotten about that. It was a friendly noise.

"The gas will help to warm this wee room up a bit, but don't take your coat or hat off yet, Helen. Go and bring me the pillows and the blankets from the bed."

Helen stood for a moment, unsure of the reason for this strange request.

"Go on! I'll need to air them at the fire. Hurry, please."

Helen dragged the blankets through the house. It was nice to be doing something and she felt a bit warmer as she ran about.

Eventually the fire blazed up and with the gaslight burning, the small sitting room was not quite so cold, although the draughts still attacked from all sides. Annie had brought some soup in a jar and when that was heated they ate it, still wearing their outdoor clothes. Helen even kept her gloves on. The paraffin heater was lighted in the bedroom and it seemed as though it might be possible to sleep in the house that night after all. Annie shivered at the mournful sound of the wind howling at the back door and when she washed her hands, the water felt like liquid ice.

"Brrrr that water is *painful* it is so cold!"

"I'd forgotten Pittenweem was so awful cold." said Helen.

"Yes, it's a bit more like the Arctic than Glasgow. We'll just have to start wearing extra clothes. You know, I think we shouldn't go into that bed until it's been properly aired. Let's just go up to the pictures while everything thaws out here. I've no idea what's on, but it'll be warmer there than this house. I wouldn't like us to sleep in a damp bed. Damp beds can affect you for years to come, you know."

That phrase *for years to come* was new to Helen and it seemed particularly serious and ominous.

She was to remember it clearly always, for that night she *was* affected for years to come, not by the damp bed, but by the film that they saw.

It was called "Frankenstein" and it was the first horror movie that she had ever watched. She was transfixed by the whole concept of the ungainly, inhuman monster in its rough sheepskin jerkin. As she watched its lumbering struggles through the mist-shrouded forest and against the eerie background of the ramshackle castle, her imaginative mind laid down images which would haunt and terrify her for the next eight years.

She did not mention her fears to her mother, although she stayed very close to her on the short, pitch-black walk home.

"Well, I didn't think much of that film at all, did you? Lot of rubbish, I would say. Eh? Don't you think so, my wee lamb? Anyway we were nice and warm for a couple of hours and the house should be a bit cosier now."

Helen grunted noncommittally, but the blood was frozen in her veins and might never flow warmly again, for that terrible film had completely changed her life. Where previously she had had a few unformed and easily dispelled night fears, she now had a horror which would constantly materialise in darkness, assuming the massive shape of the monster in his sheepskin jerkin and walking with his stiff steps ... *nearer and nearer*.

Because of the stringent blackout regulations, Annie had heavily curtained the sitting room and the downstairs bedroom.

No window in the rest of the house was adequately covered, which meant that most of the house was left in darkness, for any light used in those other rooms would be visible from the street and incur the wrath of the ARP warden. Nobody wanted to hear the dreaded rattle at the door and the shout of,

"Ye're shown a licht there! Pit oot that licht or ye'll get a fine!"

As Annie prided herself on having excellent night vision and Helen followed her example, usually the reflection from the sky and the sea gave enough light to make a sandwich or boil a kettle. It was also possible to brush your teeth and use the lavatory last thing at night with the glimmer from outside. This had seemed a perfectly sensible arrangement the previous winter but now, with her new fears, Helen found that the journey upstairs to the bathroom at night was almost more than she could deal with. Of course she went upstairs by herself. At nearly nine, she was much too big a girl to need her mother with her and she would never have thought of asking for company. Twelve stairs led up to the yard-square landing. The bathroom lay directly ahead, while a bedroom door opened to right and to left. Overhead, a never-used trapdoor to the attic was set into the ceiling. Each night, as Helen sat terror-struck on the WC, she would imagine the various ways that the monster might approach her. Whichever way It came, It would cut off her escape route to the safety of her mother in the lighted room downstairs. The monster might be pacing ponderously around the large bedroom before stepping on to the landing, just as she was about to go downstairs. Or It might drop down heavily from the trapdoor, Helen could hear the thump through the banging of her heart and she could feel the vibration of the floorboards through the soles of her feet. Then, after a moment of waiting just outside the bathroom, with Its bulk filling the small space, the inhuman beast would walk in Its terrifying, lop-sided way, into the smaller bedroom where a *sheepskin rug* lay beside the bed. The scarcely breathing Helen could clearly visualise the monster, as It picked up this rug and slung it round Its shoulders ... *then It would turn awkwardly and come back towards the bathroom for her ...*

At this point the trembling child would jump to her feet, pull the chain and rush down the stairs in an agony of terror. Somehow Annie, loving and sensitive mother that she was, seemed strangely unaware of Helen's distress. Sometimes she would comment on how quick Helen was.

"My, you're a speedy wee creature! You're down those stairs before the plug has properly pulled. Are you trying to break some record?"

But Helen said nothing.

Sometimes if Annie were already in bed, she would comment on how Helen was shivering when she jumped in beside her mother.

"You must be frozen, my pet. Cuddle up and I'll get you warm, my wee love."

In no time at all, Helen would be very warm. Annie often wondered how she would have tholed those bitter winter nights without Helen's little body in the bed. The child was like a small machine that generated heat.

Whether from pride or from a fear of being laughed at, Helen never spoke to her mother or to anyone else about the monster. She knew that there was no monster and she felt stupid to be so overpowered by her terrors, but she could not control her imagination and for years she suffered and felt ashamed of herself for suffering. Even in daylight, she shivered if she heard the word 'monster' or Boris Karloff, the name of the actor who had played the monster.

No other film was ever to affect her so strongly again.

A lot of Annie's energies were required to keep the house warm that cold winter of 1940-41. It seemed cruel that as well as the enforced food shortages, the weather should also be so severe. The pretty summer holiday house without electricity, without carpets or heavy curtains, without bath or hot water supply, was inadequate for a normal winter and almost impossible for a bad one. Besides, the house could never be quite the same to Annie again, after the scenes she had witnessed in the Forth at the beginning of the year.

Each night before sleeping, Annie winced at the strange pin-prickings in her legs and re-lived that sea-battle in her mind, and wondered if there would be further violence enacted before her eyes or unknown pains ravaging her body. Both horrors seemed very likely.

She had moved about from house to house so much this year that she felt displaced and there was nowhere that was home.

Bruce was talking about renting out the Hyndland flat, as there was such a shortage of housing. Of course it was costing money as it lay empty, money that could ill be spared. She was unwilling to have strangers using her possessions, but that seemed a very petty attitude in the face of what was happening in the world and she determined not to think of it.

Bruce would not be called up, because his work was vital to the war effort. That was something to be very thankful for. Annie tried to count her other blessings. Lots of children had been evacuated and were living far away from their mothers, while she had her wee Helen with her. She was lucky and she tried to appreciate it. She was lucky to have this house to come to, though it *was* so damnably cold.

Perhaps Bruce would lock everything of value safely in a cupboard in her Hyndland flat, or perhaps these strangers would be careful of all her small treasures.

She smiled ironically to herself at the unlikelihood of either possibility.

To stop herself thinking along these lines before going to sleep, she would plan something to do the next day. Perhaps bake a cake with the new dried egg powder that everyone said was just as good as the real thing. You were advised to measure it carefully and mix it with the exact amount of water ... that was called reconstituting the egg ... such a big word for a simple procedure. Or perhaps it would be nice to give the sitting room walls a coat of bright yellow distemper ... as long as she did not tire herself too much ... she could soon paint a room with such a low ceiling and perhaps she would use a colour similar to reconstituted egg ... perhaps she could use reconstituted egg ... she wakened up with a jerk at such a crazy idea ... the important thing was to keep cheerful and as well as possible, for Helen's sake.

◊

Annie painted the sitting room yellow. She found it quite tiring, but the bright colour lifted her spirits wonderfully.

Next she wrote to Bruce about her electric sewing machine, which was of course no use in Pittenweem. She had heard of an electric machine being converted and having a handle fitted. Could this be done for her? And if so, could he see about it please and send it through on the train?

A unexpectedly prompt reply came from Bruce. The machine would arrive in Pittenweem on Saturday, with a handle fitted. Bruce could not have pleased her more. She was delighted and longed for it to arrive. Somehow she felt that sewing helped her more than knitting did. She had regretfully left her Readicut rug in Glasgow as too bulky to carry on the train.

Annie visited Murray's, the large draper's shop in the High Street, which sold everything from overcoats to linoleum, top hats to blankets, long underwear for fishermen to fine angora wool and embroidery threads. There she chose some soft brown woollen fabric and a pattern for a dress for Helen, which was cut out and ready to sew when Archie the porter delivered the heavy box on Saturday.

Bruce had not visited them yet, as he was finding it difficult to acquire the special travel permit or buy petrol. He was also involved in trying to let the flat in Clarence Drive. He wanted to get the 'right sort of tenants', he said, but had not yet succeeded.

He arrived on a Saturday in the second week of December, bringing a leg of lamb, half a dozen eggs, a pound of butter and a large jar of jam as well as other parcels.

"This is all marvellous, Bruce! Christmas has come early! I hope this is not what you call the Black Market."

Helen listened carefully. What on earth was the black market? She considered a few possibilities, but gave up.

"Oh, no, no. Just a few gifts from good friends, y'know. Alastair has a branch in Maryhill Road you know, and they don't go in much for roasts there .There's sausages and bacon and a bit of black pudding, too and I wouldn't mind if you got the frying pan on soon, m'dear. Hungry work, driving. That other stuff is from a bloke I know in the Gallowgate."

Her father seemed to fill the little house with his loud voice, his laughter and his quick tramping from room to room. He did not sit down until his meal was ready. When he went upstairs to the bathroom, he made a loud thump on every stair, then slammed the door with a crash. Even the water from the cistern flowed out with more energy and noise when he pulled the plug, and his footsteps were even louder when he galloped downstairs. He smelled strongly of cigarettes and he lit one as he watched Annie cook. Helen saw the smoke pour from his nose and mouth and drift upwards to the low ceiling. He seemed to produce more smoke than her grandmother did. Could that be possible, she wondered?

When the meal was ready he gazed at it strangely for a moment or two. His cheeks were very red and shiny, Helen watched him and wondered if he did not like the look of the food. Then he coughed loudly, but politely behind his hand, and started to eat his meal with terrific relish, taking large mouthfuls and stopping at intervals to lick his moustache, or wipe it with the back of his hand. He ate five rolls with the meal. Helen counted them. Then he asked for the jam and had a sixth.

While she would not have called him bad-mannered, he did eat in a very different way from her mother and grandparents. He seemed to be so very hungry, starving almost.

Helen had been looking forward to his visit for weeks, but now, when he was actually here, she did not feel as happy as she had thought she would. She had forgotten how overpowering his presence was. When he gazed at her mother with the same sort of hungry look that he had given the plate of food, Helen found herself longing for the next day, when she would wave goodbye to him. It was very confusing.

Occasionally he turned his hungry glare on Helen and she felt very uncomfortable, almost angry.

He asked her questions too, strange questions to which she did not know the answer. He hardly seemed to expect a reply, for he often turned to her mother immediately and asked some other question. Helen noticed that her mother often did not give an answer either. But her mother looked quite pleased and happy and pretty. Helen was glad about that, because her mother often spoke of Bruce in an irritated or sad, disappointed way.

Bruce suggested a quick trip to St Andrews and Annie was delighted.

"We might have a wee treat in an icecream cafe, Tuppeny. What d'ye like to have?"

"Horlicks."

"Horlicks! That sounds a bit boring, but whatever you say, Nellie old girl."

He occasionally used this form of her name. Although Helen's face was completely expressionless, she churned with inner fury and Annie looked at her nervously, for she knew well how she felt.

Annie had been thinking that Helen might have started music lessons by this time, if she had been in Glasgow. She herself had been much younger when she started to study music. As there was no piano in Pittenweem, perhaps Helen could start with a recorder and learn some elementary theory.

At Annie's request, they went to the music shop first. Helen was intrigued. It was like no other shop that she had ever seen. Her father asked the young man behind the counter,

"We're looking for a, what is it ye call it Annie?"

"A recorder, a descant recorder and a beginner's book of instruction, too."

Helen wondered what this was all about, for Annie had not discussed it with her.

When the recorder was brought, Bruce started asking questions.

"So you blow into this, do you?"

"Yes, sir."

"And which end is it you blow? And what about all these wee holes?"

"The instructions are in the book, sir. It's fairly simple and straightforward."

"Is it easy enough for a child to start playing?" Annie asked.

Helen realised with a little thrill that it must be for her. Bruce spoke again,

"Now is it a wee bit like a mouth organ? Remember that awful clever wee joker that played the mouth organ, he was a wee Jew boy, what was his name, Annie?"

"Larry Adler, but this isn't a bit like a mouth organ, Bruce."

"Oh, he was great that wee fellow, if she could learn to play a mouth organ like that she'd be doing well, the wee yin. Then I saw another bloke a few weeks ago at the Alhambra. An enormous fat guy he was, Teddy something or other, and he was playing ... I don't know what it was he was playing, but it made a great sound. It was like a table and he hit it with wee sticks. Boy! could he move fast, though he was about five stone overweight. What a marvellous musician he was. An absolute elephant of a man, but light on his feet. Big fat people often are light on their feet, aren't they? What sort of instrument would that be that he was playing, d'ye think?"

"I expect it would be a xylophone, sir."

"And he was hitting it with wee sticks, sometimes two in each hand. Would that be the same thing, whatever you called it. What was it again?"

"A xylophone."

Bruce laughed,

"Damned funny name, isn't it. D'ye have one in the shop?"

"Yes, sir, we have various prices and sizes. They're very popular just now. Was it for yourself you wanted it?"

Bruce exploded with laughter,

"No, no. That's not quite my style. It's for the kid. D'ye have you one of those what-d'ye me-call-its suitable for a kid this age? And Helen, if I get this for you, ye'll need to get an awful lot fatter, to play it as well as that chap did! Eat up yer dinner every day."

Helen could hardly believe her ears. She was getting *two* musical instruments bought for her and it wasn't even her birthday.

They left the shop and went straight home, as Helen was very anxious to try out the instruments.

Sitting in the back of the car, she had mixed feelings. How kind her father had been to buy these things for her, yet she had felt very embarrassed in the shop. His loud voice and his questions were unlike the way that other people acted in shops. Why *did* he act like that? It was funny to feel angry with someone that you should feel gratitude towards.

Annie was very pleased that Bruce had bought the recorder and the music, for that had been her idea. He could be so very generous sometimes.

Back home, after a cup of coffee and two more rolls, Bruce asked Helen,

"And how's your wee pal Geraldine doing, Tuppenny?"

Helen had to think for a moment.

"It's Josephine. My friend's name is Josephine."

"Oh yes, of course, Josephine. Now she's the postmaster's daughter, isn't she?"

"She's the stationmaster's daughter."

"Is she, be jabers. Well I'll be jiggered. I could have sworn she was the postmaster's daughter. Annie, did you not tell me ...? Maybe not. So you have fine times together do you, you and your wee friend ... Josephine, is it?"

But later that afternoon when Josephine came to play, he called her Clementine several times, roaring and laughing when he was corrected. Helen would learn that Bruce would always make a point of calling her friends by the wrong name. It was his way of making fun but she never learned to appreciate it.

In order to show her gratitude to Bruce for sending her sewing machine so promptly, Annie had rushed to have Helen's new dress finished for her father's visit. She had worked hard and was delighted with the result. It was comfortable, warm and unusual. Annie had allowed Helen to stay up quite late the previous week and turn the sewing machine handle for her. At first Helen found it nerve-racking to deal with such a grown-up machine and was very cautious. However her mother was sure she could do it and encouraged her. It was nice to feel that she was helping to make her own dress.

"This is an easy bit and you can go just a wee bit faster now." Then Annie would warn her to slow down, then,

"STOP" and Annie would hold up her hand like a policeman and Helen would stop immediately.

"My you're fairly getting the hang of it. What a help you are. We'll have this dress done in no time at all. Now this is a tricky bit, so just go gently" and Helen would go very gently, then,

"STOP"

"You're *great* at stopping. Now have a wee rest, while I pin these bits together.

It was a wonderful game and Helen felt proud of her quick reactions and pleased to be helping her mother as well as getting a new dress. Annie was delighted to be sewing again and with her daughter's help, it was almost as easy as with the electricity. It was an amusing way to follow the constant advice of the government, *to save electricity*. Perhaps she should send this tip to the radio doctor?

WAYS OF SAVING ELECTRICITY.

Select Committee Recommendation.

Less Broadcasting Suggested.

Valuable economies might well be secured if it were found practicable to close down home broadcasting at an earlier hour.

Glasgow Herald 1st Nov 1940

The night before Bruce's arrival, Annie had stayed up very late to appliqué a yoke of abstract shapes in felt around the neck of the dress. She had seen some smart and artistic felt decoration in a magazine, and had found some rich coloured felt in St Andrews. She herself was pleased with the result. Helen was delighted, proud of her dress and her clever Mummy. No doubt there would be cheeky remarks from her classmates, for nobody wore anything like that, but her clothes were always different and she was getting used to their teasing. She ignored their ignorance with a superior dignity which was unlikely to endear her to them. She realised this. She would always choose to please her mother rather than those uncouth children. Her own special friends, Josephine, Ina and Jean, would admire the dress properly.

She felt the dress was very like something Shirley Temple might wear. Shirley still represented a luxurious fairytale existence, far superior to her own workaday world.

Helen confidently expected that her father would admire her new dress, for had they not finished it specially for his visit? On Sunday, Helen wore her new brown dress.

"Now what is that ye've got round your neck, Tuppenny? Is that oranges? I've never seen a dress like that, Annie"

He pronounced her mother's name in a quick sharp way that changed it somehow, and he seemed to make her own name sound more like Eln, than the two sounds of Helen.

"Now is this the latest fashion? Is this what ye've made on the machine Annie? You've been very speedy. I think it looks like a string of oranges round your neck. Is that what it's meant to be, Tuppenny? A string of oranges, is it? It suits you fine. D'ye like it fine yerself, Tuppenny? It's unusual, right enough, but it suits her, doesn't it Annie. You've certainly been quick making it. Are you pleased with your machine? I'm glad I was able to do that for you. Is it working well? A bit slower without the electricity, I bet. Oh, is wee Helen helping you? Ca'in' the handle round is she? That's a good girl, that's good. Everyone should help their mother."

As he spoke, his unblinking eyes seemed to pierce through Helen's head and he continuously shrugged his shoulders and jingled the loose change in his pocket. His large white teeth shone out from under his square, black moustache.

Helen sat self-conscious and unsmiling. His scrutiny angered and paralysed her. She wished that he would stop talking about her. His comments on her dress did not please her. They did not sound like compliments.

She wished he would shut up altogether.

He never stopped talking. He spoke about things which did not interest her, people that she did not know, boring games of golf and the club where the Home Guard met each night and drank so many bottles of whisky. When her mother would start to tell of some small adventure they had had, she was continuously interrupted by his unnecessary questions, questions which seemed to have nothing to do with the story that was being related. Helen found it very strange and unbearably irritating and she could see her mother felt the same. Helen enjoyed listening to her mother tell about their life in Pittenweem. She made it interesting and funny. Did her father not want to know any of the things that they had been doing, or laugh at the things that they had laughed at? Eventually Annie would give up the struggle and let him take over again.

He talked even more than her grandmother did! Helen could hardly believe it.

She felt guilty about how little she liked him. Surely it was wrong to dislike your Daddy?

She was disappointed that he seemed to be so uninterested in what she did. Yet she felt uncomfortable when he did pay her attention and she knew that was unreasonable. What did she want exactly? Without realising it, she was experiencing the same confusing feelings about Bruce as her mother did.

She wished the weekend was over and he was back in Glasgow, leaving them alone in their quiet, happy life.

She could see her mother was becoming less friendly to him too.

She hoped that one of the big shouting matches would not happen this weekend.

If only he would just go away.

He did leave quite early on Sunday afternoon and she was relieved that her parents seemed friendly enough when he left. She had not heard any raised voices the previous night.

The peacefulness of the house after he had gone, was wonderful to Helen.

"Y'know, you should really try to be a bit nicer to your father, Helen. He does his best and he's very fond of you."

Her mother did not sound angry, just very tired.

On the Saturday night, because of Helen's tearful determination to sleep with her mother as usual, Bruce had slept alone in the small bedroom upstairs.

When Annie was tidying up after his departure she saw something glinting in the thick pile of the sheepskin rug. It was a florin. She picked up the rug and shook it and seventeen and sixpence in silver and coppers dropped noisily on to the lino! It was more than two weeks' housekeeping money, quite a little fortune. It must have fallen from Bruce's trouser pockets when he carelessly undressed. At first Annie was pleased that her husband's cavalier attitude to his money had benefitted her for a change. Then she worried that he would be short of cash before he reached Glasgow. Then she rationalised that if he had not missed it from his pockets, he could not need it so very much.

Two hours later, she suddenly blushed. It had occurred to her that the money by the bedside seemed like payment for that brief draughty coupling on the hearthrug, which had taken place after Helen had finally been settled in bed.

She put this thought away and remembered how often she was astonished at Bruce's extravagance and open-handedness with tips. He obviously had an amount of money at his fingertips that she knew nothing about. For her, every penny of her allowance was important and there were few unexpected treats or luxurious purchases in her life. However as he earned the money, he had the right to spend it, she supposed.

Later she described her treasure trove to Helen.

"We'll be able to have a nice treat. Perhaps we'll go to St Andrews on Saturday and buy you a book. Would you like that, my wee jewel? What a lucky sheepskin rug, isn't it?"

But for Helen, the sheepskin rug could never be anything but a garment for the terrifying monster.

Helen worked her way diligently through the exercises and simple tunes in her beginner's book. She found the tunes quite boring. As she went further on, they became more difficult to play but remained boring. She had always been able to pick out tunes by ear on the piano, and she discovered she could do this on the recorder too. This made it a bit more fun and for the next two years she spent an hour playing her recorder each evening. She would practice the exercises and tunes in the book first, then play her own choice of popular songs. Her mother's favourite was "Dearly Beloved" and Helen always finished with that one. The xylophone was fun too. Annie was happy to hear how much use Helen made of these two instruments, and to know that she was at least learning the rudiments of music.

Exhortations to save for the War Effort were everywhere, in newspapers, on the the wireless and on printed posters. The last were hung in every shop and public building urging the population to save money, save fuel, save paper, save tins. Saving had become a mania in the land. Helen discovered one little way that she might help. She decided that each sheet of toilet paper could easily be quartered and still remain efficient. After carefully folding it twice, she tore each sheet into four pieces and made a little secret stash in a corner of the bathroom for her own use. She tried not to use more than three pieces each day, which meant that a small surplus grew and was there for emergencies. She continued the practice until she left Pittenweem some years later, and told no one of this small personal contribution to the war.

By the third week of December there was deep snow on the ground. Everyone kept exclaiming how unusual it was and how cold it was, but the draughty little house was in fact warmer with all the gaps and crevices sealed up by the dry powdery snow.

One morning when Helen collected the milk from the front door, the two bottles were practically hidden in a snowdrift. She thought they looked like little birds peeping out of a white nest. The milk had frozen and expanded and the cardboard tops were pushed up an inch or so and balanced precariously on a column of frozen milk. Helen had a pleasant memory of the ice cream that she had eaten before the war and thought this might taste the same, but she was disappointed for it was watery and tasted only like ice.

By half past four, it was dark as night and shopping was exciting. Shops which looked closed and forbidding from the outside, exploded into brilliance when you walked inside. The chemist's shop was particularly bright and festive. It also sold newspapers and sweets and had paper chains festooned around the walls.

The chemist was always joking and asking riddles and

knock-knock stories. Helen liked him but not everyone enjoyed his jokes. He had lost a customer called Mrs Cunningham to the other chemist in town when he had playfully called her Mrs Flybacon. He had also once addressed Annie as Mrs Sorefooting, but Annie had looked at him sternly and coldly and he had apologised and explained that he meant no offence.

Annie had chuckled all the way home about it. Helen suspected she was laughing at the dismayed look on his face, rather than his joke. Anyway her mother was pretty often making jokes like that herself.

At nearly nine years old, Helen had still not quite placed Santa Claus. Of course she was well aware that there was no fat old man in a red coat, struggling down the chimney. That was a stupid idea. She was not a curious child and had no siblings with whom to discuss the problem. She had never come across hidden presents in her house, or even looked for them. She was not close to the children at school and would not have credited them with truthfulness anyway. They were always talking rubbish. But because she trusted her mother so implicitly, it had never occurred to her that her parents were the providers of Christmas toys and other delights. Her parents always seemed to be very hard up. The annual treasure trove was a mystery, a very wonderful one. A possible explanation that she had turned over in her mind, was that the big department stores like Coplands sent out presents to children as a sort of advertisement. It would cost them a lot of money and it was not an entirely satisfying explanation, but it was the best that she could come up with.

There as usual, at the foot of the bed on Christmas morning, was the lumpy pillow slip. Socks were not considered as receptacles for the Christmas bounty, because what toy or book would ever go into a sock?

First of all Annie got out of bed and lit the paraffin heater. That was unusual, for it was normally only used at night time. Then the unwrapping of the presents began. It was so exciting and charming. There was a large book called The Triumph Annual. It was full of school and adventure stories, poems and puzzles and was just the sort of book Helen liked. There were other books, a pair of very nice mittens and a box of paints. There was a box of pretend chocolates from the Joke Shop. They looked terribly realistic, but there was a secret button underneath and as your friend reached to pick a chocolate, you pressed the button and sparks flew out of the box with a loud sizzling noise! Helen wondered which children at school she would trick with this fiendish box. Of course the surprise only worked the first time, except for her mother, who seemed to forget very quickly that it was a trick box of chocolates. Another thing from the Joke Shop was five shiny metal rectangles, about the same size as playing cards. When they were dropped on the floor, it sounded exactly like a plate or a jug breaking. That would be an excellent trick to play on her grandmother, who got so very, very angry if anything was broken.

Would she be able to stop being angry when she found out her mistake?

There had been one special toy that Helen had asked for. It was something she had seen advertised in a comic paper and it was called a Seebackroscope. It was like a short telescope, which, if you put it to your eye, enabled you to see what was happening behind you! It was almost unbelievable! Helen had found this so intriguing, that she had asked Santa Claus for a Seebackroscope in the note, which she was careful to let her mother see before it was thrown up the chimney.

Sadly there was no Seebackroscope, but there was a note from Santa!

The note was in block capitals and explained that like a lot of other things just now, there was a shortage of Seebackroscopes, but he, Santa, hoped to find one very soon. When he did find one, he would give it to her daddy to bring with him the next time he came to visit. The letter called her 'dearie' once or twice. Nobody in the family ever called Helen 'dearie' and she giggled when she read it. Dearie! The note said Santa hoped she liked her trick chocolates and he was sending her Mummy a box of real chocolates.

It was a very big box of chocolates and Annie wondered how on earth Bruce had acquired it. It was very nice anyway and she thought the note was very nice too and very clever. The use of 'dearie' as an endearment was masterly. She was pretty sure that Helen had no idea at all that the note came from her father, nor any idea who Santa Claus was, unless her daughter was a better actress than Joan Crawford.

Annie sometimes wondered about that.

They decided to ration themselves with the chocolates. They would allow themselves two chocolates each per day. Annie counted it out and that meant that they would still have some to eat in January of 1941. It was terribly difficult to choose which ones to start with.

"We must be sure not to eat the best ones first and be left with all the toffees in January!" Annie warned.

But in a life where so much was limited and scarce, it was hard to deprive oneself unnecessarily. They had five each on Christmas Day, because after all it was Christmas Day. They had six each on Boxing Day and six each the next day, too. Then, feeling guilty, they restricted themselves to three each the following day, because they had reached the bottom layer and the box was looking so empty. Then at bedtime, as there were only five chocolates left, they finished them, Helen carefully biting the odd one into two equal pieces.

As Helen said,

"This box will be very handy now it's empty. We can keep hankies in it. Or something else maybe."

The box retained its rich chocolatey aroma for many years and Helen would sometimes sniff it and evoke that last Christmas that she was ignorant of Santa's identity.

◊

One of Annie's friends, Georgina, invited them to visit her at the New Year.

"Will we stay up very late, Mummy?"

"I don't know about you, but I'm not staying up late. It's far too nice to get into bed, these cold nights. No, we'll go and have a little evening visit, just as we usually do. I expect there will be something delicious to eat, shortbread and blackbun and ..."

"What is blackbun? It sounds horrible!"

"Oh, it's scrumptious. Full of currants and raisins and orange peel. I've always wanted to make a blackbun, but I never have. You must have seen Oor Wullie and the Broons having blackbun at New Year. It's traditional."

"But we've never had it."

"You'll taste it tomorrow night and I'll bet you love it."

Helen always enjoyed visiting Georgina. She was tall and more like the ladies that her mother visited in Glasgow, because she dressed well and talked without the strong accent of most of the villagers. She also made Helen very welcome. Georgina had no children of her own and she seemed to treat Helen like another grown-up. Her husband was doing war work somewhere far away and Helen had only seen him once. She was really surprised, because he was a very little man, smaller than her mother and much, much smaller than his wife.

Georgina was a great knitter and more than once had declared her ambition of knitting combinations for her husband.

"It wouldn't take me long, you know," Georgina would declare in her deep rich voice, "because he's quite wee."

Helen was astonished that she would say that, even though it was certainly true.

Statuesque Georgina stayed with her little wee mother, who was seldom seen, in the smallest house that Helen was ever to visit in her life. The staircase was particularly steep and narrow, and seemed to Helen to be too miniature for adults to climb. In later years, Helen would wonder if Georgina really was such a very tall lady, or if she only seemed so because of her surroundings.

Not only was the house special because of its size, but it had a much stronger smell than other houses. Not really unpleasant, but stronger. Of course all houses had their own smell and even blind-folded, Helen's nose could have told her in which house she stood,. But a less finely tuned olfactory organ than Helen's would have recognised the rich atmosphere of that particular house. Georgina's mother, always referred to as Maw, supported herself by making potted meat and tablet. The heady mixture of constantly boiling bones and beef, as well as milk and sugar, had impregnated every part of the little house in the market place and the atmosphere was thick and unmistakable.

Annie could not understand how the old lady could continue her business, what with the wartime restrictions, but whatever she was using, her production line had not been interrupted. Customers, with an empty enamel basin from their last purchase under their arm, would regularly knock at the low door and they were never disappointed.

Usually Helen and her mother were entertained in the tiny sitting room which lay at the top of the minuscule staircase, while Maw stayed downstairs in the kitchen with her odoriferous bubbling pots and her striped cat, Ecky. Helen loved to pore over old Weldons pattern books and thick knitting journals. There was a pile of these well-thumbed periodicals from the thirties and their dated designs made them even more appealing to the child. Meanwhile Georgina relayed the copious village gossip to Annie, dropping her voice to a whisper at the more scandalous parts and silently mouthing those words unsuitable for a child's ears. Helen paid no attention. She would be deeply immersed in the section which showed the magnificent outfits which could be knitted for dolls of every description. Baby dolls could have long lacy christening robes of incredible complexity or charming little striped romper-suits with matching bonnet and bootees. Little school-girl dollies could have pleated skirts or gym tunics, blazers, hats and even a striped tie, all knitted. Then there were the fancy dress pages where clowns and ballerinas posed. There was even a flamenco dancer with a cascade of scarlet frills on her long skirt. Helen ached to knit something wonderful for Topsy and wondered if it were difficult to knit frills.

On New Year's night, however, Annie and Helen were ushered into the kitchen where Maw was obviously expecting them. The table was nicely laid with an embroidered cloth and little plates of all the delicacies that Annie had promised. No pots were boiling. They sat around the table and smiled happily at each other. Georgina did not seem to be so talkative with her mother there, but Annie chatted merrily and Helen thought the old lady looked pleased. Helen had always wondered if Maw was lonely downstairs in the kitchen all by herself.

Suddenly Georgina announced.

"Let's have a New Year drink. It's not midnight yet but who cares? What will you have Annie, whisky or sherry?"

"Oh, you know I never take anything."

"Just a wee glass, it's a special time. We'll not see 1940 again after tonight. Maybe just as well, too. It hasn't been all that damn great."

For a moment Helen was surprised to see Georgina look very sad. She always seemed so jolly and untroubled.

"What will you have, Annie, make up your mind!"

"All right, a sherry, please."

"And Maw?"

"Ah'll hiv a dram. Jist a wee yin."

"And Helen will have a shandy. Yes she will, Annie, ye can't leave our wee heroine out. I'll make it really weak, don't worry."

A few drops of sherry were added to a glass of ginger beer. It seemed very grown-up to Helen and it tasted good too.

When she had drunk half of the glass and her knees were feeling rather tingly and weak, she was startled by a strange noise at the window behind her. It was a rhythmic beating with a scratching noise as well. She looked round nervously.

"That's jist wee Ecky wantin' in. Get him, Georgy."

When Georgina pulled back the curtain, there was the large tabby cat standing on his hind legs, with a determined expression on his face, beating continuously on the window with his front paws, as is the habit of many cats, but Helen had never seen this phenomenon before. The standing cat looked enormous in the aperture of the small window and his concentration and effort impressed the slightly tipsy child. It was as though she had never before appreciated feline beauty. She fell in love with Ecky and with all cats at that moment and for the rest of her life. When the window was opened, Ecky rushed first to Maw and rubbed against her legs, then he rushed in the same eager fashion to the younger women and last of all to Helen. Then jumping on her lap, he immediately settled down with neatly folded paws. He had a loud growly purr and Helen was enchanted.

"He's lovely! Why did you call him Ecky?"

"Well that's short for Alexander. Now, you couldn't call a cat Alexander, could you?"

"No." said Helen though she was hardly satisfied.

"Totty Ecky was a potato merchant, that's why he was called Totty Ecky, and he liked a drink. Have another one Annie?"

Annie shook her head hurriedly and put her hand over the top of her glass, but she was not quick enough to cover Helen's glass and a few more drops of sherry and some ginger beer were poured into Helen's glass. Helen could see that her mother did not want her to have this second drink, but she felt it would be rude to leave it. Besides, she liked it.

"Well," Georgina continued with a sly sideways glance, "Totty Ecky came home one Saturday night and he was pretty drunk, very drunk. Drunker than wee Helen there ... no, no ma

wee lamb I know you're not really drunk ... Anyway, when Totty
Ecky came into his back yard, he stumbled over a few things and
made a noise and all the sleeping hens-did I say his wife kept
hens? Well all the sleeping hens were wakened up wi' the racket
that he made and they all started to go ..."

Here Georgina stretched her neck out and put on quite a
strange face and made a gurgly sound in her throat that sounded
as though she were repeating Totty Ecky, Totty Ecky, Totty Ecky,
over and over again with her mouth wide open. and it sounded
just as hens sound when they are quiet and sleepy. Then she
stopped the funny noise and, frowning, put on a deep angry
voice with a broad Fife accent,

"Dae you ken Totty Ecky tae? Totty Ecky! Eh? Ah'll gie ye
Totty Ecky."

Georgina paused dramatically and then continued in a voice
less correct than her usual accent.

"An' then he thrawed a' thur necks."

It was a strange story. Helen did not quite understand it, but
she still loved the name Ecky.

After a pause, Annie asked Maw about a piece of furniture
that stood against the wall.

"Aye that's a harmonimum, but naebody plays it noo."

"Is it like a wee organ? How do you get the air?"

"Aye, ye jist pump it up'n doon wi' yer feet ye ken, whiles
yer playin' it."

Helen was very interested. She missed her grandmother's
piano in Glasgow. Perhaps she might be allowed to play on this
instrument. She gazed at it longingly and gently pushed Ecky to
the floor.

"Here, I bet a clever wee girl like you could play us a tune."
Georgina winked at her.

"I could play 'Oh, I can wash a sailor's shirt'"

"I was just sure you would be able to entertain us, Helen. I'll
open it up for you."

First of all, Georgina poured herself another small sherry,
then removed ornaments from the top of the harmonium,
opened it up and put a cushion on the stool.

It was not easy for an eight-year-old to put the necessary
strength into the working of the pedals. Her legs were not quite
long enough, but she was a determined child and her inhibitions

had been wiped away by the sherry. She valiantly rolled from side to side in her efforts to pump the instrument and as she played, she started to sing the words.

Helen seldom sang and Annie was astonished and not a little amused. When she caught Georgina's eye they started to giggle and Maw joined in.

Then Helen who, apart from her own compositions, had no other tune in her repertoire, gave an alternative word version to the same melody.

My father died a month ago,

The adults were helpless with laughter by this time, but Helen did not care. She felt a little like the cat when he was beating at the window. She was using all her body strength to push alternate pedals and she had the same determination to finish the job. She felt she could go on all night, singing and making the grown-ups laugh heartily.

When it was time to go home, Georgina insisted that she accompany them along the High Street.

"Georgina, it's only a couple of hundred yards. I'll be fine."

"No, it's been snowing again and it's not safe for you. Your wee helper there has been drinking and you can't rely on her."

"I don't need any help at all, from anyone. I'll be fine. *I* only had *one* drink."

Helen thought her mother looked cross, but Georgina insisted and put on her coat and hat and Annie started to laugh again.

Even Helen could see that Georgina was more of a hindrance than a help on the walk home. Helen took her mother's right hand firmly and Georgina grabbed Annie's left arm, but the tall woman slipped and stumbled and even fell right down at one point. It was all that Helen could do to help her mother keep her balance. Luckily it was a very short distance and Helen could not be angry with Georgina, she was such a very nice person.

It was almost midnight and several groups of people were walking about talking and singing and shouting "Hullo". It did not feel cold and the snow made everything bright and strange. There was a sharp smell in the air. Helen realised that it must be the smell of snow.

BURWOOD HOUSE, LONDON

New Century Show, Post-war Housing

Plans of modern housing design from Glasgow, Oslo, Rome, Tokio, Paris, New York and Berlin are on show at Burwood House. It will be seen that this show was conceived at a date before the European storm had broken. These plans bode well for the future, even those from Germany, where interesting beehive shaped buildings were going forward before the military fever swept such schemes aside.

Glasgow Herald 2nd January 1941

Throughout January, Annie worked hard for Helen's ninth birthday on the 5th February. Everything in their lives seemed so dreary that she was determined that this birthday would be memorable. She had also started to realise some of her daughter's unhappiness at school. Not that Helen discussed her problems, but often the child was very dejected and low and spoke longingly of life back in Glasgow. Annie had come to the conclusion that doing interesting things was the only way that they would survive the shortages, the cold weather and the general gloom. Industry seemed to be the best defence against depression. She racked her brains to remember various occupations to amuse her daughter. Card games and cooking were useful and of course knitting, crochet and embroidery, then now and again she would remember some other long-forgotten craft. They listened to plays, comedy and every sort of music on the wireless, while they worked. After a specially enjoyable programme, Annie sometimes switched off before the news bulletins started. Why become saddened by a reality, which was almost certainly violent and depressing?

She was determined to keep herself busy too. She had procrastinated too long and now she would act. As soon as the right time arrived, she would plant tomatoes and cucumbers in the glass studio. Those fresh tomatoes in Millport had inspired her. There was the piece of ground adjacent to their house which had never been cultivated. That was too daunting a task for her, but she would employ a man to dig. She could plant it with wonderful vegetables. Last summer in a friend's garden, she had admired scarlet runner beans, growing tall and effulgent against a wall, so beautiful, so healthy and full of vitamins. Her imagination leapt forward to rows of crisp cabbages and towering brussel sprouts, crunchy little carrots and turnips. Most wonderful of all would be the abundance of shining, golden onions ready to add their special flavour and aroma to the simplest of dishes. Annie had found the scarcity of onions was the very worst part of rationing. It was ludicrous to have just one or two onions each month.

Also, and this was the most difficult decision, she determined to go to Glasgow and see the doctor to find out what exactly was wrong with her. She and Helen would just go through for a few days specially for that reason. It would not matter if the kid missed a day or two of school. She *must* find out what was the matter and set about regaining her health and strength. She had been a coward. She could not believe it was anything serious for often she seemed full of energy. She was really optimistic about what the doctor would tell her. Just now for instance, she felt great. She was making a dark green, woollen suit for Helen. It could not be a complete surprise, because Helen considered herself a partner and insisted on her rightful place at the sewing machine handle, but after her daughter was in bed, Annie stayed up late with her secret preparations. The jacket would have flowers embroidered in fine wool around the neck. She was also knitting a pretty jumper in soft pink wool, that Helen knew nothing about. For good measure, she was knitting a toy camel. She had never seen or heard of a toy camel before, but when she spotted the pattern in the draper's she was sure that its strangeness would appeal to her daughter.

On her birthday, Helen would have some friends in for tea and Annie meant to make a splendid layered sponge, pink and white and chocolate, with the new fatless recipe that she had heard about on the radio. The layers would be sandwiched together with a chocolate spread made of margarine, sugar and cocoa. Annie rather enjoyed the challenge of the shortages. It was wonderful what you could do, if you used some ingenuity. She might even boil some sugar up and try to make a substitute icing. She did not take sugar in her tea or coffee and so did not suffer from the stringencies of rationing, as much as some others. In fact the half pound of sugar each week was far more than she would ever have bought normally. She smiled to herself as she remembered her bright idea for making marshmallow. It had been a ploy to cheer up Helen one night and keep her busy when she was feeling low. Sugar, gelatine and flavouring had been melted, whizzed to a froth with the faithful Horlicks plunger, then poured into a buttered pie dish. It was an unsuccessful experiment, for when Helen tested it, she came through from the kitchen shaking her head dolefully and said

"Mummy, it's not a bit like marshmallow, but I think we've found the answer to the rubber shortage!"

This was a favourite catchphrase on the radio at the time, and very apt for the caoutchouc type of sweet meat they had invented. They had laughed long and hard at their failure and Helen's comment. Annie smiled every time she brought it to mind. How lucky she was to have such a witty wee girl. There was nothing as healthy as a really good laugh.

Nor was the 'marshmallow' wasted, although strong jaws were required to chew it.

In January, the toy shop in the High Street closed down. Toys were not a priority in the war effort, and besides a lot of them came from Germany. Annie managed to buy some of the last of their stock of charming little party favours for a few pence each, enough to give two to each guest at the tea party. Though German, they were very attractive little artefacts and puzzles. Annie realised that British propaganda was constantly denigrating the entire German race, but she once again pondered sadly on the strange mixture of whimsical charm, extreme cleverness and war-like aggression which seemed inherent in the German character. Were they really as black as the papers painted them? How had so much European culture come out of a country that was depicted as brutish and uncivilised. How could these ordinary people, just very like ourselves, worship an idiot like Hitler? The man was mad, yet they followed him and seemed to love him.

◊

When Helen saw her suit hanging behind the bedroom door on the morning of her birthday, she was almost speechless with pleasure.

After her first crow of delight, she whispered,

"Did you *make* this Mummy? It's like something from *Paris!*"

Annie was happy that it was such a success and not a little astonished that her daughter knew anything about Parisian fashion.

The jumper and the camel were adored and the tea party was all that Annie could have hoped for. Annie was very touched by the gifts which the little girls brought and Helen found everything just perfect.

"Girls! I want to thank you all very much for the lovely presents you've brought Helen."

"Aye, but jist look at a' the grand things we've hud!"

That remark came from Ina, a little girl whose widowed mother lived in one room with her three daughters, cooking on the fire and supporting her family in whatever way she could. Annie admired her and knew that she took in washing and helped out with spring cleaning, though she was unaware that the brave woman was also out early and late, milking cows. When the inconveniences of the Pittenweem house became too much for Annie and the house-keeping money had melted away too soon, she thought of this other mother along the street and how much harder her life must be and tried to shake herself out of any self-pity.

Sometimes it worked.

Tonight, the colourful cake had certainly been a favourite with the wee girls, for only a small broken portion remained on the plate. The birthday had been altogether successful.

In spite of wartime restrictions, in spite of her unpredictable health, Annie had accomplished what she had set out to do and she was satisfied.

Bad News

It was difficult for Annie to know whether she were better off here or in Glasgow. It was a lonely life here, and boring. Of course there was Georgina and old Mrs Hill, but Annie missed her Glasgow life, her friends and her parents. She missed Bruce too, in a funny way. Their sparring was amusing. She was honest enough to realise that physically her life was easier without the demands of her husband or parents. She saw it as her duty to care for them and they took it for granted that she was a willing servant. Now Annie had to admit to herself that it was not just her numb fingers or the recurrent tiredness which was a problem. Since Helen's birthday, the problems with her left leg had returned and it started to drag by the end of every day. It was not very noticeable yet, but it seemed as though that foot were weighted, almost as though part of the foot had turned to lead. It tended to throw her off balance, as though she were tipsy. It was a horrible thought that people might mistake her for being drunk!

Before Christmas, Annie had been able to walk along the High Street with the athletic stride that Bruce had always admired. Now, especially in the afternoon, when she was tired, she made sure that Helen was with her if she went out. Helen held her mother's right hand and took pride in giving just the gentle support that was required if Annie momentarily lost her forward impetus. There was no power required from the child, just sensitivity and a firmer grip of her mother's hand with a small tug in the right direction. Helen enjoyed the physical challenge of judging exactly what she must do. It was almost like dancing. There must not be too much pressure in the grip and not too little. It must be done at exactly the right moment to work correctly. Helen paid attention and had an excellent sense of timing and she found her mother's approval and gratitude very pleasant. Though no real strength was needed, she became interested and aware of her muscles and their capabilities.

The walk back from the cinema in Anstruther was now punctuated by several 'rests'. Annie found that even a slight upward incline slowed and tired her. Luckily, the second half of the walk home was all down-hill. Helen was such a little brick. Patient and helpful with her steadying hand, she seemed to accept helping her mother as quite a normal thing for a kid to do. What would she do without her wee daughter!

She must really act. She would get back to Glasgow *soon* and see a doctor. Perhaps a specialist could help her.

By mid February, the mother and child had become more closely dependent and involved with each other than ever before. They went to Glasgow and Annie saw the family doctor.

After discussing her symptoms and a brief examination, he sadly informed her that she had disseminated sclerosis.

"I'm sorry Annie, there is very little we can do for you. It's a nasty illness, very unpredictable. It's an unpleasant and strange disease and we don't know much about it. It can take various forms. You are quite old at thirty-nine to have started it but I believe you have had the symptoms for several years, haven't you? Now I suggest that you do *not* overtire yourself, take an orange every day and have nothing to do with *quacks*. They cannot help you. Come and see me the next time you are in Glasgow, if you want to. I'm sure the fresh sea breezes of the East coast are the best thing for you just now."

Annie left his surgery in a daze. He had taken less than twenty minutes to pronounce a life sentence. She knew very little about disseminated sclerosis, but she could tell from his face that it was serious. *What did he mean, have nothing to do with quacks?* Which quacks? And how could she eat an orange a day? Oranges were almost unobtainable. She was afraid to break the news to her parents and Bruce. Afraid to see the fear and pity in their eyes. What could she say to her wee girl? Disseminated sclerosis! Such a large frightening name. What else was it called? Did many people have it? Could she meet her friends and admit to them that she was suffering from disseminated sclerosis, an illness that was 'nasty and unpredictable'. Must everyone know that she was blighted by this 'strange disease' that even doctors did not know much about? Would she die of it? Would she get much worse before she died? Why had she not asked him more questions? Probably he did not know the answers.

Annie went into Ross's Dairy at Charing Cross and ordered a coffee. She felt unable to go home and face the family. She wished she were the sort of person that could drink herself into oblivion with alcohol and forget what he had said. No, she did not wish that, it was stupid. She wished that she had never gone near the doctor. He could not help her, yet now she was burdened with this terrible knowledge. Surely ignorance and optimism had been better than this horrible truth. Was it the truth? Could he really tell after such a slight examination? Might there not be other illnesses with the same symptoms? Perhaps he was wrong!

Strangely she did not cry.

She perched on the high stool in the snack bar, biting her lip and gazing into her coffee. She thought how Helen loved this American style snack bar. It seemed to transport her to a more exotic setting. But Hollywood or Timbuctoo, whatever unlikely place Annie travelled to, she would always be burdened from now on with this 'strange disease' that the doctors knew so little about. There was no escape from it.

She felt numb and terribly unwilling to return to her mother's flat, where they were waiting to hear some explanation of her ill health, waiting anxiously. Could she hide the truth from them? Tell them it was just a passing phase of ill health that would right itself in time? She knew that she could not lie, not for months, not for the rest of her life. And how would Bruce take the news? Such an energetic, healthy man would be repelled by her illness. He would probably still maintain that golf was the best cure.

But there was no cure. That was the hellish thing, no cure.

No cure.

No cure.

Her mind was a huge dark empty cave, with the words '*No cure*' reverberating and echoing in the stony vastness.

How terribly alone she felt.

She could not imagine receiving help or sympathy from that waiting family.

There would be shock and certainly drama from her mother, of course, perhaps sympathy from her father. She had no idea how Bruce would react. Her position in the family had always been one of support and service to the others. That was when she had been well and strong.

She took a deep breath, straightened her shoulders and looked out into the street, where shabby crowds were jostling and hurrying past in the drizzling rain.

What about the war and the hardships of all those other people in the world? Surely she was less alone than many unfortunate folk who had lost their loved ones and their homes, even their countries. She must concentrate on the hardships of others. She was not alone anyway, she had her dear little girl and her parents and Bruce, who would do the decent thing, she supposed. She had friends in Glasgow and Pittenweem. Suddenly she remembered the baby tomato and cucumber plants which were ordered at the nursery. A great determination to get back to Pittenweem seized her. She would get those seedlings planted and have a crop to eat in the summer and damn disseminated sclerosis, damn it to hell. Tomatoes were probably every bit as good as oranges and she was determined to have wonderful tomatoes. She would keep going as long as she could. She must be strong for her daughter and her ageing father and her tomato and cucumber plants. Yes, and for her demanding husband and mother, too. No rest for the wicked, she thought, and it made her smile her ironic lop-sided smile.

Finishing her coffee, she marched home to her mother and her legs felt almost normal. Perhaps she would show the doctors yet. She would overcome this 'strange disease' that the idiots knew so little about. Perhaps they knew so little that they could not even diagnose it properly.

She was able to break the news to every one in a firm and resigned way, that did not alarm Helen or her parents too much.

Bruce, however, went to the library and studied the disease.

Fortunately Annie and Helen had returned to Pittenweem before he described to his horrified in-laws the several, fearful possibilities and the sad, uncertain outlook for someone who suffered from multiple sclerosis, as the 'strange disease' was also called.

Bruce was never one to look on the bright side.

◊

There were two pleasant interludes for Helen in the sad, short visit to Glasgow.

She saw her little cousin Eileen again. The baby had grown into a sweet toddler, with enormous eyes and lots of dark hair. Helen was entranced with the doll-like creature in her pretty dress, so much more interesting than a baby. Eileen was able to say one or two words and Helen thought her a little genius. She wished that they lived nearer to each other. What fun it would be to dress her little cousin and brush her hair, show her picture books and dance to music with her. Little Eileen liked her big cousin too, and gave her a damp, loving kiss when they parted. Helen treasured the kiss, but felt sad because it might be a long time before they would meet again.

They also paid a visit to Annie's friend Elsie, in Lambhill, where they stayed overnight for the first time.

Now that they were older, the two little girls Maureen and Eleanor were much more fun to play with.

They had a truly splendid doll's house, something that Helen had always yearned for. Their mother, with a lot of hard work and ingenuity, had made it for her girls. Helen was impressed by the Hollywood style bedroom, with its triple-mirrored dressing table and swathed pink silk furnishings. Each room had been lovingly designed and the small details were outstanding. Annie was particularly impressed by the crystal perfume bottles, simply made by sticking a large and a small cut glass button together.

Truthfully the house was almost too sophisticated and perfect for such young children to play with. Elsie tended to hover over her girls as they played with her lovingly created work of art, cautioning, and interfering when the four-year-old started to move things about.

However Helen, being a bigger and more responsible girl, was put in charge and given carte blanche to enjoy all the fascinating, miniature delights.

After examining each room thoroughly and considering the four small dolls that inhabited the house, she asked the girls.

"Would you like me to make a play happen in your house?"

They both nodded enthusiastically, for big Helen was a role model for them and they had complete faith in any suggestion that she might make.

Helen proceeded to make one of her many 'pretends' come to life, moving the dolls from place to place and making each one speak in its own particular character. It was a Cinderella scenario, the best kind of all, where the heroine has many hardships and vicisssitudes to encounter, before winning the handsome hero.

The small girls sat quietly for an hour, entranced, but they were not more delighted than Helen. How she enjoyed using the furniture in each little room and making the bad people act in a horrible way, while the good people were always clever and kind. At first, the poor heroine was forced to work terribly hard all day and sleep at night in the attic. What triumph when she was finally released from her servitude, and everyone started to be nice to her! What bliss when she moved to the pink silk luxury of the large bedroom, with the crystal bottles full of imaginary perfume!

The little girls clapped and clapped at the end of the show. The two mummies were very complimentary, although as they had not watched the show, they could not know how very good it had been.

Helen was quietly delighted with her success. She knew that her presentation had been excellent.

All those years of imagining and telling herself stories had been a preparation for this doll's house play.

She hoped that they would come to Lambhill again soon, for she already knew the next story that she would make the dolls act out. It would be a drama of mistaken identity.

That night Helen and her mother slept on a mattress on the floor. Elsie kept apologising and saying that it would be better the next time they came to visit, but Helen *loved* sleeping on the floor and hoped that she would do it often and often in her life.

Bombs

In March, when the snow had finally disappeared from the garden, Helen would spend an hour after school each day playing in the street, like all the other children. There were seasons for different games, skipping, hopscotch (know locally as 'beddies'), round singing games and ball bouncing. Annie liked to see her daughter out playing as she herself had played as a child in Pittenweem. It also showed that Helen was settling into a life in the village and might eventually lose those dark moods which regularly overpowered her. Annie was running out of ideas to cheer her daughter up when the black dog sat on her shoulder. Of course knitting was always there and Helen was a keen little knitter. She had nearly finished her second cardigan now. She was certainly a determined child, but Annie was not sure that sitting over very plain knitting was therapeutic. She herself preferred something complicated and more demanding. Although they hardly knew them, Bruce's cousins in East Lothian, Nancy and Betty, always sent very nice, unusual presents to Helen on her birthday. This year, having heard of her knitting skills, they had sent some soft brown wool and a pattern for a sweater with cable knitting. Annie had found Helen studying the pattern several times, although it was really too advanced for a child of nine. Annie preferred to see Helen throwing a ball against the wall, clapping, turning around and jumping between each bounce. It was such good exercise.

Annie was surprised that she herself did not suffer from permanent depression. After the first terrible shock, the fact that she now knew for certain about her condition made very little difference to her state of mind. She tried to take each day as it came, and if she felt physically well, she was happy and accomplished as much as possible. When pain and tiredness struck, she rested and kept her mind occupied with complicated knitting, embroidery or reading. She now admitted to herself that it was better to know that she was ill and was justified in taking things easily. That guilty feeling of laziness had always nagged at her mind on bad days, and neither Bruce nor her mother had helped assuage that guilt. Annie made excuses for them, but she knew that they could have made life easier by understanding and perhaps cosseting her a little. Cosseting was a funny word and not something she had experienced often. Those two weeks in the nursing home after Helen was born had been very pleasurable. Yes, that was probably the nearest that she had ever come to being 'cosseted'.

Helen had expressed an interest in joining the Brownies and Annie had been delighted to encourage her. She was sure it would be enjoyable and that Helen would make more friends.

A letter arrived from Bruce saying that he had found tenants for the Hyndland flat. He described them as a 'very nice tidy couple', whatever that meant. They would move in almost immediately. Annie felt a pang about her house being used by strangers, but Bruce assured her that he had locked everything of value safely away. The money would be helpful for Bruce, although Annie did not expect it to make any difference to her.

A week later, a Joan Crawford film was showing at the little local cinema. It was an old film but Annie was a great fan of the dramatic film star.

"Let's go up to the pictures tonight, will we?"

"Oh yes. Let's hope it doesn't break down tonight."

Breaking down was a regular occurrence in the Pittenweem cinema. The film would snap and for four or five minutes the hall would be left in pitch darkness, while it was mended. Because of the blackout, most people carried a torch when going out in the evening. Some ingenious members of the audience came prepared for these dark intervals. Silhouettes of Mickey Mouse, Pluto or butterflies or flowers were stuck to the torch, which was then shone at the dead screen and the well-known characters were made to dance about or flicker on and off. Other members of the audience joined in with suitable remarks, often amusing, sometimes ribald or even outrageous in the safety of the darkness.

"I think it's quite good fun when they shine their torches at the screen, don't you? Just as long as it doesn't break down completely."

This had happened once when the projector bulb exploded. It had seemed a tragedy, as the disappointed customers tramped home an hour earlier than expected. They never did see the end of that film and Helen often referred to it with a sense of irretrievable loss.

When the Crawford film finished, it was a beautiful moon-light night as they left the cinema, Annie wiping a furtive tear from the corner of her eye.

"No one needed a torch tonight, Mummy."

"And they don't need one to walk home either. Look how bright it is, almost like daytime."

"It's really cold, though, let's hurry, if your leg's all right, Mummy."

Annie loved the fact that Helen had taken the news of her mother's illness in a quiet matter-of fact way. While the kid did not forget that her mother was not as able as other mothers, she did not fuss or weep or even mention the disability much at all. Her steadying arm was becoming more and more important to Annie. Bruce had wanted to get a stick for her, but Annie felt that a stick advertised her infirmity too much. Besides, she did not need support so much as a nudge, just a slight push or pull, and Helen's quick, controlled reaction to her mother's loss of balance was superior to any inanimate stick.

As they walked home, Annie heard the sound of planes in the distance. The siren had not sounded so they must be our own fellows up there, in the bright, cold night. She wondered if their planes were cold and if they were afraid. It must be pretty fantastic to fly over the earth when it was so brightly lit by the moon. She almost envied them. To travel so fast and directly must be a marvellous experience. Before she could unlock the door, another wave of planes flew past. They seemed to be coming in from the sea and passing over Anstruther, heading west. She could not see them, but it sounded as though there were a lot of them. She lit the paraffin heater in the bedroom, made two mugs of Horlicks, filled the hot-water bottles and opened the front door to put out the milk bottles. Still, the sound of many planes flying through the bright night disturbed the silent town. Suddenly she felt a throb of fear. Those planes sounded relentlessly determined. Those were not British aircraft on manoeuvres, she was sure. All at once she felt positive that these were enemy planes flying over Scotland. Their destination must be Glasgow, that centre of ship-building and industry.

All her relatives and friends were in Glasgow. Her home and all that she possessed and loved, lay in the path of that sinister flock of destruction.

She stood at the door and grew colder and colder. When she finally climbed, shivering, into bed, Helen found her strangely quiet and unwilling to discuss the film.

Annie lay awake all night on the east coast, while on the west coast, the Luftwaffe destroyed Clydebank.

When the news of the terrible attack was announced Annie phoned her mother.

"Yes, yes, Annie we're fine and Willie and Eileen and the baby and Bruce too and his folk. He phoned this morning. We're all fine, don't worry. John and I went down to the basement last night with all the other people in the close. Haven't seen some of them in years. Some of them had thermos flasks of tea and Mrs Bathgate had a bottle of whisky, but your father wouldn't take any. They had sandwiches too and I baked pancakes."

"Sounds almost like a party."

"No, no, it was damnably uncomfortable and cold. Your father coughed most of the night and I've got a stiff neck."

"At least you were safe."

"Safe? I suppose so, but we'll not go down there again. Couldn't stand it and it's not good for your father's chest."

"Are you sure? I worry about you, y'know and all that glass in the studio. Did you have no breakages at all?"

"No we're fine, but we took the tram out to Hyndland today and what a mess! I don't think there's a whole window left in any street. There were several landmines dropped there evidently and not all that far from your house. One family was wiped out without a trace."

"Maw, how terrible. I wonder if I knew them? And I wonder if the new tenants had moved in to 46 yet and if they're all right, and poor Mrs Walton next door. Did you see anyone to speak to? What did our house look like?"

"Pretty much of a wreck. The bedroom curtains were shredded and flying out the broken windows like ribbons, and the heavy curtains were closed in the sitting room, but open to the elements, for there wasn't a pane of glass left. However the velvet didn't look torn or anything, that was a very good heavy quality, that stuff I got for you and a great bargain. But oh dear, Hyndland looked as though a tornado had hit it. The pavements were *piled* with broken glass. But poor Clydebank is the worst, I suppose. A lot of deaths and terrible damage."

"I knew something awful was happening when I heard all those planes going over and over. I've been so worried. When are you coming through? I'll get your bed ready today. I suppose you'll come as soon as you can get organised and I'll feel a lot better when you're out of Glasgow."

"Oh, I don't think we'll be coming through, Annie. It wouldn't do for your father to leave Glasgow just at this moment."

"I can't believe you're staying there in that dangerous place. They'll come back again to finish the job, y'know. This is just the start. *Please* come through here where it's safe, Maw."

"No, I think we'll wait and see if it gets any closer."

"*Closer*! Clydebank's only a few miles away. Just moments in a plane!"

"Yes, but we'll be all right, don't worry, Annie. We'll be fine."

"Won't you go down to the basement at least. That would be some protection."

"No, no, I'll never go down there again. Too damned miserable and having to talk and be polite to all those folk. No, no, I couldn't face it. And your father wouldn't go either. We'll be fine. Phone me again next week and don't arrange anything for us coming through. Not just yet, at any rate. We'll be fine."

Annie hung up and sighed. How unreal it all seemed. She tried to visualise her beautiful brown velvet curtains with the wind and rain blowing in on them. What a mess. And what had happened to the tenants? They had been in the flat for less than two weeks!

Poor Bruce would have a lot to see to. Would insurance be paid on war damage? She had no idea.

Only one thing was certain. The war had really started now.

Annie said as little as possible to Helen about the bombs. It was too horrible to discuss with a child. Instead she taught her daughter to crochet and that was a big success. For years, Helen had admired the patterns in the Weldons books in Georgina's house. Some of those very desirable doll's outfits were in this strange skill about which she knew nothing. The instructions used a complex code for an unknown language. Knitting was Helen's metier and crochet seemed quite beyond her reach. Since her birthday, the present of brown wool and pattern for the cable jumper had been very much in her mind. Almost an obsession. It was a lovely jumper and she was sure that she could make the cables with the extra needle. She had read the instructions over fifty times. Her mother was less sure. However when Helen learned how very simple the basics of crochet were, she was at once full of plans. Topsy needed shoes, a jacket, a handbag. Helen would crochet all of these in no time at all and how smart her darling would look. The cable jumper could wait.

Annie's friend Mrs Hill was a champion exponent of the art of crochet. She was of the same generation as Mary, but she was a lady who had always had to make one shilling do the work of four. A lifetime of 'making-do and mending' had prepared her well for the difficult war years. One instance of her economy and industry had impressed and amused Annie. Unusually, they were taking tea in Mrs Hill's front room, and Annie admired the colourful antimacassars of wool crochet on the backs of the chairs and couch. Although this was not an accessory she chose to have in her own home, they were bright and beautifully neat.

"Do you like them, Annie?"

"Oh, they're really lovely. Lovely old rich colours. Where did you buy the wool?"

Pittenweem had five or six shops selling wool to the keen knitters of the town, so unusual yarn or bargain lots were eagerly sought.

Mrs Hill smiled slyly.

"Ye'd never guess, Annie!"

"Go on, tell me."

"Well, you know how your mother and I both like the sales of work."

"I know she hates to miss one."

"Just like myself. But she likes to go to the bric-a-brac stall, while I go to the old clothes. You've no idea what bargains I get there. I cannae understand why people are throwin' things away these days, but they are. They must be daft. Good things too. Plenty wear still left in them. That crochet mat only cost me tuppence. It was an old strippit jumper that I ripped out. Got it at the Episcopal church last year. That's always an awful good bazaar, that one. All the toffs chuckin' things out y'know. It's nice colours, isn't it."

"It is, it's really nice. Was it easy to unravel it?"

"Oh, aye. I'm a dab hand at 'ruggin' doon'. And look there's another and another."

To Annie's astonishment, Mrs Hill lifted and displayed mat after mat. It seemed as though there were six or seven piled one on top of another on every chairback.

Mrs Hill smiled at Annie's astonishment,

"Aye, I just love making them and putting the colours together. Once I start, I hate to stop until I've finished one."

At intervals over the last two years, Annie had been crocheting complicated roundels in fine cotton. Several of these were then sewn together to make a place mat. some mats were larger, requiring more circles. Though a very labour-intensive hobby, it was a popular occupation at the time, for lacy mats were considered a very elegant setting on a well-polished, dining-room table. At any rate, all women's magazines constantly assured their readers of that fact. Perhaps elegance was a useful dream and aspiration for housewives who daily struggled with severe shortages of the basic necessities of life. There were other ways of decorating the house with crochet. There were various ornamental baskets which required the finished article to be soaked in a saturate sugar solution. It could then be moulded into shape as it dried and was stiff and free-standing, rather like a lacy vase when finished. Helen often saw these displayed in the windows of the Pittenweem houses and rather fancied them, but her mother obviously did not care to produce one of these strange ornaments. Towels, pillow slips and tablecloths could be edged with narrow or deep bands of crochet, according to taste and devotion to the work. Annie had tried the fine crochet out of curiosity and as an alternative to her knitting, but it was a slow process and as she had no particular deadline to meet, she often wrapped her cotton work up in a dishtowel and put that particular hobby away for days or even weeks. However she had seen some ideas for wool crochet in a magazine, hats, slippers and purses. It was quicker and the bright colours were jollier, probably more therapeutic than the boring ecru cotton. The finished articles were certainly more useful. There were plenty of scraps of wool around and she made three purses and a pair of slippers. She also made a little cap for Helen, more of a small bonnet. The pattern was in the Woman magazine and was described as an Easter bonnet. It looked very sweet to Annie. It was trimmed with small flowers, also in crochet and tied under the chin. When it was finished and presented to her, Helen smiled and said thank you, but her heart dropped. That bonnet was just *too different* from anything that anybody else wore in Pittenweem. She had put up with many cruel comments about her unusual clothes, but the bonnet was the worst. She did not even like it herself. However she wore it and steeled herself for the hoots of derision.

It was worse than she could have imagined. Not even her friends liked it, and in the streets, the boys constantly shouted 'Here's Auld Mither Riley'.

Old Mother Riley and her daughter Kitty had been a husband and wife music hall act, which had transferred successfully to the silver screen. The husband, a very plain man dressed in drag, acted as the old mother, while his wife was the daughter. The old lady's outfit was pure pantomime, and on top of her grey curls she wore a small flower trimmed bonnet tied under her chin. It was a bizarre act and perhaps only the fact that it was wartime could explain their popularity.

To be described as Old Mother Riley was perhaps the worst insult that Helen ever suffered and after a few days of misery the bonnet was hidden in a drawer.

A much more successful accessory was the fur muff. It was just as unusual as the bonnet and Helen had to put up with the usual jeering remarks about it, but she had carried it all winter with pride and enjoyment. It was actually a deep fur cuff from a very splendid evening cloak of her grandmother's which had graced some important Art Club event of the twenties. Annie had found it in a drawer and had immediately seen its possibilities in the severe winter.

"You'll be able to keep your hands nice and cosy when we go to the pictures!"

Helen thought the muff 'old-fashioned' in the best possible sense and it was also very comforting.

One night Annie was frying the remnants of the previous night's Yorkshire pudding for supper. She had left things till the last minute and it was nearly time to catch the first house at the cinema.

"It's going to be far too hot to eat, Helen. I'll wrap it in a paper bag and you put it in your muff and we'll eat it there."

It made a wonderful warmth in the muff which lasted through the evening. When the big picture started and the pudding was brought out to eat in the dark, a delicious aroma spread around the cinema, for the pudding had been fried in roast beef dripping. From all sides could be heard the murmurs,

"My, whit a grand smell!"

"Is that ingins Ah'm smellin'?"

"Naw, Ah think it's meaty-like,"

"Wha's eating chips? They smell awfy tasty."

"Ma Goad, that's an awfy grand smell Ah'm gettin'!"

◊

Helen had joined the Brownies at the beginning of the year. She felt smart in her brown cotton uniform although she had reservations about other aspects of the experience. First of all the Brown Owl had a very high, affected voice which Helen hated. She also found it difficult to call a person Brown Owl. It seemed rather silly. Then it was necessary to make a vow to God and the King, and she wondered if those two should be put together like that. She did not know the word blasphemous, but she understood the concept, and as the king was just a man, it seemed not quite right to put him in the same class as God. When they started talking about fairies and elves, then she knew that was certainly wrong. There were no such things as fairies and they should not be getting mixed up with God.

That first evening, the Brown Owl had a little present for each Brownie. When Helen saw it, she frowned. It was a draw-string purse of the simplest construction, just a piece of gathered fabric with raw edges and with no attempt to finish it. Although it was kind of the high-voiced lady to give them all a present, Helen could imagine what her mother would say when she saw it! Her mother, who made so many well-crafted garments and purses and slippers, would think this a very poor piece of work. In fact all her friends had mothers who knitted and sewed beautiful, well-finished things. How could Brown Owl hand out such rubbish? Did she not know how *very bad* the purse was?

There were four Brownie outings that Spring. The first outing was boring compared to a walk with her grandfather or her mother, who were always happy to point out things of interest and stop and examine them for as long as Helen wanted. Also they were both great story-tellers and would have something good to eat in their pockets. The pack of Brownies just walked along in a single line, with Brown Owl at the front and a big girl at the back. Sometimes they sang a song and sometime Brown

Owl shouted something over her shoulder, in her strange voice but Helen often did not hear it or understand it. It did not seem like much fun and the paths were slushy and muddy.

The second event was an Easter Egg competition and Annie made a very fine one. It was a little old man with a fringe of white cotton wool setting off his bald head. He was tremendously realistic and Helen had no doubt that she would take first prize. However, her feelings of superiority towards the other children at school had not prepared her for the creativity of their mothers. There were many exotic, ingenious and realistic eggs, all much more impressive than Annie's egg. Helen was astonished and abashed by how insignificant her little old man egg looked beside the Carmen Miranda egg, the Donald Duck egg and the Winston Churchill, complete with cigar, egg. However when they rolled their eggs down the steep hill above the swimming pool, she was glad that hers was not such a work of art, for it was a shame to see the ruination of the more glorious ones, as they were battered to pieces in the rough descent.

There was to be a church jumble sale for the War Effort where the Brownies and Guides would have a stall to sell the various artefacts which they had created. This tied in nicely with the Brownie badge for knitting, for which a toy must be knitted. The result of this industry would then be sold at the jumble sale.

Helen chose to knit an elephant. Its structure was of the simplest and she quickly finished it. It was brown and looked very plain and ordinary to mother and daughter. When Annie made her suggestion, Helen received it with enthusiasm. Annie said,

"Wouldn't it look better with a nice coloured blanket on its back and a little brown boy, he's called a mahout, riding on it?"

It just so happened that they had a nice little brown china doll just the right size for this role. When the miniature mahout was seated and sewn into position on the crochet orange and green rug, with tassels at each corner, it was a splendid sight. Helen was entranced. He was just like a little Sabu, the talented young Indian film star who rivalled Shirley Temple in Helen's Hollywood role models. Sabu had won her heart with his liquid brown eyes and beautiful smile when he had starred in "Elephant Boy."

It was only as she was going to sleep that night and thinking about her elephant and how very special he looked, that she suddenly sat up, horrified!

If her elephant were going to be sold at the jumble sale, some other person would own that charming elephant and, more important, the mahout.

The truly terrible fact was that the china doll that was the mahout, was also *Topsy's baby!*

She leaped out of bed and rushed to her mother with such distress, that Annie was quite frightened at first. However she was able to calm her daughter down by reassuring her that they would certainly be first in line to buy the elephant back again.

And they were, although Helen was in a state of stress until the money was paid and the elephant, complete with mahout, safely in her arms once more.

The third Brownie expedition was to gather primroses. The pack was to meet at Lawson's shop at ten thirty on Saturday morning. Unfortunately there were three shops of that name in Pittenweem and obviously Helen had not paid enough attention to which of these was the rendezvous. Helen found no Brownies at the first Lawson's shop that she went to and, as she had been rushing at the last minute, she thought they had started without her. She returned home, despondent but philosophical.

"I was too late. They've gone away already."

"Oh, surely not, it's only two minutes after half-past now. Are you sure that it wasn't the other Lawson's, along at the town clock you were suppose to meet?"

"Oh I didn't think of that."

She ran off, but they were not there and some of her stoicism deserted her. She would have liked to gather primroses.

Back in the house there were a few tears.

"Let's go up to the other Lawson's at the Toll. Maybe that's where you should have gone."

"They'll be far away by now."

"Well, don't worry, I'll come with you and we can surely catch them up. Two people can travel faster than a crowd."

Helen was too tactful to point out that her mother's walking was pretty slow.

At the third Lawson's shop they learned that yes, the Brownies had met there, but had set off fully ten minutes ago.

"I'm sure we'll find them, my pet."

Helen did not have her mother's optimism, but her goal was

no longer that of meeting up with the Brownies. Her overpowering desire was to find primroses.

Eventually they did find them growing beside the burn where she had first seen them with her grandfather. Annie sat down to rest, relieved that they had not needed to walk further.

Helen saw a hawthorn tree and remembered eating 'bread and cheese' with John.

"Look, mummy, a bread and cheese tree."

She picked some of the budding leaves to eat and found them just as good as she remembered, although not remotely like bread and cheese.

Just then the Brownie pack came into view on the other side of the stream. There was no way of crossing at that point but Helen and the other girls waved to each other and chatted.

"Whit's that ye're eatin' Helen?"

"Well it's called bread and cheese, but it's just the new little leaves. It's supposed to taste like bread and cheese, but I don't think it does. Look, you have a tree beside you, try it."

Four little brownies clustered round the tree and sampled the small green buds.

"Aye, that's grand 'n tasty."

"Ah'm thinkin' it diz taste like breed'n cheese."

"Naw it duzny."

"It niver tastes like breed'n cheese."

"Thur braw, though"

"Aye, thur braw, richt enough."

"Ah widnae hae thocht Ah wid hae likit tae eat leaves, but thur grand an' tasty."

The girls had forgotten their primroses and now the whole pack crowded round the hawthorn tree on their side of the burn. Annie watched in amusement. They were like a little flock of brown birds demolishing the crop on a fruit tree.

Suddenly, in the distance, Brown Owl's quavering voice could be heard calling to them. They were not quick to respond, but when she blew three sharp blasts on her whistle, they abandoned the tree and rushed off out of sight. Only one little girl waved cheerio to Helen. It seemed very quiet when they had gone. Annie wondered if Helen felt bereft at their disappearance, but she seemed perfectly content with her mother's company as they slowly wended their way home.

The fourth Brownie expedition proved to be the final one. This time Helen arrived at the correct meeting place, at the correct time. However three hours later, she returned, pale-faced and accompanied by an apologetic Brown Owl.

Annie listened with an expressionless face, as the older woman explained that Helen had slipped and scratched the back of her leg, while climbing over a barbed wire fence.

"I am extremely surprised that a nine-year-old was expected to negotiate a barbed wire fence."

Brown Owl was explaining how it happened, but Annie shut her front door firmly.

She was even more furious to discover that it was much more than a scratch. The large deep cut was bound up with a hanky and not a very clean one.

"That's the end of that. You're not going back to the Brownies. She's not fit to be in charge of children. I wonder if I should take you to the doctor. That might need a stitch or two. What an idiot that woman is. She didn't even have a first aid kit. Would you be sorry to leave them?"

"No, not at all. I thought it was all a bit silly. Are we too late to go to the pictures, now Mummy?

◊

Fisherwomen are being given the novel opportunity of "doing their bit" for the War Effort. The Ministry of Supply requires large amounts of netting to be used in connection with camouflage. Older fisherwomen are urged to pass on their skills of netting and mending nets to the younger generation.

Glasgow Herald 8th June 1941

One Saturday they went to the neighbouring town of Anstruther.

Annie had seen an advertisement for women required to make and mend nets. She had a great longing to earn some money, it was something she had never done. Nowadays everyone was working towards the war effort and, in spite of her worsening health, she felt that she could surely do something like sit and mend nets. It could not be so different from crochet. Just crochet on a grand scale. Perhaps she could work while Helen was in school, as there were all sorts of changes in working hours now.

She felt strong and adventurous that morning and they walked along the street mentioned in the advertisement. It was a long street and the building was farther from the bus-stop than they had expected.

The manager clumped down the steep stairs in answer to his wife's loud shriek

"Davey! Ye're wantit."

He seemed in less than a happy mood and as soon as Annie spoke, he glared at her then turned his head away shaking it vigorously.

"Ye'll no' ken naethin' aboot mendin' nets div ye? Whaur d'ye come frae?"

"Pittenweem."

"Aye, but ye're no' a Pittenweemer, ur ye? Ye divnae stey there, div ye"

"I do stay there now,"

"Na, na, ma lass, there's nae wark fur ye here. I'll show ye the loft if ye like, an' the lassies daein' thur wark, but it's no' fur the likes o' you."

The stairs were steep, almost like a ladder, and Annie climbed them with some difficulty. The walk from the bus had been tiring.

The net loft was large, but stuffy and pungent with the smell of the bark preservative with which the nets were treated. About ten women of all ages were working at the tan-coloured nets. All were dressed in bright print crossover pinafores over warm jerseys and skirts and all wore something to protect their hair, the older women with small frilled mob caps and the younger girls with a scarf tied in the fashionable turban. Some of the nets were slung from the beams and others were draped across the knees of the workers. A large skylight gave an idyllic view of a calm blue sea, with the purple streak of the distant coastline. It was a picturesque scene and the artist in Annie was delighted by it. At the same time she sadly realised that the journey here and the work itself, was probably far beyond her capabilities.

She listened glumly as the man spoke of the hardship of the work and the speed required. He mentioned each girl by name and although they continued working, they seemed to smile a secret smile to each other at the arrogance and stupidity of the city woman who thought she could come and do their specialised work and deprive some local girl of her rightful employment. When the man spoke of what they earned, Annie was appalled. It sounded like slave labour. She thanked him and apologised for wasting his time.

"Na, na ma lass. That's nae trouble at a'. Noo watch they stairs noo, thur shoogly and it strikes me ye're a wee bit unsteady oan yer pins, ur ye?"

He was smiling now and in a thoroughly good mood. He had fairly put this city woman in her place.

Annie did not answer him but bowed coldly. After negotiating the steep stairs with great care, she grabbed Helen's hand and walked away from the building as fast and as steadily as she could, until they turned a corner.

"Well that was a bit of a waste of time!"

Helen said nothing. She was glad that her mother was not going to be working.

Before they reached the bus stop, they bumped into Helen's teacher. Helen liked Miss Peebles rather better than the fiery tempered Miss Don of her first year at Pittenweem school, but she was still wary of an adult who used the leather strap so regularly. She had, in fact, felt the sting and humiliation of the belt herself that winter. On a bleak snowy day, when the hard-packed, hard-thrown, icy snowballs from the boys' playground had seemed too threatening, Helen, with five other timid girls, had hovered in the school doorway, rather than go outside at the morning break. But the school rules insisted that children must go out into the playground, use the toilets and play, whatever the weather conditions or dangers. Not to do so was a crime which must be punished, and the six girls were belted. Perhaps Helen found it marginally more bearable because she was one of a crowd, or perhaps it was not really as sore as she had feared. Perhaps Miss Peebles was more generally complimentary and appreciative of the well-informed and hard-working child than her predecessor had been. Whatever the reason, Helen had forgiven Miss Peebles and was pleased, though astonished, when her teacher and mother greeted each other like old friends.

Helen had no idea that they knew each other and the next thing, Annie was asking how Miss Don was! And almost immediately after that, afternoon tea was mentioned. Helen felt dazed as the two women made their affectionate farewells, arranging to meet at Annie's house the following weekend.

"I didn't know that you knew Miss Don! Or Miss Peebles either! Were you all friends?" Helen's voice went very high on the word 'friends' and she could not avoid a tone of disbelief. Teachers seemed such a separate race from her nice ordinary mother. Helen was incapable of imagining members of that profession taking a bath or peeling potatoes or laughing at something naughty or washing their knickers. She could not even imagine what sort of knickers they would wear.

"Oh, yes, we used to play tennis together long ago."

"Tennis?"

"Yes, and golf and go to dances and we all bicycled about in a crowd. Ellen was wild on a bike. She could go so fast and her red hair streamed out behind her."

"Who's Ellen?"

"Miss Don."

"*Miss Don went fast on a bike!* What did Miss Peebles do?"

"Florence? Oh she was pretty mad on dancing. She was good! Her legs were almost too quick to see when she danced the Charleston, and she was great at the Black Bottom." Annie laughed. "I wasn't so bad myself in those far-off days. It was a good crowd."

It was rather too much for Helen to believe all at once. Fancy teachers bicycling and dancing dances that sounded quite rude!

Of course her mother was talking about the olden days.

"What on earth is the Black Bottom?"

"It's a dance. I'll teach you when we get home. Let's go for the bus now."

Annie was starting to feel very weary. Her foot had the horrible dragging sensation, but meeting Florence had cheered her up and reminded her of good times and the strength and energy of her youth. Perhaps some of that strength would come back if she could find the right doctor to advise her.

Helen had her own problems. Why had Miss Don and Miss Peebles been asked to tea? What on earth were the two teachers and her mother going to speak about? It seemed to Helen that there was only one subject that they had in common and that was *her.* How awful to sit there and be discussed all afternoon! She dreaded it and thought of little else in the intervening days.

But on the Saturday afternoon visit, the three women talked gaily for nearly four hours without referring once to Helen.

What relief she felt! And just a morsel of astonishment and a touch of disappointment.

Mrs Hill's two granddaughters came to stay with her in Pittenweem that summer, and Helen had a wonderful time with them. Marion was the same age as Helen but sadly she was affected by a birth defect and was rather slow. Jessie, her young sister, was a quick and clever little girl and the three of them got on well together, with Helen taking a maternal, dominant role. Many hours were spent playing games of imagination in their grandmother's house, which had just as many strange and wonderful things in it as Helen's Grandma had in her house.

At night Helen put them to bed, just as proper middle-class children in storybooks were put to bed. She insisted on thorough hand and face washing, tooth brushing, then prayers. When they were in bed, she told them a story. Then she returned home to her own much later, less conventional and unsupervised bedtime, where only tooth-brushing was part of the routine.

Before the summer term ended, there was the War Effort Week with various ways of making money, bazaars, concerts, fancy dress parades and lots of raffles.

Annie thought that, quite apart from the financial side, it was a good way of cheering people up as rations became smaller and the end of the war receded into the distance.

Annie brought out Helen's bridesmaid's dress which still fitted her, although it was no longer ankle length as she had grown tall and thin. Annie threaded a springy curtain wire through the hem and the dress stood out in a pleasantly Victorian way. Helen was not too sure about the lace-edged pantaloons that Annie assured her were what little girls wore in those far off days.

"Are you sure they should hang down below the dress like that? I think it's a bit rude to have your knickers showing."

"They used to think it was rude to show your legs then!"

Fortunately Annie found an illustration to convince her daughter.

Helen was pleased to be wearing her pretty pink dress again and with a little pre-war straw bonnet, mittens and a posy of flowers from Mrs Hill, she looked authentic and very sweet. Her grandfather painted a small watercolour of her in her Victorian costume. The judges awarded her a prize of one 15/- savings certificate, with which she was delighted.

War Savings were a very positive part of each child's self-image at the time. Buying them was seen as a duty to contribute to the war effort, as much as chance to build a nest egg. Schoolchildren were encouraged to contribute a weekly sixpence, perhaps only threepence, until they had built slowly up towards the goal of a savings certificate. Even this small sum must have been difficult for the mother of a large family to find for each child, regularly. Annie found it hard enough with only one child.

The teacher, who fulfilled the role of banker, had an impressive amount of extra paperwork in the collection of these sums.

Grumbles were discouraged, for there was a war on!

It was to be a very lucky week for Helen for she also won a yellow teapot, with half a pound of tea in it. This was considered to be stupendous luck, as no one ever had enough tea. Although Annie mostly drank Camp coffee, it was nice to bask in the envy of other less lucky folk and it was a fine china teapot. Then Helen won a pair of Fair Isle gloves, which were redundant as Annie had knitted many pairs herself, but warm gloves were always handy. Lastly and best of all, she won a model yacht. It was quite a simple craft, but large. It was something that she would enjoy sailing until her mid-teens. She found a nine foot pole in the coal shed, which was just long enough to keep control of the yacht in the swimming pool. It was a perfect toy for Helen because she could take a friend to share the fun, or she could go alone and indulge her imagination. In the many months when it was too cold for swimming, she would spend an hour or two each day at the pool with her yacht.

◊

That summer, their visit to Glasgow was disappointing. Everything looked gloomy and dirty. Although the windows had been replaced in the Hyndland flat, Bruce had advised Annie to stay at her parent's house.

"I haven't had time to clear it up yet and it's still a bloody mess, I'm afraid. Wouldn't like you and the wee yin to deal with it on your holiday. I'll get round to it sometime. Poor tenants were only in the house for four days when the blitz came. They've skedaddled up North somewhere and I can't say I blame them. Must have been a terrible night. Lost money on the deal of course, but what the hell. There's a war on."

This last phrase, delivered with a shrug and a grin, was now used regularly in most conversations.

The problem with the Renfrew Street flat was the stairs. When Annie discovered how daunting the climb to the top now was for her, she realised that she had lost a lot of strength since her last visit. How depressing that was. She must limit her outings to once a day and conserve enough energy for the long climb upstairs. Tears came to her eyes as she remembered hauling baby Helen in her pram upstairs twice and sometimes three times a day. How she had delighted in her own strength. It was not so very long ago, but she must not give way to depression. She tried to hide the effort required to climb the stairs from her daughter.

"We'll just have a wee rest on each landing and then we won't get out of breath."

Helen was fully aware of the situation and enjoyed the fact that they spent most of the day away from home, shopping, visiting, lunch in a cafe and often popping into a cinema in the afternoon, to give Annie a rest. The King's cinema was very near the flat and they went there several times. It was a strange long narrow hall, hardly broader than the screen and quite different from any other picture house that Helen knew. It tended to show old films and Annie liked to see a movie that she had enjoyed previously. That holiday they watched 'King Kong' and 'San Francisco'. Each film left a strong impression on Helen and inspired her imagination, but neither terrified her as Frankenstein had done.

Helen was disappointed that the Arlington was closed, but it was a relief to her mother.

They visited the aunties Gerty and Beatrice in Kelvindale. They seemed terribly frail to Annie. She wondered if the horrible news and the wartime restrictions were too much for them? Would they live to see the end of the war?

Next door, she was cheered up by seeing Eileen, who was always jokey and positive. Helen delighted in playing with wee Eileen. That was a very good day for them both.

Helen decided that she would like to be a mummy when she grew up. She had previously thought that being a teacher would be best, but of course you could not marry if you were a teacher. After playing with her delightful wee cousin, a maternal future seemed the only possibility. Just a pity that they had to be messy for the first few months. Eileeen's soft little feet reminded her of the toddler on the beach in Millport and she wondered what she was doing now. She would be at school.

Before they left Glasgow, they went to the King's theatre to see the Ballet Joos. This experience would give Helen's life a new direction altogether. There were three, very different, pieces that day. The first was graceful and fascinating, with apparently several mirrors onstage and one dancer, but as she danced, the reflections became other girls, who stepped from the mirrors and joined her. At the end she was once more alone. It was magical, the dresses were flowing and delicious colours and Helen was entranced. All those stories and scenarios which she had created in her head now crystallised. She started to realise some of the infinite possibilities of movement in telling a story. The leaping, turning and flying that a ballerina could accomplish on her toes determined Helen that she would one day dance like that. The second piece was ugly and hard and very avant-garde. It did not appeal to Helen, for she did not understand it and thought it peculiar. It was called 'The Green Table' and ten men with false bald heads and beards danced and gesticulated around a table. Its message was political and downbeat rather than exquisite and lyrical like the first piece. In fact 'The Green Table' was an early and seminal piece of modern dance which won many prizes, and Helen would one day be pleased and proud that she had seen it. The third piece was the 'Cracow Wedding' with wildly exciting music, crowds in bright peasant dresses and thrilling acrobatic dancing. Annie was delighted that it was such a marvellous show. For Helen it was a watershed. She would never again listen to music without creating an inner vision of movement to match the sound.

In August they returned to Pittenweem, where Mary was giving more than maternal care to the tomatoes and cucumbers. One cucumber had grown so large that it threatened to overbalance or even break its parent plant, and Mary had fashioned a sling to support it.

Annie laughed and complimented her mother on her ingenuity, realising at the same time that the plants were no longer her own project. Mrs Mackay had adopted the leafy jungle in the studio and made it entirely her own.

Helen had been fascinated by the doll's house in Lambhill. Previously she had thought that lots of money was required to set up a doll's establishment, but Elsie's splendid house had demonstrated that an ordinary person could make perfect miniature things for a doll to use. As far as Helen was concerned, of course, the only doll that required a home was Topsy.

There was a little cupboard under the eaves in the smaller bedroom upstairs. Helen judged that it would be a possible bed-sitting room for Topsy, only a little cramped. She emptied it of the few things it contained and gave it a good scrub. There was a miniature chest of drawers and she asked her Grandma if she might have it for Topsy's room.

"Topsy's room, my wee jewel? I didn't know she had a room."

"Well, I'm just getting it ready for her. It's that wee cupboard beside your bed."

"Have you got a bed for her room? She'll need a bed to sleep on, won't she."

"Yes, here's her little wooden bed."

"It's not very comfy looking, is it?"

For a few nights, Mary was very busy after Helen went to bed. By Saturday, the wooden bed was furnished with a proper ticking mattress, hem-stitched sheets, blankets edged with the correct wool stitching, lace-edged pillows and a silk eiderdown quilt. When Helen opened the cupboard door and saw Topsy, in her striped pyjamas, sitting up in her new bed, she was enraptured. Topsy was like a real person in a real bed. When a small vase of tiny flowers stood on top of the chest of drawers, and a birthday cake candle burned in the miniature brass candlestick beside the fine bed, the shadows on the wall seemed specially satisfying to Helen. It looked such a cosy little bed-sitting-room.

No one seemed to fear that she might set the house on fire.

One day Mary shouted to her family,

"Quick! Come here to the kitchen. Something's happening in Pittenweem. There are crowds passing the house and they're all carrying things. Come and see!"

John and Annie joined her and peered out the window.

"It's like Sauchiehall Street, Maw."

"Where can they all be going.?"

"It's like a mass flitting, they're all carrying bags and baskets. Even furniture! Look there's someone with a bird in a cage."

Just then Jean Hughes, a dependable source of town gossip, made her familiar rat-tat with the knocker on the front door.

Mary nodded and smiled,

"We'll hear all about it now."

The stupendous and shocking news was that two unexploded bombs had been dropped at the bus stop on the main road through town! It was unthinkable and just for a moment, Annie felt faint. This quiet little corner that had seemed so terribly safe throughout her life, was once more attacked. First of all the episode at sea and now this. What would come next? Where could they go to be safe?

Jean was busy telling the story,

"Ye see this Messerschmidt, Ah think that's whit Wullie said it wiz, Ah dae ken whither it wiz or no', but it hud goat separated from the ither Jerry planes, an' it hud loast height an' it wiz fleeing at ower low a latitude. So he hud tae dump his boambs, tae get back oot tae sea again an' awa hame. An' he dumpit thim richt in alow Geordie Miller's gairden. Ye ken hoo the wall's high at the bus stoap, weel that wa' is haudin' up Geordie's gairden, jist whaur he grows his totties. An' the twa bombs is stuck faur, faur intae the wa'. An' richt unnerneath Geordie's totties. An' he's tellin' me he hud an awfy grand crop comin' oan this year. Awfy grand, faur better than usual. Whit a shame, eh? His guid totties a' wasted. An' the bomb disposal squad's comin' the morn's mornin' and the bairns havenae tae gan tae the skill, fur it's closed a' week."

"But it's very lucky that no one was killed and no house damaged." Mary was trying to keep a serious face as this story poured out.

"Aye richt enuff. Ah'm gled naebody wiz staunin' at the bus stoap. Ye see it wiz hauf past ten when the boambs fell, an' the Elie bus had passed twenty meenits afore that. They wid hae been killt richt enuff, if they'd been staunin' there. But the bus hid gone afore that. Naw, they widnae hiv hid a chance, pair sowls. But still an a', it's an awfy peety aboot a' they grand totties. Whit a shame, eh!"

The schools were given two day's holidays, which pleased Helen.

The first day, Annie came home from shopping to find her father and Helen both sitting reading in the garden studio, where they were surrounded by glass walls and ceiling.

Trying to repress her anger, she shooed Helen out of the studio, then coldly asked her father,

"Don't you think that sitting in a glass house is rather inadvisable, considering that there are bombs in the town which might explode at any minute. Can you imagine what it would be like if all this glass fell on top of you and on top of my wee girl."

"Oh, I'd quite forgotten about the bombs, Annie. I suppose it might be dangerous in here. I'd never thought of that."

He turned over the next page of the newspaper and folded it carefully, showing no signs of moving from his seat.

"You're not going to stay sitting here, are you!"

"Och, I don't suppose anything'll happen yet, my dear."

Annie turned on her heel and walked away. She blamed her mother too, for not noticing the danger. Really, her parents were worse than children.

She quickly put together a picnic, and she and Helen walked along to St Monance and spent the day out of town. Helen really enjoyed having her mother all to herself like that. It was unusual when her grandparents were there. There was more cooking and housework to be done when they were visiting and also Grandma liked to have an audience to listen to her stories.

Willie came through one weekend with wee Eileen. Helen was so happy to take the toddler to the beach and to hold her hand as they walked slowly up and down the steep wynds.

They paid a visit to St Andrews on Saturday and had lunch at the Tudor tearoom. Eileen was a little afraid of the cuckoo clock, although Helen tried to tell her how nice it was.

While Mary drank her tea, Willie took the two girls out to the garden at the back of the tearoom. Helen had never seen it before, but she would always remember it with shame. The baby was bending down looking at a flower in the path, when cacoethes struck Helen like a bolt of lightning. She was seized with the urge to do something which she knew to be foolish, but which she could not resist. She took a running jump and leapt over the crouching child. Unfortunately Eileen stood up at the wrong moment and was bumped by Helen's bony knee. Not surprisingly, the child shrieked her astonishment and pain for several moments, while Helen stood aghast, filled with remorse and horror at her own stupidity. What an idiot! What had made her do such a thing? Would uncle Willie ever speak to her again? What would Grandma say, for no doubt the screaming would be audible inside the cafe?

That was when she discovered what a kindly man her uncle was. All he said was,

"Don't worry Helen, that was just a wee mistake. She'll be fine in a minute."

What a wonderful understanding man! Helen remembered all her years of adoration and her early desire to marry him.

When they went back inside the cafe, Mary asked,

"Did I hear the baby crying out there, Willie?"

Helen held her breath in horror, but Willie only said,

"Och, she just had a wee fall. She's fine now."

Helen sometimes heard worried family conversations about Willie and his money problems, but to Helen he would always be a hero.

Thimble

That autumn it became obvious that a family of mice had moved into the house. Packets of cornflour and semolina were ripped open and little black droppings appeared in the cupboards.

At night, the scratchings and scufflings kept them both awake.

"I must do something about those mice. I'll need to get a trap I suppose."

Annie was far from enthusiastic about the idea of a cruel trap.

"P'raps we could get a cat, Mummy?"

"That would be awkward when we go back and forth to Glasgow."

"Maybe we could just get a loan of a cat? What about Ecky?"

In fact Georgina's cat often walked along the High Street to visit them, knowing that he would be welcomed with a tasty snack.

"I don't expect he would stay with us. He never stays long after he has eaten. We need a cat-in-residence"

Georgina was asked for her advice and she knew of a young cat, not much more than a kitten, which wanted a home for five weeks, while its mistress was visiting a sick relative. Perfect!

Helen was terribly excited about this addition to the family.

"What will we call it?"

"I expect it already has a name."

Helen was disappointed.

"Can I feed it?"

"Certainly. What will you feed it, darling?"

Tinned food for animals was unknown in those days of rationing

"I expect there will always be things I can get for it, wee bits of whatever we are having. I have that little doll's saucepan that I can use to cook in,"

Annie looked doubtful and suggested,

"Perhaps she will just kill and eat all our mice, and she won't need anything else to eat."

Helen was silent. She was in love with the beauty of cats and their pretty, purring ways and had not considered the schizoid killer side of the feline race.

As it happened, Thimble did no killing during her stay. She may have frightened the mice away, for Annie's neighbour caught many in his trap, but Thimble saved her energy for playing and chasing. Much to the delight of Helen and her mother, the small black and white cat was a 'retriever'. She would carry the hank of string or the ball of paper in her mouth, back to the feet of the person who had thrown it, just as a dog would. Annie said this was very unusual in a cat.

"She's a very special wee cat, Mummy."

"It must be all that food that you cook for her. Remember that she is on *loan* and has to go back to her rightful owner."

Annie worried that the future parting would be hard.

Helen was always on the lookout for any morsel that she could add to Thimble's daily stewpot. Sometimes a fish head or skin formed the basis, with small crumbs of bread, sardine, cabbage, a pinch of mince, corned beef, sausage, potato, cheese, just anything that might taste good. It was cooked at the side of the fire, beside the large pot that was usually full of simmering soup or stew.

Helen developed her culinary skills on Thimble and no matter what strange mixture she produced, Thimble ate every scrap with relish and grew large and plump. It was an excellent, affirmative training for a cook. Soon Helen started to read cookery books and learned to make biscuits for herself when she felt like a treat.

The house was very quiet the day that Thimble returned to her owner. Annie wondered if there would be tears, but Helen was a pragmatic child and only said rather sadly,

"I expect Thimble is happy to be home again."

"I bet her owner hardly recognises her, she's grown so much."

"Y'know, I'm looking forward to when I have my own wee cat and I want a striped one, like Ecky."

Mary came through to Fife for a few days in October.

"What a cold house this is. I'm absolutely frozen. You never realise it's so draughty when you're here in the summer."

"Well, this is nothing. Wait another few weeks and it'll be colder, then in January it's worst of all."

"I had no idea, Annie. Your father and I often worry about you through here all by yourself."

"Och I'm not by myself. I've got Helen and we do not badly the two of us. My wee paraffin heater is a great comfort at bedtime. Don't know what we'd do without it."

"I see you're still not wearing stockings."

Annie made no reply.

"Pettigrews had a great show of fur boots in their sale last week. Some were only about three pounds a pair. I nearly bought you some, but I suppose you're better to try them on yourself. I'll give you the money and you can maybe get some in St Andrews."

"That's very kind of you, Maw. They have nice boots here in the shoe shop in the Marketplace. I'll just get them there."

"Your father was saying we should give you a wee present, as he's been selling quite well recently. Surprising isn't it, with all the terrible news."

"That's good and it would certainly be very acceptable and very kind."

"Yes, well we've had to give Willie a bit of financial help this year. What with the baby and everything, he and Eileen had got themselves into a bit of debt."

Again Annie said nothing. She wondered just how much debt it was. She knew she would never learn the actual sums involved. It would not be the first time that his parents had come to Willie's financial rescue.

"Another thing that Pettigrews had in their sale were some wonderful fur coats, dyed Canadian squirrel. They were really lovely, so stylish. I wondered if you would have liked one of those to help you through the cold winter."

"Oh, that's *very* generous of you, Maw. What a lovely idea. Fancy you thinking of that! The problem is that really a fur coat is too heavy for me to wear nowadays. I have my old musquash there, but it just tires me out when I wear it to the shops. I've tried it once or twice, but no go. I've reluctantly hung it away until I feel better."

Her smile was quizzical and slightly lop-sided.

"Anyway, it's really in the house that I feel the cold most. When I'm outside, just walking and keeping my balance is enough to keep me warm. Anyway, how much were these gorgeous fur coats? They must have been quite a price."

"Yes, they were dear, seventy nine and eighty nine guineas,

but that seemed like a bargain to me. My grey squirrel coat cost a lot more than that in 1937."

Annie's breath was quite taken away. How wonderful if her parents decided to give her that amount of money instead of the coat. What a difference it would make to their lives. No more pinching and scraping for years.

When Mary left for Glasgow, she gave Annie twenty-five pounds.

"That's five pounds for boots, Annie and twenty just to make life a wee bit easier for you. Not much to spend it on these days, I'm afraid, but your father was keen that you shouldn't feel left out, when Willie had been helped."

It was a very nice present and Annie was properly grateful, though it did seem hard that because she did not want the fur coat, her present was so much reduced. Her mother was a strange woman. Annie wondered again exactly how much had been given to Willie to save him from his difficulties.

◊

Helen had been slow to learn the skills that other children had. She was timid at jumping into skipping ropes and often missed her beat when they were 'keeping the pot boiling' That meant that she must take the rope-end and do the boring job of 'ca'ing the rope round' until the next person missed a beat or stumbled. She did not feel she was as good at kicking the tin in hopscotch either, although she often practised by herself on the pavement outside her front door. She was quite good with a ball and also practised that in the autumn evenings after tea.

One night when she came into the house, her mother said,

"Turn around a moment, let me see your dress."

It was the brown woollen dress with felt applique that had been made the previous year. She loved it and had worn it a lot.

"My goodness, you've worn right through the skirt! There's quite a big hole and I can see your knickers shining through!"

What horror Helen felt. She had been out in full view in the High Street, for at least an hour, with her knickers showing through her skirt. She felt so ashamed. She thought that she could never forget it.

The shame faded with time and when she could forget about the embarrassment, Helen found a strange satisfaction in wearing something until it was really finished and of no more use. So often she had found herself outgrowing favourite garments which, although in perfect condition, had quite suddenly became too tight or too short. Then she suffered a real sense of loss when they were discarded, almost a bereavement. Although she had loved that dress, it was certainly worn out now. It had been getting rather small anyway.

It set a standard for the future and for the rest of her life, Helen continued to feel that an article of clothing should always be worn thin or torn before it was discarded.

There are now air-raid shelters for 20,000,000 people in Britain. More bunks and rest centres will be provided and more tubes are to be used for shelters.

Glasgow Herald 20th Oct 1941

When Annie lay in her bed at night and longed for more heat, she tried to imagine what it must be like sleeping in a tube station, as the poor Londoners were doing. She remembered her honeymoon and how she and Bruce had struggled to find their way through the vast, labyrinthine corridors of the London Underground. They had gone up and down escalators, asking for help from officials and other travellers. It had been a nightmare for no one seemed able to help. Really, she should not complain about her squeaky old brass bed and the coldness of her little room. It was sheer luxury compared to a thin mattress on a narrow concrete platform. Then there was the lack of privacy added to the fear and discomfort. How *horrible* it must be! It was quite beyond her imagination.

NEW RATIONING SCHEME FOR CANNED GOODS

Distribution of Pink Books in Glasgow this Week

The allowance will be sixteen points every four weeks.

Full sixteen points required for 1lb of following goods, canned or bottled.

Tongue, Brisket, Australian minced meat loaf, Australian or New Zealand canned rabbit, Eire stewed steak, USA canned meat loaf, sausage meat or sausage bulk, salmon, sardines, crayfish, lobster, crab or tunny.

Herring and pilchards require only thirteen points. Canned beans in sauce are four points.

Glasgow Herald 9th November 1941

Another Christmas passed. The New Year of 1942 showed no signs of the war ending.

It was a quiet narrow life that Annie and her daughter led in Fife. There were no visits to museums, exhibitions, botanic gardens or department stores, no regular swimming at the baths club and no theatre visits. Although that night with Rena Hall had certainly been a wonderful show, there had been only one or two local concerts to attend since then. Annie was impressed by the local talent, there were many good singers and the children were always nice to watch. Even the little ones who forgot their lines were sweet. But these outings could not compare with a professional show. There had been a Brownies concert while Helen was still a member of the troop and she had been asked to recite a poem which described the wonderful life that a Brownie led. Annie suspected there was more than a touch of irony in the emphasis which Helen gave to certain sentimental phrases. However it had given the kid the idea of learning poetry and Annie supposed that was a good discipline. Helen had thrown herself into learning poetry wholeheartedly. Each day, Annie could hear her daughter reciting large chunks of Tennyson to the toys in the studio. That was probably the only influence that the Brownies had made on Helen, but it was a habit which would last for several years.

Helen lived for the holidays spent in Glasgow, and Annie herself missed the stimulation of a bustling city and its various inhabitants. Annie worried that Helen's perception of the world beyond Pittenweem was too much influenced by the films that they saw. Probably everybody was very influenced by Hollywood. Perhaps she herself was more influenced than she liked to admit. Younger women certainly were, for in spite of all the wartime restrictions, their clothes, make-up and hairstyles mirrored those of the transatlantic film stars. The world depicted on the screen seemed so luxurious and idyllic compared to the austere reality of life for most people in Britain.

Annie supposed that they were sort of fairy stories and Helen would take them as such. She certainly felt cheered up by them herself.

She particularly loved the musicals with their ridiculous plots, splendid dancing and gorgeous clothes. The slight plots might be interrupted at any moment by a song or dance. She adored

Deanna Durbin, who could smile and look so lovely as she sang, for not all singers look good as they perform. Helen liked more action; Sonja Henie skating on a romantic pool under the stars, wearing a charming fur-trimmed skirt which whirled out and showed her neat little knickers as she spun around faster and ever faster; Johnny Weissmuller swinging from tree to tree on conveniently placed ropes and finally diving into a jungle pool, probably sharing his swim with a wild animal. How she would love to do that herself! Esther Williams with her magnificent powerful stroke and her charming smile, no matter how deep the water. Helen practised some of Esther's balletic manoeuvres in the water, although always avoiding any immersion of her face.

When she first saw Vera Zorina in the Goldwyn Follies, Helen knew what she must do when she grew up. She would be a ballerina. Zorina was even more wonderful than the lady dancing with the mirrors in Glasgow last summer. Helen had often watched dancers on point in films before, but they had looked bizarre and awkward, with little skill and no grace. They struggled, where Zorina soared. Zorina was a real ballerina, whose work was choreographed by her husband, the as-yet-unknown Balanchine. While Helen did not know anything about dance, she recognised poetry and perfection. Zorina would be her role model forever after, with Esther Williams a very close second.

Annie enjoyed the heavier dramas, especially if Joan Crawford or Barbara Stanwick were in them, but she knew that they held less interest for her daughter.

The B feature was almost always a cowboy film, which bored the mother and daughter, although it elicited happy cheers from the Pittenweem boys in the front rows.

There was little to balance these entertaining but unrealistic film. Annie had small faith in the news bulletins. The unreal accent of the 'voice over' seemed to have a false jollity and optimism. Of course this would change immediately when bad news could no longer be ignored. Sometimes jokes were made about unpronounceable foreign names, which seemed very undiplomatic to Annie. How much of what they saw was propaganda? How little was truth?

Occasionally there was an American documentary which Annie really enjoyed because it was informative. It was called the Passing Parade and opened to the strains of Dvorak's New World symphony. One episode described the impressive hydro-electric schemes which had been built in America, showing the landscape of vast mountains and rivers. These projects had meant work for thousands of unemployed men, at a time when families were starving. Annie thought it was a wonderful story and wondered why the government in this country had not helped the unemployed in the thirties in a similar way. There must have been money there to finance this beastly war that they were now waging.

Another Passing Parade episode pictured a very different aspect of the USA, the poor whites of the Appalachian Mountains. These people of the backwoods lived in hovels and were dressed in rags. Without crockery, their small portion of food was served in shallow indentations hollowed out of the wooden table. The half-clad children were seen squatting in the dirt eating crumbs of clay, from which they derived the minerals necessary for survival. This primitive existence and appalling poverty, in the midst of America's wealth, seemed incredible. She had thought that such backward societies were only to be found in Africa or other distant deprived lands.

Sometimes a cartoon would be part of the programme, though not nearly often enough for Helen. Mickey Mouse was the favourite, for Helen could not understand Donald Duck's quacking voice and Popeye was very violent.

Sometimes there was a twenty minute 'short' with various 'turns' a sort of showcase of unknown talent. Generally it started with a band and a girl singer. The band-leader then introduced the different acts. There was usually a couple in evening dress who did a modified Astaire and Rodgers number. Although not as magical as the famous pair, they were usually good and finished with the man swinging the lady round and round through the air rather dangerously. One time as Annie watched a glamourous dancing couple, the girl made a slight slip. It was hardly noticeable. A moment later, the man stumbled slightly, so slightly that Annie wondered if she really had seen it. Could they have meant to do it? Or were they just not rehearsed? Annie felt herself start to giggle, from nerves as much as anything. Then they really made a mix-up, and the man just stopped the girl from falling. It was very understated and subtle, but they were parodying the usual performances. Annie and Helen began to laugh and others around started to join in. Soon, with each further disaster on the dance floor, the whole audience was helpless. Annie and Helen were wiping the tears from their cheeks. It was a wonderful act and the two dancers gave no sign that they were anything but serious and perfect. Annie always hoped to see them again, but never did.

Quite often there was a troupe of three or four negro brothers, who would sing in close harmony then tap dance with amazing brilliancy, incorporating acrobatics into their act.

Helen was fascinated by the bodily contortions achieved by these agile young men and often copied their movements, as far as she could. Sadly, she tried one that went beyond her capabilities. Placing both hands flat on the floor between her feet, she hooked her bent knees over her shoulders and tried to balance on her hands. Unfortunately she lost her balance and was unable to stop herself from crashing forward on to her face. As she said afterwards sadly,

"I bit a hole in the linoleum."

And there was a small indentation in the green lino, where she had broken a corner off her nice new white front tooth.

It was very sad and the dentist advised waiting until the tooth was fully grown before doing anything to it. The future possibility was of filing it away and capping it and Helen did not much like the sound of that. She hoped that in the future, when the war was over, there would be lots of apples to eat and she felt that a capped tooth might not deal with eating an apple very well. The broken tooth was still quite efficient for the few apples that came her way.

Although Helen continued her acrobatic experiments, she put more thought into safety from then on.

Films were not the only American influence in their lives. After the United States entered the war, a distant relative of John's started to send them the Saturday Evening Post. What an amazement the first one was. It came in a heavy, tightly rolled bundle. When it was opened, there seemed to be enough newspapers and magazines to stock a newsagent's shop. Annie and Helen had become used to meagre daily papers of only one or two folded sheets, of very soft light newsprint. Here was the Post printed on marvellous heavy duty paper with lots of colour. It included a full length novel, a magazine of short stories, the funnies, the sports page, the magazine with its Norman Rockwell cover as well as several other sections. They could only laugh that first time, for it seemed impossible that anyone would ever finish reading it in less than a month, yet it was a *weekly*! Helen loved it and read all the fiction, some of which was probably beyond her ten-year-old understanding. The comics were hilarious.

Because of the strong colour prints, Annie remembered another craft to teach Helen.

A long strip of paper was cut, narrowing at one end. The side which was the least colourful was spread with wall paper paste then, starting at the broad end the paper was wound round and round a knitting pin to form an elegant long bead, fatter in the middle. The colours blended beautifully, and once it was dry, the beads could be strung together. No one would guess that the glowing beads owed their existence to a Coca Cola advertisement or perhaps a Popeye comic.

The same relative sent one or two food parcels as well. Helen did not find these very tempting, there were cake mixes, sweets and rather dry biscuits. One item, however, made them laugh just as much as the Saturday Evening Post had done, and for the same reason. It was a plain metal tin about the same size as a large tin of treacle. It had no label or description on it. Annie thought it must have been soldiers' rations.

"Shall we open it up and give it a try?"

Helen nodded.

The tin was full of sausages, *very full*. Indeed they were so tightly packed, that they would hardly come out of the tin. They were not in skins, but extruded and chopped off square at the end. Annie opened the tin at both ends and pushed them out and pushed them out, and still more came, threatening to overflow the large plate and cover the kitchen table. It was like a conjuring trick. When they were counted, there were forty-eight sausages and Helen and her mother were giggling help-lessly.

"How on earth will we eat all those sausages?"

Georgina and her mother and Mrs Hill were able to help them and they were certainly very tasty pork sausages. Mrs Hill said,

"My, those were *awful good* sausages. Just like pre-war, weren't they. I wish we could buy those in the shops. Mind you, the pilchards are very tasty too, and very good value and not many points. And I think they're healthy. D'you try the pilchards yourself, Annie?"

Annie smiled and nodded slightly, not to seem rude, but Helen knew that her mother was quite snobbish about the pilchards and the thick tomato sauce that covered them. Her mother was snobbish about several things. They never ate pilchards or Spam or margarine. Margarine was pronounced with a hard g and was only used for cooking. When the small ration of butter was finished, they ate dry bread.

That superabundance of newspapers and sausages would always be intertwined and associated with America, in Helen's memory.

Editorial Diary.

Notice in a garage in centre of Glasgow,

"In the event of a direct hit, all doors to be closed."

Glasgow Herald 10th January 1942

Expeditions

Helen had developed such sensitivity to her mother's failing strength that in her mind she had two separate perceptions of distance. There was her own sort of distance, when she was by herself or with adults other than her mother. Then she could walk, run or skip and never notice if it were uphill or rough underfoot. She was an energetic child and hardly knew the meaning of physical tiredness. However she held a separate and special attitude towards her mother's distance and was aware of every difficulty when walking beside her. Annie's progress was governed by the terrain, for even the slightest upward incline made it harder for her. If the ground were rutted or stony, this would be a further drawback. Even a windy day would add to her problems. Helen learned to judge all these handicaps, as she held her mother's hand to steady her, and was able to ignore them completely when by herself. In fact she rather enjoyed the extra effort required on a steep hill.

The mile between Anstruther and Pittenweem was now about the limit of Annie's endurance, and even that short distance entailed several rest periods. Just two or three minutes standing still and breathing deeply seemed to help her.

"There I am," she would say, "ready to go again, just as good as new."

But Helen knew that was not true.

Annie's ambitions were not always moderated by her capabilities. When she heard that Winston Churchill was to visit Elie, she was really keen to go and see him. No one was sure if it were only a rumour, but there were certainly to be some morale-boosting army exercises along the coast. As it was also known that several important Army and Navy men had houses in that town, Churchill's presence seemed a strong possibility. Annie knew that they were living through historic times and thought how fine it would be if Helen, when she was a mother herself, could tell her children that she had seen the famous war leader in the flesh.

Helen was less enthusiastic, but her mother tried to paint a vivid picture of the old warrior and how important he was.

They took the bus to Elie. The town was quiet and empty. Annie asked in a shop, but they seemed to know nothing about any event happening that day. Were they just being cautious with a stranger, she wondered? Posters everywhere warned you to 'Keep it Dark!' and 'Walls have Ears!' Surely she looked innocent enough with her limp and a child with her. She asked a passer-by and he shrugged and shook his head. Another thought that "perhaps there is something happening in Earlsferry, I think I heard that, yes." Earlsferry was nearly another mile to walk and Helen started to feel downcast. They continued to walk slowly through Elie. One or two armoured cars passed them and Annie felt a bit more optimistic.

"There must be something happening after all, Helen. We'll get there yet, darling."

"Will we see Churchill?"

"I'm pretty sure we will."

But Helen was worried, because she knew that Annie was tiring and there was no further sign of troops or gold braid. They stopped while Annie leaned against a wall for a short rest. There was no tearoom or cafe in sight. It all seemed pretty hopeless. Annie wished that she had found out a bit more about it before setting off. Helen had a worried look on her face. If they decided to give up and go home, they must walk all the way back to the Elie bus stop.

Just then a very opulent car with dark glass windows drove past.

"D'ye think that was Winston Churchill, Mummy?"

"Well, if it was, there wasn't much chance of seeing him. I wonder if he'll get out the car and give a speech in Earlsferry?"

"I think we should just go home. I'm not caring about seeing him."

"It seems a shame to give up, when we're nearly there."

Helen's face showed that she did not agree.

"All right, my love, you're right I suppose, probably going home is the best plan."

It was a long, slow walk back to the Elie bus stop, with several pauses for Annie to rest and recover. When a squad of smart soldiers marched past them, heading for Earlsferry, Helen was afraid that her mother might change her mind about going home, but Annie knew her limitations. She was almost at the end of her tether. They were both very thankful when they arrived at the bus stop and were just in time to drop into their seats on the little blue bus.

A few weeks later, the news came that a whale had beached itself at St Andrew's.

Once more they set off with Annie enthusiastic to see the whale and Helen wondering if they would have to walk far to see it.

The distance from the bus stop to the beach was further than Annie had remembered and this outing was again a failure, for when the beach came into sight, columns of thick black smoke could be seen and the air was full of an acrid unpleasant smell. Annie spoke to a passerby and learned that they had started to cut up the dead whale and burn it the previous day. She immediately turned round to leave the horrible scene.

"We're just a bit too late, Helen."

At first the child could not comprehend quite how they could be too late for a dead whale. She was anxious to reach the beach for a closer look at the dark mound in the distance, but Annie hurried away as best she could.

"I'm afraid your old Mum's been too slow to get here. It's another disaster, like the day we went to see Churchill. Never mind, let's go and have a cup of Horlicks to warm us up."

"It's not such a disaster as the day we walked to Elie, Mummy."

"That's what I've just said!"

"No, I mean long ago, when we walked along the shore to Elie. That was a disaster."

Annie laughed

"I'd forgotten that."

In their first few months in Pittenweem at the beginning of the war, they had walked along the path to St Monance, then onwards to Elie, without realising that there was not a continuing pathway, nor how far or how difficult it would be for a seven-year-old. There were times that they had to climb over rocks, slither over masses of deep seaweed and occasionally wade through the incoming sea. They had got tar on their clothes and shoes and had been exhausted when they finally caught a bus home.

It was not true that Annie had forgotten that demanding journey, for it was the first time that she had fully realised her lessening strength, and a terrifying inkling of what the future might hold had dawned on her.

Other Husbands Other Wives

Helen had gone to bed long ago for it was after eleven, but Annie still sat at the fire. She had foolishly piled on more coal than necessary and it seemed such a waste to leave it. Especially as, for once, the small sitting room was really cosy. It must be a very calm night, Annie thought, for the usual draughts were not creeping in at every crevice. It had certainly been bitterly cold when she had put out the milk bottle, but there was no wind.

It was terribly quiet and she wondered if she would describe herself as lonely, but decided that being alone was not lonely. Not even unpleasant, in this warm and pretty little room. She felt rather content.

Smiling to herself she remembered that she had offended Helen that day. She was unrepentant because honestly she sometimes got a bit fed up with the importance that Topsy still held in her daughter's life. Surely at nearly eleven, she should be outgrowing dolls. Helen still had a habit of pouncing on any miniature object and saying,

"Wouldn't that be just the right size for Topsy!"

or,

"Wouldn't that make a nice table (or cake or book or anything) for Topsy!"

Today Annie had been cleaning out a cupboard and had found a cedar cigar box. It was well made and smelled delicious, Annie could not resist showing it to Helen and saying,

"Wouldn't this make a lovely coffin for Topsy!"

Helen had not been amused. The fact that Annie could not stop herself from giggling, did not help. There had been no tears, but certainly there was a look of fury, not unlike the expression that Mary could summon up in her displeasure.

By tea-time, Helen had obviously decided to let such an insensitive statement fade into that void of things best forgotten.

Annie picked up the Herald again. How could one be sure that the news in it was correct? She was pretty sure that lots of bad news was suppressed. Most people were obsessed with the latest news, listening to every radio bulletin and searching in every paper, but facts could so easily be twisted around or just missed out. Perhaps the most believable things in the paper were the advertisements? Annie smiled at that crazy thought, for she normally felt extreme cynicism about all advertisements.

She turned to the Woman's Page where a headline caught her eye.

"CANNY WITH THE COUPONS"
Women who have patriotically refrained from major dress purchases since war began, now regard their wardrobes with extreme disfavour.

What rubbish! Patriotism was hardly the main reason for her, or her friends', lack of new purchases. Plain old shortage of cash was a more immediate drawback.

On the same page, Coplands advertisement for lady's wear proclaimed.

Ladies flannel slacks	25/6	8 coupons.
Tailored tweed skirt	35/-	8 coupons
Housecoat	55/-	6 coupons
Woollen combinations	18/6	6 coupons

She already had several skirts and she ignored the housecoat. Were there many women who could afford to drift around in such an impractical garment? She had considered getting herself a pair of slacks, but no doubt her mother and Bruce would disapprove. She'd never hear the end of it and the Pittenweem folk would certainly gossip, for women in slacks were not often seen in that quiet corner.

She smiled to herself as she remembered the time when she had her long hair bobbed, nearly twenty years ago. It was the latest style in the city, but it had not yet reached the rural areas. Her neat bouncing hair was the talk of the town. One day she heard two young Pittenweem women in conversation in the street. Their voices were loud and it was obvious that they intended her to hear.

"Aye, then Jessie, Ah'll see ye nixt week."

"Aye, that'll be grand, Bella."

"Weel, cheerio the, noo!"

"Aye, cheerio the noo. An be shair and no' hiv yer hair cutten oot, afore Ah see ye again."

But it would only be a few weeks before the short style was adopted by many local ladies.

Annie could not make up her mind about slacks. Woollen ones were probably very warm and sensible. Those Hollywood stars looked good in them. Katherine Hepburn was often pictured on the golf course in slacks and Annie was certainly thin enough to look stylish. Somehow she just could not find the courage to wear them.

The previous winter Annie had given up the struggle of donning a girdle each morning. The strong elastic garment had to be subdued, then manoeuvred and forced over her hips, slender as they were, and the procedure made her tired before breakfast. Without a girdle, she had nothing to hold up her stockings. As tight garters did not seem very healthy, she had decided that woollen socks and a long tweed skirt were just as warm and a great deal easier to put on quickly in the cold mornings. Her mother disapproved, of course.

"You should think of your health, Annie. You haven't enough on. Those socks aren't *nearly* warm enough. You should be wearing a corset and stockings in this cold weather."

Her mother was of the generation that saw corsets as a necessity and Annie had been kitted out with one when she was fifteen. She had discarded it after a week and refused to wear one ever again, in spite of the ' health-giving comfort' described in advertisements.

Helen did not like her mother's socks either, for other mothers did not wear socks. However it was more practical for Annie and besides, Katherine Hepburn also wore ankle socks with a tweed skirt and looked very stylish.

The last item on Coplands list of bargains, the combinations, reminded her of another of her mother's purchases and Annie burst out laughing at the memory.

How strange, but enjoyable, to laugh out loud when you were by yourself! She was not sure if she had ever done that before.

She had probably been about seventeen when she was presented with those lambswool combinations. They had one drawback. The neat round neck was small and defied the entry of a well developed body. The only way to clamber into the garment, was through the bunkerlid and that required an advanced degree of agility. When her mother had come into her bedroom one day and witnessed her daughter's contortions, her first reaction was of anger.

"What on earth are you doing, Annie? You'll *ruin* the shape of those combinations and they were very expensive!"

Annie's red face and untidy hair pushed through the neck at last.

"Well, Maw, you'll need to show me some other way of getting into them."

Mary was apologetic, unusual position for her, but she transferred her righteous indignation to the manufacturer, who happened to be a personal friend. Poor Annie had cringed, as the man was given a description of the awkwardness of donning his product. She hoped that he did not have too vivid an imagination.

The combinations had been so beautifully soft, she could still feel the fabric in her imagination. It all seemed so long ago, and Europe had been at war then too. Now another war was raging over Europe and nobody knew what would happen next. Here she was, a married woman of nearly forty, with a husband who was hardly a husband. For years there had been that feeling of waiting and not knowing. It was a strange sort of limbo. Even her health was just one big question mark.

She wondered what Bruce was doing just now. Perhaps at the golf club, drinking whisky with the rest of the Home Guard. They seemed to have a very social time of it. Perhaps he was with some ladyfriend. She could not worry about that too much. Romance seemed a very distant prospect, even if there had been the opportunity. Too hard to be a femme fatale, when just keeping warm and fed was such an effort. Nor was one bath per week, in a small zinc tub, helpful towards feminine allure. She laughed aloud again.

In a way, compared to the other husbands she knew, Bruce was not so bad. He sent her cash regularly each month, and brought treats when he visited. He obviously cared for Helen. Many of her friends were not so lucky. There was Nancy, whose husband had embezzled money, then left her completely in the lurch. Then there was Elsie, whose husband had to be practically carried home from the pub each night, and Annie suspected that Derek Dickson was in much the same boat. Then, although her own brother was a devoted husband and father, his addiction to gambling meant that his family was always desperately hard-up. So strange that he continued to feel that *next time* he would make his fortune. That terrible optimism of the gambler never faded.

Then poor Laura in Edinburgh, her husband had punched and beaten her.

In fact Bruce stood out as a very fine husband. What a pity that they could never live happily together.

What about wives? She thought of her friend Jean Brown, who had died last year. Jean had hardly been a model wife. Easily the wealthiest of all her friends, Jean had always had a maid and her own car. With her two daughters in boarding school, she had more time than other women, and obviously more inclination, for affairs. She lived in Edinburgh with a holiday house in Elie. One summer she had conducted a torrid love affair during her summer in Fife, using Annie's Pittenweem address for secret telegrams and letters. Annie was not proud of deceiving poor Andy, Jean's husband. He seemed to work so hard for his large salary, and with little return, for Jean was often on the golf course, when not secretly meeting some amour. If the maid could cook, that was fine, but if she had not the skill, they ate disgusting messes. Annie had tasted appalling meals at their house.

Poor Jean though. Cancer had taken her very quickly before she was forty. She had been a great believer in Spiritualism and had attended seances regularly. Annie did not believe in any of that sort of thing, although she remembered when the family had great fun with the Ouija board. It was still kicking around the house somewhere. They and their friends had laughed their way through each session and had never taken it seriously, although some of the messages had seemed eerily to the point. Then, purely as an entertainment, Annie had always read teacups, using her imagination and with her tongue in her cheek. There again, it was surprising how many people would tell her later that her prophecies had hit the mark.

She shook herself and thought it was damned silly to be thinking about things like that, at dead of night. Just as well there was no wind, because sometimes a high wind could get under the linoleum and make it rise and fall gently, as if it were breathing. She and Helen were able to laugh at it together, but now she was alone and she glanced sidelong at the green lino. How horrid if it moved just now!

Jean had been so positive that there was another, spiritual world. If there had been such a thing, Annie rationalised, Jean would most certainly have tried to get in touch with her.

Just then she turned her head towards the fire, where a dish-towel was hanging from the mantelpiece to dry. Her blood froze.

Had the towel moved? Or were her eyes just tired?

Why was Jean so much in her mind just now?

Was Jean trying to get in touch?

Annie hurriedly jumped to her feet and poked the fire to pieces, decided against going upstairs in the dark to brush her teeth and was soon in bed, cuddled up close to her sleeping daughter.

Ice Cream

There was a snowfall while they stayed with the Mackays at Renfrew Street that Christmas of 1942. John asked Helen if she would like some ice-cream.

She smiled politely, as she thought he was teasing her. However, when he said that he would just make some custard, she really thought that he was talking nonsense. Mary was always complaining about how forgetful John was and Helen thought that must explain his strange suggestion. Once the custard was made, he picked up an enamel basin and beckoned her to follow him upstairs to the attic bedroom. She was very puzzled. There John opened the window, scooped snow into the basin, then embedded the pan of custard in the snow and started to stir it vigorously.

"We'll soon have some delicious ice-cream. Helen!"

She did not believe a word of it and felt terribly sorry for him as he stirred and stirred. She even took a turn at stirring herself, although she knew it was hopeless.

He opened the window and added more snow round about the pot and stirred and stirred.

"Aha! Here we go!"

It was the nearest thing to magic that Helen had ever witnessed. The bright yellow custard had turned into pale ice cream, just as she remembered it from long ago, before the war. It even tasted just the same.

"I don't think you thought I could make ice cream with custard and snow, did you? You'd no faith in your old grandad."

Helen blushed and mumbled that yes she did, but she felt very guilty.

Helen had received a book for Christmas which delighted her and affected her whole philosophy. It was the Jungle Book, Kipling's story of the boy Mowgli who was reared by wolves and lived amongst the wild animals. It had a great influence on Helen, changing her attitude towards wild animals and to herself. She approved of the idea of sleeping whenever you felt tired, as Mowgli could do. That seemed a very sensible skill to Helen and she tried to develop it.

Another present was a kaleidoscope. She was fascinated by the wonderful, ever-changing abstract shapes and colours which formed, then disappeared, never to be repeated.

The third present was a perfect sphere of Pears soap. She loved to hold it and to look into its mysterious, golden depths. It smelled clean and unlike other soap. She often gazed at it and it seemed too precious to waste by introducing it to water. She would never again see a soap ball like it.

◊

Annie came back to the house in Pittenweem with little enthusiasm. The house felt bitterly cold after two weeks of being unfired. There was still a lot of winter to deal with, probably the worst part was yet to come. Again she felt how unfair that these extreme winters should have hit Europe at such a difficult time. As usual, in order to suppress her self-pity, she scolded herself and tried to realise the tribulations of those who were homeless in much more severe climates than Britain. It helped slightly.

Her general strength was depleted by the constant cold. In the mornings her limbs were stiff and unresponsive, and by nighttime she felt an aching tiredness.

She was cheered to hear from her plumber that he had finally found an old bath for her. It was delivered and installed in the wash-house. No plumbing was necessary as the hot water would be scooped in a little pannikin straight from the boiler to the bath. When the plug was pulled and the bath emptied, the water would flow across the concrete floor to a drain. It was amazing how excited Annie and Helen were about their new bath, scratched and scabby as it was.

On Saturday Annie filled the boiler with a hose-pipe and made a fine fire underneath it. Helen was waiting with her towel and soap.

"It might take an hour or two to heat up, you know!" Annie warned her daughter, "They say that a watched boiler never boils."

Helen did not quite understand her mother's joke, but she smiled politely.

When Annie came to the transfer of the water from the boiler to the bath, she warned her daughter out of the wash-house.

"This is very hot water and it would scald you if it splashed."

It was harder work than she had bargained for. The government had issued regulations that a bath should be no deeper than five inches, so Annie felt justified in stopping at that point. Helen looked slightly disappointed. She had pictured it being much fuller, like the ones that she remembered at the Arlington Baths. She was compensated by the discovery that one could be much wilder in the wash-house than in a conventional bathroom. You could splash as much as you liked! By soaping the sloping end of the bath, she made a spectacular chute, displacing high waves of water each time she slid down it. The floor was soon awash.

Annie was pleased to see how much her daughter was enjoying herself, but also glad that Mary was not there to see such pandemonium. There was no damage to be done in the simple wash-house, but somehow her mother was apt to frown and dampen any spirit of spontaneous enjoyment. She wondered if Bruce felt that she, herself, was a killjoy? She knew that she did often try to curb his enthusiasm, but that was because there often seemed to be a thoughtlessness and the possibility of danger in his extrovert enthusiasm.

She sighed, she was far away from all of them just now, so why was she worrying? She shook herself and smiled. The bath was a marvellous success, for it added *luxury* to their narrow lives.

She enjoyed thinking of the summer and the tomato and cucumber plants which she had ordered. She had been successful for two years. How wonderful to have as many tomatoes as one could eat. She had followed a tip from the Radio Doctor, who had so many good ideas to help make life better. He had suggested that if you had green tomatoes still on the vine when the frosts started, you should pick them, wrap them in tissue paper and lay them carefully in a drawer until Christmas, when they would have ripened and be a welcome addition to the winter larder. Helen had been very dubious about this.

"I don't think they'll ripen. I bet they just go bad, mummy."

However in December they had been scarlet and firm and Helen had certainly enjoyed eating them.

◊

Helen would never be a popular child amongst her classmates. Her shyness and timidity was taken for pride or unfriendliness. No doubt she did have feelings of superiority towards many of her classmates, for certainly a greater degree of snobbishness, or at least class distinction, existed at that time. The local children had their own suspicions and prejudices of the city stranger. Helen spoke and dressed differently, her general knowledge and vocabulary were wider and more sophisticated than her fellow pupils. She tried hard in class and was considered a teacher's pet. And although boys and girls all knitted, Helen's cardigans and cable jumper were more ambitious than the scarves and blanket squares of her own age group. There were many things to set her apart. She did have some close friends, who tended to be on the periphery of the class 'inner circle' for one reason or another.

Jean was also an only child and had no local accent. She too, worked hard in school and she and Helen jockeyed for the top of the class. The two mothers were friendly and Jean's mother confided to Annie that she was determined that Jean would have the education that she herself had missed. Annie was doubtful about this as she considered Jean's father was a 'rolling stone'.It was the first time that Helen had heard the phrase. He had a history of a series of different jobs, with his wife often expected to take the heavy end of the stick . At present he worked for the Coast Guard, and because of the war, it was probably one of his longest periods of steady employment. His long-suffering wife had travelled from place to place. Jean had been born in the distant Falkland Islands though they had returned to Britain while she was still a baby. They had run a boarding house in Pittenweem just before the war. It was now commandeered by the Polish soldiers who were stationed in Fife. Jean's family lived in a small attached annexe. Although these lively and wealthy young officers were friendly and their quarters were completely separate from the family, they were also noisy and high-spirited. A washhand basin had been shattered by a rifle shot. Annie felt that she would rather not have a crew like that in such close proximity.

Ina, another good friend of Helen's, was of true Pittenweem stock. Her mother had been left a widow with three daughters and had a 'very hard row to hoe' although Helen was unaware of the family's financial distress. Certainly, their house contained only one large room, with two double beds built in recesses on one wall. The house always looked friendly and cosy, with a fire flickering on bright brasses and a good smell of cooking soup. But Ina's mother must have had a terribly difficult life in her struggle against poverty for she milked cows early each morning, took in washing, mostly the heavy flannel shirts belonging to the Polish officers. She also did any house-cleaning jobs that might come her way. Her daughters were always nicely dressed and well spoken and Ina excelled at mental arithmetic. Because a lack of money was a very big part of her mother's life, Helen tended to feel on a financial level with Ina, and had no idea of their poverty. She was surprised one evening when Ina came to her door about some homework. Helen was wearing cosy little house bootees with zips and Ina exclaimed, with loud and dramatic astonishment,

"OH! Look at the baffies, look at the baffies! She's wearin' baffies!"

'Baffies' is the local word for house slippers and poor Ina thought of such articles as luxuries far beyond the ken of ordinary mortals.

Another family showed Helen that there were degrees of poverty, much greater than her mother's.

Margaret was clever in school but poorly dressed. She lived with her father and two brothers in a small house with an outside stair. There was no mother and Helen did not ask why.

"Are ye comin' in tae visit us the nicht, Helen? Wur hivin' puddin'. C'moan in, it's awfy guid an ye'll get some. It's a grand wee treat. Ma Dad's awa oot the nicht."

Helen was curious to climb the outside stair and see the little house. She wondered if the pudding would be like the 'clooty dumpling' that her grandma made or the apple sponge that was her mother's speciality.

It was a very tiny house, the rooms smaller than any she had ever seen before. It seemed not quite right that the three children should be alone in the house without an adult.

In the crowded little kitchen, Margaret's thirteen-year-old brother was stirring something in a pot and he did not look pleased to see Helen. She could hear him muttering,

"Mind, ye'll need tae gie her some o' yer ain puddin'. Ah'm no' sharin' oot mine wi' her."

Helen felt very awkward and suggested that she just go home, but Margaret would not hear of it.

"He's jist an auld moaner, him. Dinnae pey ony attention, thur's plenty puddin' in the pot."

Four little bowls were laid out on the table and the older brother, in spite of what he had threatened, meticulously divided the thin clear pudding into four, small, equal portions. Helen was aghast. She did not like milk puddings.

As the others were eagerly delving their spoons into the mixture, she took a small sip. It was horrible! It had a faint sweetness and smelled very like the paste that her mother had used to stick on wallpaper.

"I'm really sorry, but I don't like it, Margaret."

"Niver mind, that's awricht."

And her bowlful was snatched, divided amongst the other three, and almost immediately devoured.

"I'm sorry I didn't like it. What sort of pudding was it?"

"Cornflooer puddin'.

"You see I never eat milk pudding at all."

"Thur wisnae ony mulk in that puddin'."

"Oh."

Helen felt pretty stupid and that night told her mother about the 'treat'.

Her mother's eyes filled with tears.

"Poor kids! They must have made it with just water. Was it sweet?"

"Just a wee bit sweet."

"Poor things. What a shame. And they were all by themselves? I wonder where their father is tonight. Their mother died several years ago."

"Was she quite young to die?"

"She must have been, I suppose."

Helen felt very sorry for that poor family and also worried that mothers could die when their children were still so young. How terrible not to have a mother and have only that horrible pudding for a treat.

1943

School was hard work in those months as the 'qualifying exam' approached. As well as the usual spelling, reading and arithmetic, there was a great deal of general knowledge to learn. Then there were strange puzzles to solve, which Helen really enjoyed. These were problems of logic or pattern, using numbers or letters and they marked the introduction of IQ testing.

Helen and Jean both worked well and vied for top of the class. There was no doubt that they would move into the A stream when they went to secondary school and take double languages, science and mathematics. Annie often thought of how Jean's mother had been determined that her daughter would have the education that she herself had missed.

The two girls were close friends now, although there was a certain amount of bullying. Jean was twelve, nearly a year older than Helen, and taller and broader. If Helen were unwilling to follow Jean's wishes, the older, stronger girl would grab her wrist and twist it until Helen squealed and complied. Helen always felt surprise that Jean, a friend, would treat her like that for what seemed paltry reasons. She was even more surprised at herself that she allowed it to happen and yet stayed friendly. She was never forced into doing anything that she absolutely hated, the disagreements were minor, it was more a question of power. They had good conversations and as Helen had no great wish for power, she accepted that a bit of pain was part of their friendship.

After Easter Jean divulged a secret, with many admonitions that it must remain a secret from *everyone*.

One of the young Polish soldiers who lived in part of Jean's home, was called Bolek. He was a lad of nineteen and often visited Jean when her parents were not at home. Jean described to Helen how he would take her on his knee and kiss her.

Helen listened to this with shocked astonishment. She did not know what to say. It seemed that Jean was just a child like herself and yet she was kissing a soldier and *sitting on his knee!*

"Your mother doesn't know?"

"Of course not, stupid! She'd be furious."

"What would she do?"

"Blow up I expect. You won't tell your mother! You *mustn't*"

"No, no, of course I won't tell her."

Helen thought it would be impossible to tell her mother a thing like that. Yet she wondered if she *should* tell her. Knowing nothing of the facts of life, she yet felt that Jean was too young to be kissing a soldier.

Each time that Helen walked home after hearing about Bolek's latest visit, she worried about it. Perhaps she should really tell her own mother? Perhaps Jean was making it up? Could she be making it up? She just looked the same as always, a slightly plump little girl.

Each time they met, Jean obviously wanted to speak about her adventure and, while Helen felt curious, she also felt anxious. There were no further details, but Jean looked very pleased with herself and did not finish some of her sentences, as if there might be more to be told if she wanted to tell it.

Before the results of the qualifying examination were published, Jean's father had decided to move on once again. They were taking over the YMCA in Dunfermline, so Jean would not go the Waid Academy with Helen.

Helen met Bolek once or twice and she was not impressed by his looks. She never found out if the kissing was in Jean's imagination or not. Could that be the reason for the family moving away?

◊

The summer holiday in Glasgow was spent very quietly. It was hot and humid and Annie had little energy to see friends. Helen was left to herself and read her way through all the short stories of Rudyard Kipling. They were very different from the Jungle Book and she did not always exactly understand them. Some of them were horrifying! But she loved the picture that he painted of an exotic unknown world and the brave and sometimes foolish people in that world. At the same time, she had discovered the satisfying properties of peanut butter and ate spoonfuls of it as she read.

The health shop around the corner had lots of other unusual things to eat. Annie always bought a packet of Vegetarian Rissoles. These needed water added to the dry mixture, then little patties could be formed and fried. The packet made several servings and often stayed in the cupboard for months, for it was not the tastiest meal, but it was a change and as Annie always said.

"It's a good standby."

One day Annie bought some small, dark brown sticks that did not look tempting, but were delicious. These were dried bananas and not often available. Helen ate them with bread and butter and thought they tasted more like dates.

Liquorice root always made Helen smile, for it looked like the most unlikely thing to eat! Helen enjoyed it very much and she took some back to Pittenweem for her special friends to chew.

There was a very nice fruit shop on the way to the baths and one day she bought redcurrants which seemed so cheap that she bought two pounds. Delicious as they were, she realised that she would be unable to finish them and the idea of making jam popped into her head. She had never made jam and was not sure if redcurrants were a fruit often used. She had never actually heard of redcurrant jam. She did not mention her intention to her mother, but lay in bed that night planning how she would get up very early the next day to make jam.

She arose about seven, feeling adventurous. It was not that her mother would have fobidden her to do it, but she might have thrown cold water on the idea. She might have said that no one ever made red currant jam. Helen was now determined to do it and do it all herself.

She added the same weight of sugar and some water to the berries and hoped that it would work. It smelled delicious and bubbled prettily in the pot. She took a little on to a plate to test if it were thickening. Disaster! She realised that she had not separated the currants from their stalks. However that was a problem which must be dealt with at the point of spreading it on bread. It was beginning to thicken and it tasted delicious. It was her first jam and although not perfect, for the stalks were a nuisance, she was proud of it.

Annie suppressed any sarcastic comments as she ate the jam and disposed of the stalks with as little fuss as possible.

One highlight of their visit was Helen's little cousin Eileen. What a delightfully quaint child she was, with enormous eyes and a nervous, fluttering manner. Beautifully dressed in very short skirts showing little matching pants, she was dainty and helpless. Helen thought she was just what a three-year-old should be. It was hilarious when this little thing was persuaded to sing and she chose the sophisticated song, 'Jealousy' although she pronounced it 'Delouthy'. She sang it in tune and lisped all the passionate words.

Helen did not know whether to laugh or not. She wanted to, but thought the child might be hurt. She gave her a cuddle and took her on her knee. Then Eileen took Topsy on her knee, because the doll had worked her magic on the toddler.

Although there was a seven year difference in their ages, the two cousins would always have a very special relationship.

◊

It was never easy for Annie when her parents came to Pittenweem in the summer.

What had been her home for a year, became once more her mother's demesne. The rooms resumed the full and cluttered look that her mother admired, and Annie abhorred.

The fireplace was painted with the stinking mixture of whiting and sour milk that Mary swore was necessary to keep it white. Pieces of furniture were replaced in their old accustomed corners, and ornaments were brought out of storage and given a prominent position once again. Not a great deal was said, but there was a sense of pressing determination in her mother's movements and a look of displeasure on her face, as she carried small tables and stools to their original site. Sometimes she would tut-tut under her breath, and say to herself

"I don't remember that scratch on the table there before!"

And sometimes make a disparaging remark,

"I see you've still got that yellow paint on the walls, Annie. I thought you might have got fed up with it and changed it by this time."

Only the tomatoes and cucumbers met with Mary's approval

In previous years, Annie had always given her parents breakfast in bed. It was not entirely unselfish. Her mother would be sure to stay in bed reading the newspaper until eleven, and that made for a peaceful house where Annie could please herself.

Helen would run along for the rolls and the paper, then take the trays upstairs when Annie had prepared them.

One Saturday, Helen had arranged to spend the day with Jean in St Andrews and had left after collecting the rolls. When Annie came to carry the tray upstairs to her mother, she realised that to balance the tray while climbing twelve stairs without the help of the bannister was not possible for her. She stood and bit her lip. Her mind was a blank. However she put the tray on a step and sat down on the lowest step. By edging herself up a step at a time and always moving the tray up ahead of her, she managed to reach the top. She felt rather pleased with herself to have met the challenge.

"Oh you've brought it up today. Where's Helen gone?"

"She's off to St Andrews today, remember?"

"Oh yes. Have you made your father's breakfast?"

Mary was obviously not in the happiest of moods. Annie felt like saying, "Don't I always make it?" however, she held back the retort and nodded with a smile.

Downstairs once more, then a repeat of the bumping from stair to stair and shifting of the tray. It was hard work.

As Annie left the room, Mary said,

"You might bring me up yesterday's Glasgow Herald the next time you're coming upstairs, Annie."

Annie closed the bedroom door with a sharp click. She had had no intention of coming upstairs again that morning, if possible. Had her mother no idea how difficult life had become for her? Not even a please or thank you! It was as though she were some sort of serving automaton, and the fact that she was running down was inconvenient rather than tragic.

She walked slowly to the sitting room and picked up yesterday's newspaper. Leaning on the table, she looked out at the sea which was calm and beautiful. Should she struggle up those stairs again? She was an idiot if she did, for she was really ready to sit down and rest. It was only nine-thirty and the whole demanding day stretched ahead. Perhaps the paper would keep her mother in bed for another half hour and mean that she was in a better mood when she did get up? Annie could not make up her mind.

◊

Perhaps the peanut butter had something to do with it, for Helen grew a lot that summer. Upwards and outwards. It was with dismay that she saw a favourite skirt become rather short, then much too short. A jumper with a Fair Isle yoke that her mother had knitted and that Helen particularly liked seemed to shrink each day. Her shoulders became broader and her breasts swelled. The two horrid little mounds which poked her jumper out at the front were embarrassing. She felt angry and sad, for she knew they would only get bigger. She considered that they might be better, if they would hang down a bit, instead of pushing out in that too obvious way. Already they wobbled slightly when she ran. She hated them.

Two lovely jumpers and two skirts became too short and too

tight in a month and must be discarded. Her summer dresses looked terrible. It was heart-breaking. She had hardly any clothes! Her skinny little childhood was behind her and at first, this new, bigger Helen kept bumping into things.

Just before the summer holiday ended, they took a trip to Dunfermline to visit Jean's family. The journey required two long bus journeys, so they were invited to stay the night.

Dunfermline was much more like a city, than they had expected. It was a long walk uphill to the YMCA building and Annie had to stop and rest quite often. No one seemed to know exactly where it was and they were given conflicting instructions. As on other occasions, Helen thought that they should not have come. Her mother had been too optimistic about her own strength. All the same, she felt sorry for her mother and wondered how they would ever get there. Eventually they found the large shabby building. It was enormous, four storeys high. Did it all belong to them? How different from the compact boarding house in Pittenweem.

It was good to see Jean again and the two mothers were soon deep in conversation.

"It seems very quiet. Do you have many Christian young men staying here at a time?" Annie asked.

"Just wait till eight o'clock tonight. The lads get off the boats at Rosyth and come up to Dunfermline. Not so sure about the Christian, but we'll be busy enough with young men."

Just as Helen was thinking that they might go to bed soon, the men started to arrive. Crowds of them crammed into the dining room, laughing and shouting to friends. They all wanted tea and buns or biscuits. Jean and Helen were kept busy carrying trays of teas, then collecting empty cups and plates and washing them ready for the next orders. It was fun!. At one am they were still busy in the kitchen. It was like another life to Helen. Jean was used to it by this time and would have preferred to go to bed, but Helen found it exciting and thought that she would rather like to run a YMCA herself.

On the bus back to Pittenweem, Annie shook her head,

"I wonder if Jean will ever have that good education her mother spoke about."

Helen said to herself,

"I wonder if Jean will find another man to kiss amongst all those sailors."

◊

Helen was eleven when she started secondary school and she felt a quiet satisfaction in becoming a woman. There was no doubt that someone who studied French, Latin, Mathematics and Science and had breasts was a woman. She did not speak of the fact to anyone. They might have been foolish enough to disagree with her, but she knew it was the case and she would never waver in that opinion.

The local secondary school was called the Waid Academy and it was was not as Helen had expected. It was not too large, nor was it too daunting. Although she lost sight of some of her school friends in the streaming, the faces in her class were not all strange to her. She was delighted when her timetable directed her to science, for she had always been fascinated by laboratories. She remembered the one in Girls High School, where they had knitted and been warned so often about the Bunsen burners. Now she would be using the Bunsen burners! She had read about them in school stories and also those dainty little scales in their glass cases. It was as exciting as a school story. She had learned a little French when she was younger, so the strange pronunciation did not astound her, as it did the other children. Latin made her feel very proud and part of history, although there was an awful lot of repeating and learning off by heart. Her first reaction to algebra was incredulity. How could a number be a letter? It seemed very strange. Science was certainly her favourite subject. There were only two girls in a class with twelve boys. The IQ test must have suggested that she would be good in that subject. The teacher was a very handsome young man, who was kindness itself to the two girls and absolutely *rotten* to the boys. Helen felt embarrassed when he would treat a boy with rudeness and even cruelty. He actually threw rulers or balls of crumpled paper at any boy who misbehaved or did not know the right answer. However she could not help liking him as he was so sweet to her and Catherine, the other girl in the science class.

Catherine became her special friend for the four months that she spent at the Waid. They both knew that they would be leaving at Christmas, Catherine going to Edinburgh and Helen to Glasgow.

Catherine invited Helen and another two girls to tea one Sunday. Her house was in the country, several miles from Pittenweem. Helen took a country bus and was met at the bus stop and taken to a large lonely house, in its own grounds. The house seemed very swell to Helen and she judged that Catherine's family was much wealthier than her own. It was probably the sort of family that would have a real Christmas tree, with hanging parcels and candles on it. Catherine's bedroom had its own washhand basin, with hot water flowing from the tap. How luxurious it seemed! After tea, they played Monopoly, which Helen enjoyed tremendously, believing that it might be a game that only rich people would play. She was surprised and delighted to win. There was a small windmill outside the house and she learned that it made electricity. This seemed another wonder, though Catherine assured them that it often broke down and they needed to have torches and candles all over the house. Even this necessity seemed pretty extravagant to Helen.

The girls were driven home in Catherine's father's car and the visit took on a dream-like quality for Helen. She would never find out exactly where that house was located, nor would she ever see Catherine again after the Christmas parting.

◊

Annie's friend, Mrs Hill, was visiting her one day in October.

She was a shapeless old wheezy lady who loved to reach her own special chair, a rather high-set antique one, and plump herself into it to recover from her walk along the High Street.

Annie was very fond of her and had made a little cake. When she brought the cake and tea into the sitting room, Mrs Hill was standing up again.

"Is everything all right?"

"Yes, yes, Annie. Just put the tray down though, for I've something I want to say to you."

Annie was puzzled and put down the tray. The old lady looked very serious and took Annie's hands in her own.

"Now I'm an old woman and I'm going to give you some advice, Annie."

The younger woman nodded.

"I think that you need to get back nearer your family."

"Yes, I'm afraid you're right, Mrs Hill."

"You're soon going to need more help in your life and it's too much to expect wee Helen to deal with it alone."

Annie bit back the tears. It was all too true. She knew it herself.

They both sat down and wept a little, then Annie poured the tea and cut the cake.

"You're such a good friend, Mrs Hill and you're right. I know I need more help. Every week I get a bit worse. I'll go at Christmas time."

"I really think it's best, though I'll miss you, Annie. You know that, I'm sure."

◊

Just before Halloween, a very splendid doll's house was put on public view, the modest entry fee going to the War Effort. The house belonged to the Lawson family, joiners and cabinet makers, and was a marvel of staircases, furniture and electric lights. It belonged to the six-year-old daughter of the family, who was scarcely old enough to appreciate its magnificence.

Helen, who had always longed for her own doll's house and who had so much enjoyed playing with the doll's house in Lambhill, paid several visits to Lawson's. On one of these visits she met Alison Hamilton, an eleven-year old from Dunfermline and a niece of the local butcher. Within half an hour they were boon companions and they would become life-long friends. They were the same age and had everything in common. They were both fascinated by the doll's house and offered their services to dust and tidy it, which were kindly accepted. They wandered around town, talking of the subjects that eleven year-old girls talk about. They both loved to draw and they made sketches at the harbour of seagulls and boats. They spent their evenings making Halloween masks and Alison was not too grown up to appreciate Topsy in her bed-sitter.

"What school will you go to in Glasgow, Helen?" Alison asked one day.

"I'll go the Glasgow High School for Girls. My mother went there and my dad's mother."

"Oh that's the same school that my cousin goes to! Perhaps you'll meet her. She's the same age as us. What if you're in the same class!"

Helen knew how big the city was and this seemed an unlikely coincidence.

When the cold descended in November, Annie experienced new symptoms. Her right leg had now developed a tendency to disobey her. As well as the numbness in her fingers and the familiar, stabbing pains in her back, she wakened one night with a fierce ache in her right knee. It was almost unbearable and Annie, trying not to groan, rolled over on to her back and stretched and bent her leg several times. The pain persisted. How she longed for an easier existence, where she could get up, switch on a light and a radiator, and take an aspirin and a hot drink in comparative comfort. How wonderful that would be! She thought of the reality, where she must stand in the bitter cold, fumbling for matches to light the gas. The rest of the house would be even colder. She could not face it. After twenty minutes, the excruciating ache subsided, then a lesser residue of pain seemed to flow slowly down the front of her shin and out at her toes. Suddenly she was miraculously without pain and could relax. It was heaven. What a very strange disease this was. This symptom would recur most nights. Annie learned to keep a bottle of aspirin below her pillow, though probably the pain would have disappeared before the aspirin could take effect. She was always afraid of taking too many aspirin. It might make them less effective in future.

Two weeks after the first of these episodes, Annie was sitting at the fire one evening when her left leg suddenly cramped. This leg which had been straight and stiff for years, suddenly bent so severely that her knee almost reached her chest. The pain was terrible and she was glad that Helen was in bed and could not hear her exclamations. Her leg relaxed after a few minutes. It had been so dramatic and the relief so instant and marvellous, that Annie was able to smile and say to herself,

"Well that was a bit of a surprise! I didn't know you could still bend yourself up so well. Hope you won't try it again in a hurry, because it was *bloody* sore."

She sat there in a state of exhaustion. What was the best way of dealing with a cramp like that? Would it happen again?

Sadly it would start to happen quite frequently, usually when she was over-tired.

◊

Like many people, Helen was sure that the end of the war would make all things right again. And at long last that end might be in sight.

The End of the War!

It was a magical phrase. It sounded as if a kindly sun would shine over every life and put an end to unhappiness, hardship and fear.

For Helen, the return to Glasgow certainly held out hopes for things to improve.

It might even be that her mother would start to get better and walk properly again.

Back to the City

The tall thin eleven-year-old stood on the pavement, frowning and shivering in the cold east coast wind. She was ready to help, but knew that her mother managed best in her own time.

Annie was kneeling on the floor of the back of the car. She had stumbled as she entered and now she was leaning across the padded leather cushion on one elbow. Her other hand gripped the back of the driver's seat, while she gathered her strength to haul herself up on the backseat.

She looked over her shoulder at her daughter and, biting her lower lip with the large white teeth that Helen loved so much, smiled ruefully. Her raised eyebrow expressed a mixture of amusement at her own ridiculous position and an apology for the trouble that she was causing.

"I'll be fine in a jiffy ... just need a breather. Don't worry, I'll get up on the seat in a minute, my pet."

Her tone was bright and optimistic and Helen was unconsciously grateful.

The whole business of packing and closing up the house had been far too much for Annie now that her condition was deteriorating so quickly. She realised that she should have gone months ago, as soon as better news of the war had reached her, but she had procrastinated, dreading what awaited her in Glasgow after four years absence. It was obvious to her that before long she would be unable to walk at all. She wondered if others thought of that time. They did not speak of it. Perhaps they thought of even worse afflictions that might befall her, because of the unpredictability of this disease.

"Aye, we've goat ten meenutes t'get up the road tae catch that train." and the taxi driver slammed the boot-lid on the two leather suitcases and the three bulging paper sacks tied with string. "No' that Ah'm hurryin' ye, Annie, jist tak yer time noo."

Helen locked the front door with the big key, then with a heave and a push against the front seat and a little tug at her feet from Helen, Annie was seated and ready to go.

For Helen the future was delightful. Her vision of it was as unclear as her mother's, but the opportunities seemed infinite and exciting. She was glad to be leaving the small town and returning to the broader vistas of the city, although she might have found it hard to define exactly what it was that she would enjoy about Glasgow. Certainly she was happy to leave the more insular and uncouth village children, with their broad accents and unkind suspicions. For four years she had lived in the expectation that the end of the war and a return to the city would solve all unhappiness. Air raids, rationing, shortages, all those horrible things which loomed so large in everyday life, would be wiped out completely. Buried deeply, though not always acknowledged, was the hope that the old life would restore her mother's ability to walk properly.

Besides, tomorrow was Christmas and she knew that her present was 'very grown up'.

The train journey was cold and dirty and incredibly long. Soon it was dark and impossible to read or knit in the restricted light of the carriage. Helen gazed at her reflection in the window, alternately admiring her thick blonde plaits and regretting her deep-set eyes and sharp nose.

At Queen Street station, Bruce was there to meet them with a big welcoming smile. As usual, he bombarded them with the problems which he had surmounted in order to be there at that particular time. He had cancelled an important meeting with a big bugger from I.C.I., probably cost the firm a good few hundred pounds that, never mind, water under the bridge, couldn't be helped, Ha ha ... and the car had been in the garage for a week, had to put a bit of pressure on his good pal Jimmy to get it ready for today, grease his palm a bit, Ha ha ... works wonders ... of course hardly get petrol at all these days ... if it wasn't for old Bill ... be scuppered ... but he'd done him a few good turns ... slipped him a coupla quid.. He sounded quite cheerful as he listed the inconveniences and the apparently large sums of money cast away. In fact he laughed out loud several times as he talked, while Annie slowly and clumsily descended the awkward steps to the platform. Helen wondered if he were really pleased to see them. As usual, she was puzzled and guilty that she should feel so little affection for her father.

"Let's get to the car as soon possible, Bruce."

"Sure, sure. Just give us a sec ... plenty time, no rush, no wild horses chasing us, eh wee one? Ha! Ha!" and he ruffled Helen's smooth hair. Directing a porter, he grabbed Annie's elbow and with his nervous, bouncing stride, hurried her along the dim smoky platform. Helen watched her mother's left foot dragging and wanted to protest at the speed, but then her mother stumbled and almost fell. Bruce saved her but cursed under his breath.

"I'll have to rest for a moment, Bruce."

"Whatever you say. I *thought* you were in a hurry." He was no longer laughing.

The noise in the station was loud and echoing and it was terribly dirty and cold. Helen felt the grit crunching under her feet, but the choking smell of steam and coal and the mysterious height above her was exciting, too.

When they reached home, there was the remembered feeling of space in the west end flat, where the ceilings were almost twice as high as those in the Pittenweem house. It seemed large and empty of furniture, compared to the crammed rooms in Fife. Apart from the intermittent rumble of a tram toiling up the hill, there was a quality of silence and calm in the house, which Helen recognised from her early childhood. It was almost like being in church. She liked the atmosphere, but would she ever get used to it again? Would it soon begin to feel like home? There was a flat dusty smell that was very unfamiliar.

The house was nice and warm as fires were burning in the sitting room, the kitchen and the bedroom. She had never seen so many fires burning at one time in her life before.

"Hullo my darling wee girl." and Helen was gathered up against the predominant and well-dressed bosom of her maternal grandmother, her own thin chest pressing uncomfortably against a long strand of amber beads.

"I've just been dying to see you. And we've got all the fires on to make it cosy. Are you glad to be back in Glasgow, my jewel? This is *home* isn't it! I've made some pancakes for you, too, I think they're extra good this time and gingerbread too, really treacly just the way you like it. Grandad said it was the best he'd ever tasted. Would you like a piece just now? Or a pancake with jam? Are you not hungry, wee one? Hullo, Annie. How are you, I suppose you're tired? You don't look too great. You look pretty done in. D'ye want to get away to your bed? There's a bottle in it."

"No I don't want to go to bed. I've just arrived."

Helen was surprised at how irritable Annie sounded when she spoke to her own mother.They had not kissed each other. Annie had at once dropped into a chair, without taking off her coat or hat. Then she asked,

"Who's that banging about in the kitchen?"

Bruce coughed loudly before he answered.

"My mother's here and she brought Betty along to give a hand, if there was rough work to be done."

Annie and his mother had remained cool to each other for fourteen years and he knew that Annie suspected his mother's cleaning woman of dishonesty and disliked her intensely. Annie sighed deeply, then said on an indrawn breath,

"Quite a reception committee."

There was a silence, which seemed terribly different from the quiet times at the cottage when Helen and her mother were reading or knitting and not speaking. This silence made Helen feel breathless.

Bruce turned to his mother-in-law, who listened with a faint sweet smile.

"You know I had a lot of difficulty getting this coal and it cost a packet. If I hadn't known Kenny Sprott at the club ... and, paid through the nose for it, too, believe me! And five bags won't last long at this rate. I mean to say, three fires and it's not even very cold! Extravagance really ..."

"Well Bruce, you'll need to speak to your mother about that. It was her idea. I was rather surprised, but the house was chilly, I must say. And I don't expect Annie will be burning three fires very often."

This speech was triple-edged, putting Bruce in his proper place for complaining, insinuating surprise at the uncharacteristic extravagance of his mother and referring to the meanness which Mary often attributed to her own daughter.

Taking a packet of Gold Flake from her handbag, she lit a cigarette with a smile of quiet triumph..

"What about you? Annie? Bruce?"

"I haven't smoked since the day the war started, remember?"

"Oh, no, of course. Wouldn't be good for you in your condition I suppose, anyway. You must have saved quite a bit by now. How about you, Bruce? Cigarette?"

Bruce shook his head, breathing noisily as he poked the fire destructively and threw on another two large lumps of coal.

"Ask your mother to come in here and join us, Bruce." said Annie. "I don't want her working away in the kitchen and us sitting here like ladies. But don't bring Betty in, I couldn't face that woman just now."

Bruce returned almost immediately with his mother, a small shrivelled, still toothless lady with her hat perched straight on skimpy hair and a flowered apron over her smart, navy suit.

Betty, a gaunt woman of sideways glance and relentless speech, was right behind her.

Mrs Corning brushed her papery old cheek against Helen's.

"Hello dear, my what a big girl you are! And Annie, how are you keeping? I brought you some soup, Annie. Scotch broth."

Helen remembered her paternal grandmother's overboiled Scotch broth with dismay.

The older woman shook hands and sat down with a serious expression. Betty started to giggle and talk loudly and familiarly. She planted a loud kiss on Annie's cheek and Helen saw her mother flinch. Annie did not care for such intimate greetings even from her own family.

"Now, dear, I'm sure ye would like a nice wee cup o' tea. D'ye take sugar'n milk? An' there's lovely pancakes and gingerbread, just delicious ..."

Annie's mother raised her eyebrows at the thought of her baking having been already sampled in the kitchen.

"I never take tea, thank you." Annie gazed into the fire.

"Well how's about cocoa or Bovril? Or maybe a wee cuppa coffee? I brought a bottle of Camp that's got a droppie left in the bottom."

"No, thank you." Annie turned and looked full in Betty's face when she said this and even Betty realised that she meant it. "You can go and make some tea for the others, though, if that's what they'd like. Please."

Helen stood at one of the three tall windows. A tramcar stopped just outside and a few passengers alighted and immediately put up their umbrellas. It was exciting not to know these people, after the familiarity of the village. They looked really interesting and their clothes were smarter.

The objects in the room pleased her too, the pattern on the carpet that she had used as stepping-stones when a little girl, the leather couch with its brown velvet cushions that used to be piled on the floor for somersaults and hair-washing. Helen blushed at the memory of the fuss that she used to make. There was the brass box that always had an assortment of interesting things in it. She remembered different coloured hanks of raffia and a pack of playing cards with the face cards depicting film stars and a little glass jar of beans that they used for gambling when playing Newmarket, her favourite card game. There were storybooks, combs, beads, glitter wax, tiddlywinks, always something new to be discovered in that box. She must explore it tomorrow.

Betty brought the tea and pancakes and defiantly sat close to Annie and asked questions about her health, which Annie parried when she did not ignore them. The two grandmothers talked unenthusiastically to each other. Bruce, whistling tunelessly under his breath, crossed and re-crossed his knees and swung his foot like a restless teenager. In doing so he repeatedly kicked Annie's chair.

"Bruce, please don't knock against my chair like that. It's very painful."

Helen knew the look of anguish that could cross her mother's face when she was unexpectedly jarred or jerked. Helen could only guess how sore it was and it seemed that she herself shared the pain.

"Sorry, sorry I didn't know that would affect you so much."

He moved his legs ostentatiously to the side but still he swung his foot, and still he knocked against her chair.

"Bruce! Please!"

On the third exclamation, Bruce jumped to his feet with a frown.

"Time we were getting along now, mother, Betty. I've still a lot of things to see to ... been a bit of a wasted day so far and tomorrow's a holiday. I'll probably see you tomorrow, Annie."

Within four minutes the two women were swept out of the house, Betty talking non-stop and Granny with her beady-eyed fox fur slung around her neck, though she still fumbled to untie her apron.

Annie's mother stayed on for another three hours, talking of her friends at the whist drive and telling anecdotes of long ago, some of them interesting, but all very familiar to Annie, who was sick with exhaustion. It was cold, the fire had dwindled and it seemed too late to put on more coal. Christmas Eve was not mentioned and Helen wondered if everyone had forgotten. Eventually Mary started to fumble in her large straw basket.

"Well, I'd better get away before I miss the last tram. Here's a wee parcel for you, Helen and that's for you Annie." She put a five pound note under the clock on the mantelpiece.

"Thank you Grandma." The neatly wrapped parcel was excitingly small and lumpy. "I'll keep it for tomorrow."

"Thank you very much, Maw, that will come in handy. Very generous."

"Well, John's got a commission you know. We're pretty sure he has it, anyway. A big leather manufacturer wants his portrait. It's a while since your father painted a portrait. I hope he can manage. He's getting so forgetful. Now, don't spend that all in the one shop! Merry Christmas."

"Merry Christmas. Helen, get the you-know-what for grandma."

Helen brought one of the paper sacks. Her mother had knitted a large blanket, striped green, blue, pink and purple, then, after brushing at the woolshop, the colours softened and blended into each other like a wonderful rainbow. Helen adored it and her Grandma said it was very nice, but she would just leave it here tonight, as it was so late.

When they were alone, Helen gave the little crow of delight that showed she was excited and happy.

"It's *Christmas, Mummy.*"

"Yes, and how are we to get me through to the bedroom?"

"I think I could manage it best if I saw my present tonight!"

"D'ye think so? Really? All right, you know which suitcase."

But Helen was out of the room.

"Oh! OH! it's so ... GORGEOUS ... oh thank you, it's so ... it's *really* grown up. Oh! I love it, I love it. Can I wear it tonight? Say yes, please say yes!"

"Course you can. Mind you, it's a bit chilly tonight."

"No, no, no, no."

"It's yours to wear when you want to, my darling."

Helen draped the pale blue Celanese night-gown over a chair and gazed at it with rapture. The jersey fabric hung in graceful silken folds and lace decorated the neck and sleeves. It was very glamorous and pretty and very adult for an eleven-year-old.

"It's so lovely. Thank you, thank you, thank you. Let's get to bed quickly."

"Easier said than done, I'm afraid."

Annie could not stand up.

"Afraid I'll have to go on my hands and knees tonight. But first, would you bring me a pail or a basin from the kitchen, please."

"What for?"

"What d'ye think?"

"I don't know."

"Think! I could never make it to the bathroom ... "

"Oh!"

Helen scuttled off and returned in a moment with an enamel pail.

"Now just leave me for a few minutes."

"Will you manage?"

"Just go."

When Helen returned, her mother was crawling slowly across the carpet.

If this had happened before, Helen had not seen it and it was a shock. She felt so very helpless and so sorry for her poor mother. What could she do?

Annie paused to take a rest when she came to the edge of the carpet. Ahead of her was the wooden surround and then the icy linoleum of the hall and bedroom. Helen realised that though it might be fun for her to march around such a spacious house, it was daunting for her poor tired mother to crawl such distances. She wished that she could do something.

Suddenly her mother looked up and smiled.

"Do you feel strong tonight, my love?"

Helen nodded vigorously.

"If you bring that hall rug over here ... to my knees here, yes, and I climb on. You know how you give your wee cousin a ride on a rug? D'ye think you could pull me along the hall on the slippy lino? Whoa! not too quick or I'll fall off the back again. You're too strong! That's fine now, that's great. Now you've got it. What a help. What a great wee girl you are. Thank you my pet, that's just marvellous."

Helen really enjoyed pulling her mother through the hall and across the bedroom in just the same way that she and her friends pulled each other around on rugs, just for fun. Annie was no heavier really.

The struggle into the high bed was accomplished, eventually and the pail was emptied.

At last Helen donned her exquisite night-gown with a rush of happiness and as they lay in bed, the remains of the fire flickered on the ceiling in a pleasant Christmassy way. Helen quickly drifted into dreamless sleep.

Annie was too tired and too painful to sleep. She should have taken an aspirin, but they were in her handbag in the other room and she would not waken the kid up now.

The fire had lasted a long time. Had there been logs on it? Surely there was a faint smell of woodsmoke? Annie lifted her head and seeing just embers, lay down. After ten minutes the smell was stronger and she looked again. Around the edge of the tall, elaborately carved wooden mantelpiece there seemed to be something moving in the dim light. She switched on the bedside light and saw distinct curls of smoke escaping from the top and sides of the mantelpiece.

"HELEN"

Like an animal, the child was awake immediately.

"Don't get a fright now, but the mantelpiece is on fire, don't worry, *don't worry*."

Helen's face was pale against her blue night-gown and her eyes and mouth were wide open.

"What will we do?"

"Just go across the landing and ask the neighbours for help."

"But what about you?" Helen cast a terrified look at the mantelpiece which smoked gently.

"I'll be fine. I've had a rest and I can make a run for it if I have to." Annie could never resist irony.

"*On you go now,* I'll be fine."

It was half-past eleven by this time but the Grahams next door were not yet in bed when Helen rang their doorbell.

"What do you expect me to do about it? Who are you any-way?" was Mrs Graham's daunting answer to the child in a woman's night-gown, who informed her that "our mantelpiece is on fire". This answer confirmed Helen's worst fears and she was turning away to find another more helpful neighbour, when Mr Graham appeared and efficiently took things in hand. First phoning the fire brigade, he then produced a stirrup pump, that excellent piece of equipment which many households kept in readiness for dealing with incendiary bombs.

In half an hour of frantic activity, Mr Graham had put out the fire and Mrs Graham had fussily escorted Annie, who had recovered some energy, into the sitting room and ordered Helen to make tea for her mother,

"Tea with plenty of sugar, that is vital for shock."

Ignoring this order, Helen lingered in the kitchen. She knew her mother disliked tea, especially with sugar, and she disliked being ordered about by this unpleasant woman.

Six tall firemen arrived, dragging their unrequired hosepipe, for, thanks to Mr Graham, there was little for them to do. Although the mantelpiece had looked so imposingly solid, it was in fact quite a flimsy structure. The firemen removed the charred and damp remain to the back yard, then tramped up and down the house, checking the other fires and shouting comments to each other in broad Glasgow accents. Helen did not understand a word they said. Helen was furious to hear Mrs Graham tell the men that "the lady's a cripple, poor thing." But she was relieved to see them carry her mother back to bed.

They could not sleep after such excitement and were chatting when there was a ring at the doorbell and a loud knock at the door. Helen leaped out of bed.

"Ask who it is before you open the door."

The first deep voice answered,

"Police!"

The second younger voice said,

"The Leith police dismisseth us."

Which seemed mad to Helen.

They came into the bedroom and wrote down details of the fire. Before leaving, the young one asked if Helen's plaits were called ringlets. What an idiot.

"Merry Christmas, darling."

"And what a Christmas! I *love* my nighty and I'm glad I was looking my best. Can I pull you through the hall on the rug tomorrow night?"

"Yes, I'll allow you to do that, if you behave yourself! I'm quite sure I'll be fine tomorrow, though. I'm just needing a good rest. Now, off you go to sleep."

"Merry Christmas, Mummy. Oh, it's *lovely* to be home again!
I'm awful happy."

The firemen had replaced the cast iron grate with a few
embers still in it and, in the middle of the expanse of raw, fire-
blackened stone and plaster, a little fire started to flicker and purr
and cast gentle shadows on the high ceiling above the double
bed.

◊

The following day was very quiet and pleasant.

They opened the various small gifts for each other and Helen
was delighted with everything. The present from her grandmother was a most beautiful hand-made lace collar.

"What will I do with that, I wonder? It's lovely, but ..."

"That's a family heirloom, my pet. I think your Grandad's sisters or maybe his mother made it."

"Yes but how would I wear it?"

"Well, I'll make you a nice plain dress to wear it with. It will
be very smart and absolutely no one else will have anything like
it. It will be splendid for school. That collar will look superb on a
nice navy serge dress."

That was what Helen was afraid of, that familiar situation of
having something very special, but very different from anything
worn by those around her. So different as to be almost peculiar.
She had struggled doggedly with this problem in Pittenweem,
without completely recognising it. She had been different in
every other way from her peers, so unusual garments had been
just another thing for them to jeer at. However, now she was in
Glasgow and she had hoped that she would fit in and be more
like a storybook schoolgirl. It would be nice to be an accepted
member of a group, and she was sure that no one else would be
wearing an antique lace collar or a navy serge dress.

Helen took a slow imperceptible breath and held it for as long
as was comfortable. This was the nearest thing to her mother's
resigned sighs that she dared attempt. It was certainly not to be
compared with her grandmother's deep and disapproving breath
inhaled and exhaled through that noble nose. Helen's breath was
just a small personal statement and though it passed without
notice, it made her feel better.

At last it seemed that every present had been examined, but
Annie said,

"If you go into the bed recess in the kitchen, there is a parcel behind the ironing table, I believe. That's from Daddy."

"Do you know what it is?"

"No idea. Go and get it and we'll find out."

Helen took quite some time to return and then she staggered into the room with something which was bulky and obviously weighty.

"I couldn't see it at first. It was so much bigger than I was looking for and it's really heavy."

"What on earth can it be?"

Annie had her doubts about it. Bruce did not find it easy to tune himself to other wavelengths and Helen was at an awkward stage between childhood and girlhood.

"Come on, open it up."

The haphazard wrapping was soon removed and Helen and her mother gazed at the large lidded box covered in brown cut velvet.

"What's it for?" asked Helen, opening the lid and finding it plain and empty inside.

"I think it's maybe a workbox."

"Oh. It's a bit like the brass box in the sitting room. It's the same size."

"Well that's to keep logs for the fire, so a velvet box wouldn't do for that."

"But we don't ever keep logs in it, anyway, do we."

They continued to look at it, unsure what more they could say about it. The craftsmanship was not of the finest.

"It's a bit rough and ready but it's nice and roomy."

"I expect I'll think of something to do with it. It's no use for anything for Topsy." Helen, at nearly twelve, still found it difficult to relinquish concern for her beloved doll.

"No."

Her mother was pleased to see that the box was more of a puzzle than a disappointment to the child.

"You could always sit on it, like a little stool."

"Yes."

Annie could guess pretty accurately where the velvet box had come from. Probably one of Bruce's pub acquaintances had a friend who was an upholsterer, possibly an apprentice. Bruce would have been spun a hard luck tale and he would have offered to buy the box. No doubt he had first presented his mother with the box and when she didn't want it, he had thought of Helen's Christmas. Annie's scenario was not far from the truth, for she knew her husband very well.

They stayed in bed until nearly lunchtime, then Helen, with instructions from her mother, put on the fire in the sitting room, something she had never attempted in Pittenweem. She felt a real sense of achievement, as it blazed up satisfactorily. She was *certainly* grown up now.

In the late afternoon, Bruce arrived with Mary in his car. She was bearing a large plate of Christmas dinner which was covered by another plate and a dish towel and was still quite hot. Mary Mackay had considered asking Annie to dinner but the three flights of stairs were an impossibility for her daughter to negotiate and she and Bruce had arranged this surprise between them the previous day. A lot of organisation had gone into delivering this hot food and Annie was touched by their thoughtfulness.

Helen thanked her Grandma for the lace collar and her father for the velvet box, very prettily. No one would have guessed that she wondered privately what the hell she would do with either article. She enjoyed a little inner swearing, now that she was a woman.

"Absolutely delicious chicken, Maw. From the aunts up North, I suppose?"

Mary had two aunts, Kate and Bella, who had a croft near Bonar Bridge, a small town north of Inverness which to Helen seemed impossibly far away in the inaccessible Highlands. These aunts were only a few years older than Mary and they had always kept in touch, though she had not seen them since she was a girl. Annie had never met either of them. Throughout the war a very welcome parcel arrived every month or so. It might be a dozen eggs or goat's cheese or sometimes a chicken. As the aunts fed their excess goat's milk to their poultry, those eggs and chickens were superior in flavour to anything available in the shops. It was a red letter day when the postman handed in the limp, still beautifully-feathered cockerel, with only a label tied around its stiff orange ankles to ensure its safe arrival. Helen found that unwrapped bird astonishing and amusing and yet very sad.

Annie had written a poem about one of their delicious birds arriving and saving the day just when food was short. The aunts had been terribly pleased and impressed by Annie's cleverness. After that she wrote regular letters to them, for they loved to hear about little Helen and these far away relatives that they did not know and would probably never meet. Annie had also knitted Fair Isle gloves and lacy shoulder shawls for each old lady.

While Annie and Helen enjoyed their unexpected Christmas dinner, Bruce and his mother-in-law spoke amicably and continuously to each other.

It often struck Annie that, while in private each spoke of the other with intense dislike, almost with hatred, they got on very companionably when they met. In fact they seemed like the greatest of friends.

Mary attended three whist drives each week at the Conservative Club in Royal Crescent, and she spoke of the ladies there and their eccentricities. Bruce talked of his problems at work and also of some of the ploys of the Home Guard which, as always, seemed to be mainly concerned with drinking whisky. It was questionable whether either paid much attention to the content of the other's stories, but they had been laughing and chatting vivaciously for nearly an hour before Annie, who enjoyed underplaying any drama, mentioned in an offhand way,

"We had a bit of excitement here last night, after you left."

It was not easy to stop the other two in their animated conversation. Eventually, they both turned towards her.

"Yes the mantelpiece caught fire, about eleven thirty, though it must have been smouldering for a while before that."

Bruce and Mary turned towards the fireplace.

"Not that one, the bedroom. We had six firemen tramping through the house, then two policemen!"

They remained open-mouthed and almost speechless, as Annie and Helen recounted the happenings of the night before.

"Were you ever in any actual danger?" Mary asked with her fascination for the sensational.

"Oh, no, no, no. Nothing like that. Our neighbours next door were very helpful. Away and have a look at it. It's a bit of a mess, certainly."

They came back overawed at the damage.

Bruce said very little, but shook his head and muttered about 'too many big fires' and 'too much coal.'

"I'll see about the insurance," he said when he returned from the inspection. "We've never had a claim, so they'll fix that up all right."

"Would it not be up to the factor to claim insurance?" Annie asked.

"Maybe, maybe. I'll make enquiries and get it sorted, sometime."

"I think the most important thing is that Annie should have a telephone put in." Mary sounded aggressive. She had always had the luxury of a telephone and she saw it as meanness on Bruce's part that Annie had never had one.

"Not an easy thing to arrange nowadays, Mrs Mackay, I'm afraid." Bruce was not keen to have yet another bill for this house and he worried that women could soon run up big amounts, with their constant chatter.

"Anything might happen."

"I doubt, I doubt ..."

"I think it's a necessity now in view of ... well her father and I could be in touch with her so easily if we were required."

"Tricky to get a new installation these days. Very tricky. I might just see old Wilson. He might help. Doubt it though."

Bruce rubbed his cheek with his thumb and Helen could hear the small rough scrape against bristle.

"But surely for an invalid ..."

"I am *hardly* an invalid. Not *yet* anyway." Annie was furious with both of them and immediately stood and walked from the room with as much force and steadiness as she could muster. Out in the hall, the tears spilled over and she was racked with sobs before she could reach the bedroom. She felt powerless and unloved.

Helen wanted to rush after her mother, but felt that was the wrong thing to do. She sat very still on the uncomfortable velvet box, her hands tightly clasped. She chewed her lower lip and she had that breathless feeling again.

After a short silence, while Helen could hear everyone breathing, her father spoke,

"So you like your wee padded box, do you, Tuppenny?"

"Yes, thank you. It's nice. It will be very useful."

"Yes, your granny said you would just love it."

Helen smiled, but not too widely.

Mrs Mackay looked pointedly the other way. She thought the box was execrable and had avoided any reference to it.

Quite soon, after an uneasy silence, Bruce excused himself. Then moments later, Mary left to visit a friend who lived nearby, one of her card-playing cronies.

Neither seemed to think of saying goodbye to Annie.

Helen went into the bedroom and Annie sat up with a small rueful smile, her lips pressed close together.

"Would you like a cup of coffee, Mummy?"

"That would be lovely, my wee darling. Will we have a game of cards too, if I can find the pack."

"I know where it is."

Christmas day finished very pleasantly with double patience and Newmarket and some beautiful Beethoven on the wireless.

After two days' complete rest, Annie felt much better and determined that she would never allow herself to be so over-worked again. If she were sensible and did not try to do too much, just as that doctor had advised, she would manage fine.

There were all the practicalities of re-registering for food in Glasgow to be arranged. Fortunately the grocer, butcher and dairy were very near. Helen was surprised to see how everyone greeted her mother. It was as if she had been gone for a few weeks, rather than four years. Helen could not remember any of the assistants in the shops, but they all exclaimed over how she had grown and how long her hair was. Helen wished that they would not talk about her, besides it was not so very surprising, that at nearly twelve-years-old, she was a lot taller than she had been at seven. Although they may not have guessed it, she herself knew she was a woman now.

The grocer and the butcher both asked Annie how she was keeping and to Helen's surprise, she answered each time with the same words,

"Oh, I've been great, thank you. I'm a bit tired just now with the move back to Glasgow but I keep very well. How about your-self?"

It was wonderful to hear her mother dismiss all her problems like that, wonderful but puzzling. Helen also felt just a little bit angry to hear her mother tell an untruth. She knew that the dis-tances Annie could walk were growing less and less each day. Even the slightest incline slowed her pace. Clarence Drive was a pretty steep hill and it was lucky that the distance to the shops was short. Annie had walked up the hill very, very slowly. As they returned home, downhill, Helen was aware that her mother was striding out as much as possible.

She would learn that her mother, when asked about her health, would always make light of her suffering. Perhaps it was pride, perhaps it was an unwillingness to inflict her sorrow on other people? Perhaps the denial helped her to cope with her own state of mind? Helen could never decide, but she also knew that some people, when asked about their health, spoke for twenty minutes and went into great detail about their ailments. That could be very boring. Perhaps her mother just wanted to avoid being boring.

◊

RUSSIAN'S SWIFT ADVANCE ON POLISH BORDER.

8TH ARMY IN BITTER FIGHTING ON ADRIATIC COAST

100,000 PEOPLE HOMELESS IN GREECE

TWO JAPANESE CRUISERS SET ON FIRE

LANDINGS ON NORTH COAST OF NEW GUINEA,

Japanese troops out-flanked between Australian and American forces.

1,000 TON 'SATURATION' RAID ON BERLIN

... fighting their way mile by mile through skies filled by enemy fighters, our bombers again went to Berlin yesterday, where smoke still rose from the smouldering ruins of our previous raid, two days ago. About 1,000 tons of HE were dropped. At one stage, bombing was so rapid that 70 tons were going down every minute.

Glasgow Herald 4th January 1944

In the first week of 1944, the newspapers were full of the terrible violence which seemed to have seized the planet. In Pittenweem, Annie had thought that the end of the war was perhaps in sight, but these reports were terrifying. She wondered if these horrors were necessary in order to bring the war to a conclusion? Britain seemed to be intent in demolishing Germany, Germany was trying to wipe out London. The rest of the world was in upheaval, destruction and misery was everywhere. What would be left after it was all over?

In spite of this cataclysmic global situation, Pettigrews advertised their January sale of underwear. Annie was amused to see combinations available at only three shillings a pair plus four clothing coupons. A superior garment with sleeves was eight shillings and elevenpence and six coupons. Good old combinations! They must have contributed considerably to the saving of electricity in these chilly wartime winters!

There were many articles and readers' letters about the new pay-as-you-earn regulations which were being introduced by the Inland Revenue. She supposed it showed faith in the future which, hopefully, would offer a more normal life. Perhaps that was why it was being introduced at this time? To boost morale? More cynically, she wondered if it were being introduced just now because the public was too concerned with other things to complain about it. It would not affect her. She only wished that it could. She would love to earn some money. Her mother had taken a pair of her knitted Fair Isle gloves to the whist drive this week and sold them for five shillings. Several other people had said that they would like to buy a pair. Her mother was anxious for her to get them ready, for Mary loved making a sale. Although it made a welcome addition to her weekly housekeeping allowance of fifteen shillings, five shillings did not seem like much of a price to Annie. The wool cost over a shilling and there was a lot of work in a pair of gloves. However, her mother was positive that people would not pay more and as she could not earn in any other way, she would just get started and knit gloves until she was sick of them.

The following week there was a technicolour film on at the Grosvenor, their nearest cinema. It was a mile away in Byres Road, a popular shopping area. Helen could remember eating hot buttered pikelets in a tearoom there before the war. They had been delicious and she had never seen them since. She would find out one day that they were the same delicacy as the English crumpets, also eaten hot and buttered, which often figured in books.

"D'ye fancy going to the pictures this afternoon? You'll be starting school soon, darling, and it might be our last chance for a while. It's a musical, lots of dancing and singing. Would you like to go? I would."

"Are you *able* to go, Mummy?"

"Oh, I think I could manage that all right."

Her mother's tone was confident and jaunty, but Helen was much less sure.

They took a tram to Byres Road and slowly walked the few hundred yards to the cinema. It was a good film and they both enjoyed it, chortling at the crazy bits and delighting in the graceful dancing of Rogers and Astaire.

When they came out, it was dark and drizzling and Annie was stiff, painful and weak. Just leaving the building had been difficult for her. Negotiating the rake of the auditorium and the short flight of four stairs to the foyer had used up the last ounce of her strength and energy. Her left foot felt leaden and her right foot would not obey her. She paused on the pavement outside the cinema and Helen could tell that her mother was in difficulties.

"I'll be all right if I just take a breather."

She took a few deep breaths and gave Helen a forced smile with tightly-compressed lips.

Helen looked anxiously at the distance they must walk to the tram stop. It was only a few hundred yards, but they must cross two busy streets and Helen, measuring it through her mother's capabilities, judged it almost insurmountable. All at once, the tram that they might have caught came into view, turned the corner and disappeared. There would not be another for nearly quarter of an hour. Her mother would never be able to stand waiting for that length of time, even if she could reach the tramstop. It was such a horrible cold January night. Helen shivered and for just one brief moment blamed her mother for having come out. Her mother should have known that this outing would be too much for her. Almost at once, her filial compassion banished this blink of resentment and Helen started to wonder what they were going to do. Annie had taken one or two faltering steps away from the cinema and stopped once more. She held her daughter's hand more tightly than usual and rested the other against the wall. Helen knew that her mother was worried.

"What are we going to do, Mummy?"

"Of course we could always get a taxi. If we could find one."

There were certainly no taxis in sight.

"Would that not be awful dear?"

"Well, we'd just have to manage it, I suppose. But I don't see one anyway, do you?"

Annie walked another few difficult steps and stopped. This time she leaned her back against the damp wall.

"I wonder if there's a policeman about? He might be able to

help or something ..."

"Oh, Mummy!"

Annie smiled down at her daughter and said,

"Now don't panic. We'll manage somehow."

And they did manage, though it took many 'breathers' and Helen's skilful balancing support and all Annie's determination.

No passerby offered help and Annie felt that some of them looked at her suspiciously, as though she had been drinking. It would not have been the first time that her unsteadiness had elicited disapproval from the ignorant.

They caught the next tram by the skin of their teeth and fortunately a kindly conductor was on the platform. He jumped out and, taking her arm, hauled Annie up the two steep steps, then standing in front of her and taking her two arms, helped her up the shallow step to the interior of the tram and pushed her gently backwards into a seat.

"Oh, thank you, thank you very much."

Helen dropped into the seat beside her mother. She had never felt so relieved in her life. She did not allow herself to think of the end of the brief journey and the struggle across the broad road and up the sixteen steps to the close. Once in the close, she knew her mother could crawl those last few yards to their front door, if necessary. They would manage.

That night, when they were safely in bed, Annie tried to apologise to Helen.

"I'm sorry, wee one. I bet you were a bit worried that you'd never get your old mother home again. Were you?"

"It was a bit of a job, wasn't it!"

"Yes, but it was a good film. I really enjoyed it."

"Yes, it was a very good film. It was great."

"Well, nighty-night then."

"Nighty-night."

Helen was happy and relieved to be safely home, but Annie struggled with bitter thoughts. She would probably never leave the house again under her own steam.

◊

It was arranged that granny Corning would take Helen to buy her school uniform. Helen would have preferred to go with her other grandmother, because she felt that she hardly knew this one. Although she was always very kind and sweet, Mrs Corning just seemed a very different sort of lady to Helen, rather old-fashioned and fussy and difficult to understand. However it was apparent that Bruce was going to be very upset if his mother was not involved in kitting out her granddaughter for school. Annie supposed that she could not go far wrong buying a uniform.

"After all she has hardly seen the wee one for years now." He complained pathetically.

"Oh, I don't mind at all, as long as Helen doesn't mind."

Helen nodded and smiled politely, if untruthfully and Bruce grinned with relief,

"They'll have a rare old time together! A whale of a time. My mother's great fun y'know. Terrific sense of humour!"

Annie said nothing. She had never credited her mother-in-law with much humour or wit but she thought it rather nice for a son to stand up for his mother in this way. It often struck her that Mrs Corning was pretty downtrodden by the three men in the house.

Helen and her granny went to Coplands, the Mackay family's favourite department store.

Helen knew that she must have black lace-up shoes and kept visualising the big clumsy boots that the boys had worn in Pittenweem. However the shoe department produced the prettiest pair of soft black leather shoes, rather pointed and slender. Mrs Corning was doubtful, but as they were the only ones in Helen's size, they took them and Helen was quietly ecstatic. They were elegant and grown-up! Next they bought two pairs of long black stockings which were thick but soft and smooth. Certainly an improvement on hand-knitted three quarter socks. Helen had always felt those socks with the turn-down at the top had accentuated her muscular legs and they left your knees so cold, too.

Next they went up in the rickety metal lift that Helen remembered so well from her childhood. When they left one floor she found the sound of the metal gates crashing shut delightful. The way that the lift jerked when it started and juddered when it stopped at the next floor filled her with memories of her childhood pineapple cakes, Russian tea, small crispy rolls and sweetbreads in rich brown gravy. How far away it all was and she would never come here again with her Mummy. Before she could become too sad, they reached the school uniform department.

The school shirt was a pretty pale blue poplin and they had Helen's size so that was fine. Everyone in the class would be wearing a pale blue shirt and she would be the same. Next the glass-fronted drawer of school ties was placed on the counter. Unfortunately they only had a junior size tie for her school. Helen had not worn a tie since she was seven and did not even know that they came in different sizes. Granny was unsure what to do. Helen knew that she needed to have a tie and was unaware that there were other shops selling uniforms. The saleslady, anxious to make a sale, assured them that it would be fine and it was unlikely that there would be any larger sizes for several months. They bought the tie but its meagre proportions would be a sorrow to Helen. It would be two years before that skimpy tie reached the right degree of shabbiness, to justify buying a new one. Amazingly the navy blue felt hats were kept in a deep drawer! When she tried one on, she seemed changed into a caricature of a schoolgirl with her long plaits hanging down absurdly. She cheered up considerably when the school skirt was chosen. Wartime shortages meant that, as with the shoes, there was no choice. Only one skirt fitted her slender, unformed body. It was navy serge, but it was certainly not a school skirt. It reached to just below her knees, was longer than any skirt she had ever had and was straight with a tight-fitting belt decorated with navy studs and a little buckle at the front. It was so grown up and sophisticated that she could hardly stop herself from crowing with delight. It was a skirt to give her confidence to walk into a strange classroom, no matter how different she might be from the others. Granny Corning was biting her lip and looking very troubled. It seemed to her a completely unsuitable skirt for a twelve-year-old schoolgirl, but nothing would have stopped Helen from having it. She could have *kissed* the saleswoman, who was assuring Mrs Corning that it was the only navy skirt likely to be available for quite some time.

"I'm afraid supplies are *so* irregular and schools do realise the problems and are very understanding ..."

As they left the store with all the exciting parcels, Helen said,

"Isn't it good that we managed to get everything. I love that skirt. I'm so pleased and Mummy will be too."

"I do hope so, Helen."

"Thank you for taking me shopping."

"It was a pleasure, dear."

But Mrs Corning was thinking how much easier it had been to shop for her two boys.

◊

Helen started school in a mist of agonised confusion. Bruce accompanied her on her first day and arrived late, which made her angry as well as nervous. Her fears that she would do something awkward or stupid were compounded by the terror that her father would do or say the wrong thing. He might call someone by the wrong name, as he liked to do for fun, or perhaps he might swear in front of the headmistress. He did swear a lot. She could not trust him!

The headmistress was called Mrs Tebb and had been Annie's form mistress in the distant past, fully thirty years ago. She had sparkling pure white hair but she did not seem as old as Helen expected. She was very pleasant and seemed to remember Annie, which Helen found difficult to believe. She kindly explained that Helen would be placed in a B class. It was a double language class with absolutely the same curriculum as the A group and it was just a case of keeping numbers correct. This was a terrible blow to the pride of a girl who had been a top A pupil at the Waid Academy. It seemed shameful to be relegated to second best. Even the magnificent skirt was not enough to support Helen's dismay and shyness as she was introduced to her form-teacher and the thirty three unknown girls who sat in their pale blue blouses and watched her take her seat at the antiquated desk. These desks with their hinged seats had surely been designed for a previous generation of smaller girls with shorter legs. It would be some weeks before Helen discovered the trick of the half-lifted seat, the slight knee-bend and co-ordinated side-sway of the hips, required to seat herself gracefully, while trying simultaneously to protect her black stockings from the ever present danger of splinters. It was a skill and an art.

School work was terribly different from her previous experience. It was humiliating to be corrected when she addressed the teachers as 'Miss' instead of using their individual names and she was not as familiar or immediate as her school fellows with her 'Excuse me' or 'I beg your pardon'. For the four previous months she had been taught to pronounce V as W in Latin, but that was not the method in this school and she found it hard to change. The teaching of history and geography was reliant on text books which Helen had not yet managed to acquire. The pupils were responsible for providing their own books. Shortages meant that some books might only be found at the ABC second-hand bookstore. Helen had no idea where that was and had no adult to help her find it. Bruce was too busy working and second-hand bookshops were hardly in Mrs Mackay's sphere of interest. Helen fell further and further behind in history and geography, and grew used to having low marks in the weekly tests in those subjects. She kept up a fair standard in French, English and maths as those subjects required little study. She specially enjoyed science, art and gymnastics. These subjects were enhanced for her by the awareness that she was following in her mother's footsteps and actually using the same laboratory, the same studio, the same gymnasium that Annie had used as a schoolgirl. Nevertheless she was certainly no longer the class leader

Helen's biggest practical worry was the building itself. It was a chaotic mixture of several structures of different periods, cobbled together with illogical corridors and unexpected doors and flights of stairs. It had been enlarged over the years to deal with the ever expanding intake of middle class girls intended for professional careers. Both Annie and Bruce's mother had been pupils at the school, the latter in the nineteenth century, in buildings which were not new in her time. Other buildings had been added, as and when money or necessity dictated. In the first few weeks, Helen was constantly confused. The main building had a double staircase and it was important to choose the correct stair or one might find oneself knocking at the wrong door, in which case the teacher would be understandably ratty, or worse keenly sarcastic. She started to have nightmares about the stairs and she was sure that she would *never* get the hang of the horrible staircase. Throughout the rest of her life, her worry dreams would usually incorporate a complex staircase.

Fortunately she was always part of a group as she moved around the school. The other girls in her class had of course had several months to learn the lay-out. Helen often thought that the group made a mistake this time and they were definitely going in the wrong direction. Luckily she said nothing, for she was always wrong. She despaired of ever making her way alone. She was useless. What if a teacher sent her on an errand one day and she got lost? How humiliating.

The cloakrooms and toilets were in the basement and were ancient, cold, dark and gloomy. In the morning it was crowded, but if one went at lunchtime or four o'clock, it was often deserted and Helen found it really scary. The toilet doors had a variety of locks and bolts, some of them very stiff and unworkable. Because she had never quite lost her fear of being locked in, she investigated the locking device very thoroughly before closing it. She also considered the possibility of climbing over the partition from one cubicle to the next, if that should become necessary. Some years later, she was forced into doing just that and she was rather pleased that she had planned it well in advance, and was able to carry it out successfully.

Family Problems

School seemed unimportant compared to the drama which was unfolding at home. All those childish beliefs that coming back to Glasgow would make everything come right again!

What nonsense.

How stupid she had been to think those hopeful thoughts. It seemed that her mother would very soon be unable to walk at all. Her father and grandmother did little, except say hurtful things to upset her mother. They both came and sat in the house until late at night, eleven o'clock sometimes, and expected cups of tea and coffee. And always they talked, talked, they were always talking about the difficulties of their lives. Her grandmother seemed to be very worried about John Mackay's health. His chest was bad again and he spent a lot of time in bed. It was hard to know whether Mary was more worried or more irritated. She seemed to complain a lot about her husband, rather than feel sorry for him.

"He will insist on taking those pills and I don't think they do any good. Damn silly name they have, Do-do pills. Can't help thinking of 'dead as a dodo'. He says they help, but I can't see it."

She sounded furious and Annie said placatingly,

"Oh well, I don't suppose they do much harm do they? What does the doctor say?"

"He's useless. Just mumbles *anno domini* and says John's always suffered with his chest, and it won't get any better with the passage of time. The man's an idiot."

◊

Although life was full of new difficulties and experiences and the family atmosphere was edgy, Helen felt an inner happiness. It was true that coming back to Glasgow had not worked the miracles that she had hoped for. Much of her life was puzzling and demanding, yet she felt better than she had done in Fife. There was the feeling that something nice was just around the corner. Something good would happen soon. She could not have described what it would be, or even what she would like it to be. The happiness was just there, most of the time.

It was good to be back in her old home and she discovered things that she had completely forgotten. There was a pack of playing cards with pictures of film stars on the face cards, four small jelly moulds, unusual teaspoons, all familiar objects of her youth. A brass bell and a brass samovar stood on the hall table beside a beautiful wooden tea chest, which had two inner lidded boxes and a blue glass bowl for sugar. Just remembering and handling these objects from her childhood filled her with joy. In the kitchen was a strange metal gadget which she barely remembered. Her mother told her was an egg slicer. There were five fine wires in this clever machine and Helen plucked them like a little harp and managed to play God save the King. She repeated that often and it always made her laugh. Her romantic mother had once said that she could imagine Helen playing the harp, with her long hair all swirling around her, but Helen conjured up the crazy vision of herself on stage playing an egg-slicer.

For Annie, one of the delights of returning to Glasgow was her wireless. There was not the constant worry of the battery running down and it had better reception than the Pittenweem one. It could be switched on at any time for it was kept on a wheeled trolley and could be easily moved from room to room. Having her wireless beside her bed at night was a supreme luxury. It took her mind off her pain wonderfully and made the slow unsleeping hours pass. She switched it on each morning as soon as the Home Service started at six thirty, playing it very quietly not to disturb Helen. Helen was a light sleeper and hated the fact that she was wakened so early each day, but she said nothing. The wireless made her mother happy and she could not grudge her this small pleasure. She knew that Annie was increasingly suffering pain and took six aspirin each day. Usually Helen could ignore the whispering voices and go back to sleep again.

One Saturday morning, Helen had a very pleasant dream just before she wakened.

It was different from most other dreams, for there was no trace of anxiety in it. It had the same quality of magic and happiness as the underwater dreams of her early childhood.

In the dream, it was a beautiful warm sunny day and she was alone in the country. It was very quiet except for the birds chirping and the sound of faint music, so far in the distance that she could hardly hear it.

She stood at the foot of a small hill. On the top of the hill, trees grew thickly and she had a strong feeling that there was magic in the little wood that they formed. Magic which would make her happy. Just then the music became much closer and she realised that it was pan pipes playing in the wood. Then she awakened. It was a strange and lovely dream and it would be repeated every few months, in almost the same form, for several years. The anticipation of something delightful about to happen always remained strongly after she wakened.

And it seemed to Helen that often, something exciting or pleasant *did* happen to her just after she had that dream. Perhaps an unexpected present or outing came her way. Her common sense denied the likelihood of a prophetic dream, nevertheless that happy dream often presaged some piece of good luck.

Entirely ignorant and indeed uninterested in the facts of life, as many girls were at that time, Helen had no key to a Freudian or Jungian explanation of her dream. Her interest in mythology seemed enough to explain the pipes of Pan and the strong sense of magic.

◊

Helen's father and grandmother were once more in the house and the uneasy atmosphere hung like a mist in the sitting room. Helen wished that they would go away quickly. There was a play on the wireless at nine o'clock and she and her mother would have liked to go to bed early, to cuddle up and listen in the dark.

"Well of course, Betty could come along once or twice a week. My mother would manage without her ..."

"I'm not having that woman in my house. I cannot stand her. Prying and simpering and talking rather than working."

"My mother thinks she is a fine worker." Bruce was looking displeased.

"No idea of hygiene, if you ask me. And I'm positive she's dishonest."

"Annie needs someone that she likes. Someone she can get on with. And she needs a woman to be with her all the time, Bruce."

"No I don't! I don't want anyone with me all the time. I'm not *completely helpless*."

"Well you certainly need someone coming in every day,

Annie." Mary's voice was sharp.

Bruce coughed loudly and looked even more displeased.

"There would be a considerable cost, *that* has to be thought about ..."

"I only need a decent charwoman for a couple of hours each day. Someone to do the rough work and help me to the bathroom."

"I wonder if anyone at the whist drive would know..."

"You see, Mrs Mackay, it's very tricky for me. My time is so limited with the business. I just do not have the time to spare, to be interviewing a lot of women."

"Well, Bruce, you've just been telling us about your evening last night at the pub and the pictures and your golf arrangements at the weekend. Annie is your wife and I think you may just have to cancel some of these pleasures to get the help that she and the child are needing right now! At this very minute! I would do more myself, but I've got John to think of. He's getting so forgetful, I hate to leave him alone in the house for too long. And he has this portrait to do and I'm worried about that."

Annie who had been gazing into the fire throughout this conversation, grimaced slightly and Helen knew that the pain in her legs was bothering her again. She had asked Bruce to move his chair further from hers. With his everlasting restlessness, he was kicking and bumping her chair.

It had been a day of lowering cloud, but rain had never fallen and suddenly Helen felt very miserable and tired.

Annie shook herself and said in a business-like way,

"What about one of those shops with advertisements in the window? You might find someone that way and if you contacted them, I would interview them. That wouldn't take up too much of your precious time."

The remark was directed at Bruce, but Helen saw her grandmother frown, her lips tightened and there were the familiar signs of displeasure.

Bruce hummed and hawed and Mary collected her belongings together.

Helen brightened, if they would go away quickly perhaps, she and her mother might hear the play after all. But her hopes were dashed, when her mother said,

"Away and put the kettle on, pet, your grandma would like a

cup of tea and what about you Bruce? Coffee? Tea?"

"Aye that would be fine, Tuppeny. Coffee, please, with two sugars and no milk, remember. And if you've got a bit of bread and jam, wouldn't say no to that. Ha, ha."

Helen marched into the kitchen. Why on earth had her mother not just let them go away, when they seemed so ready to go?

She hated making bread and jam for other people.

◊

Two days later Jessie Clark came to be interviewed.

Mary had seen a cleaning woman advertising her services in a newsagent's shop and she had left Annie's address and the tram fare to Hyndland.

Jessie was fat and vivacious, with thick dark curls tied back with a straggle of ancient ribbon.

She had a personality of Shakespearean richness, philosophic and practical, quick-witted, bawdy and infinitely kind. Uneducated but intelligent, she was a typical woman of the Glasgow working classes and she was exactly the sort of person that Annie needed at that moment.

They were immediately attracted to each other at the interview. Annie explained that as well as housework, she would need a bit of personal care.

"That disnae matter, hen. Ah wid jist dae whit ye wur wantin' me tae dae."

"Even getting to the bathroom by myself is sometimes more than I can manage ..."

"Och, that wid be nae boather tae me. Ah'm used tae helpin' ma auld granny. She's hud the rheumatics fur years an' Ah aye helpt 'ur fur tae pee 'n shite, an' wipe ur bum an' a' that. It doesny worry me. Naw, it doesny. When wid ye like me tae stert? Wid ye like me tae help ye fur a pee the noo? It wid mak ye comfy fur the efternin, till yur wee lassie gets hame. An' Ah'll get ye a coffee tae, if ye like. Or ur ye hungry, hen?"

Over the next few weeks, Jessie's warmth and ready understanding cheered Annie up and helped her to climb out of the despondency which had been draining her of all energy and optimism. In return Annie could send Jessie into gusts of helpless laughter with stories and limericks.

Jessie would arrive each morning, slamming the front door behind her and shouting,

"Cooee! Cooee! Ur yiz therr Missus Cornin'? Good mornin' Missus Cornin'! See Ah'm a poet an' ye didny know it."

Then, singing loudly, she would take her coat off and put the kettle on.

"Ur ye wantin' a coffee or yer bed bath first?"

She would shout this rhetorical question from the kitchen, for the bed bath always came first. A normal bath was hardly practical, as the kitchen range required to burn for three hours before there was sufficient hot water.

Annie had not expected this sort of personal nursing and at first she was unwilling to submit to such an intimate service, but Jessie was implacable.

"A wee rub doon'll jist freshen ye up like. It's nae bother. I like it better'n washin' flairs an' yer flair's no' durty onywey."

It was an exciting process and bore no resemblance to the bed baths that Annie remembered in the nursing home. Jessie used the face cloth and towel with anything but a gentle hand and as Annie was so slender she could be lifted and turned over like a baby. Annie felt she was tossed around like a toy in the hands of a large friendly child. It was stimulating and relaxing at the same time. As she worked, Jessie talked about her relatives and their lives. Her accent was broad but she talked well, never repeating herself and choosing descriptive words and phrases that painted a picture of a community quite different from anything that Annie had ever known.

"Oh, I feel good now, Jessie, after that pounding, but I'm fair wabbit. You don't expect me to get up now, do you?"

"Aye, ye've goat tae get up and get yur wean's denner ready. Ah'll get the tatties an' ingins oot oan the table fur ye, an' pit the chair fur ye. Ur ye reelly feelin' good, Missus Cornin'? Wiz that a guid bed bath? I shud o' been a nurse. Ah aye wantit tae be yin."

"It was a delightful bed bath and I think you would make a superb nurse. You'll maybe be one yet, you never know."

Jessie would smile widely as she cleared away the towel and basin.

Most days Annie was still able to walk unsteadily around the house though she no longer ventured outside. Jessie or Helen could see to the shopping, but Annie cooked the dinner for Helen coming home, sitting to prepare vegetables or roll pastry or to iron or accomplish other small household chores.

By evening she was exhausted and Helen trundled her mother to bed on the carpet.

No one mentioned a wheelchair, but the thought of one was always at the back of Annie's mind. She dreaded the idea, yet knew it was inevitable and would simplify her life.

Jessie was married to a cook in the dockyard canteen and she had a ten-month old baby called George. She had not mentioned George at her first interview, because her mother would care for the baby, but her mother had found a 'wee cleanin' joab' on a Monday.

"Is that a' right, Missus Cornin'? It wid jist be the Monday Ah wid be bringin' him. He's a guid wee wean an' wanst he's hud his boattle, he'll jist be sleepin' an' he'll no' keep me aff whit Ah've goat tae dae."

"That'll be fine Jessie, of course it will. I'd love to see your wee boy. I'm very fond of babies. Does he look like you?"

The worried frown disappeared from Jessie's brow and her broad face beamed with pleasure,

"Oh yes, Missus Cornin', he's awfy like me. Fat, too." She chuckled heartily. "He's a *luvly* boy, though Ah says it masel' as shouldny. He's ma wee pride and joy!"

When George arrived, Annie was astonished. He was enormous, tall, broad, fat and with a full head of thick black curls and with his roving, meaningful gaze he seemed nearer three years than ten months.

"I can hardly believe George is only ten months old! He looks so big and grown-up!"

"Aye, he's awfy smert fur his age, righ' enuff! His granny says he's been here afore."

It was obvious that his mother was besotted with him. It was hard for her to remove her gaze from his person. Soon after she arrived she announced,

"The durty wee bugger's needin' a clean nappy, uren't ye ma hen. Aw the wee sowl, wid ye luk at that!"

Throughout the process of cleaning and changing the baby, Jessie directed a continuing flood of reproaches, laced with curses, at the child for his smelliness, fatness, greediness, but the tirade was delivered in tender tones of love and a beatific smile of delight wreathed both her face and the child's. Before she dressed him, she delighted him by loudly blowing several rude raspberries on his belly and genitals and murmuring,

"Aw ye wee bugger, ye. Ye're jist a wee bugger, bugger, bugger."

Annie had never seen mother love expressed quite like this before. It was fascinating and impressive. She wondered if Truby King would approve.

After George was dressed, Jessie unbuttoned her blouse and produced an impressively large snow-white breast, which the baby immediately grabbed, cramming more than seemed possible into his mouth. As he sucked, his eyes travelled constantly around the room, observing each article with careful deliberation.

Annie chuckled,

"Look at him! D'ye think he's casing the joint?"

"Aye," Jessie giggled, "He's aye lookin', lookin', lookin', isn't he! He dizny miss much, this yin. Mebbe he'll be a bloody detective whin he grows up." Then she laughed so hard that the baby relinquished the nipple and gave her a look full of pain and reproach.

"Jessie, I thought you said he took a bottle."

"Aw aye, he gets his boattle efter. Ye're aye feared o' no' gi'in' them enough, uren't ye."

"I don't think you need to worry about that one. He's more like a man than a baby."

Jessie thought this a wonderful joke and a great compliment. She laughed uproariously for a few minutes.

Annie was sitting smiling to herself and thinking what an entertaining morning she was having, when she looked round to see George back in his pushchair. He sat with one leg casually thrown over the armrest and with the opposite hand held the bottle which protruded from the side of his mouth in the same way that an archetypal American smokes a cigar. It took Annie a split second to register that the bottle George held was dark green and bore the legend *McEwan's Pale Ale*.

"Jessie! Is that a *beer* bottle the kid's got."

"Och aye, he's awfy fur crashin' his boattles oot the bed. Ah goat fed up buying new yins."

"Well, I suppose that one's just as good. He's certainly a *wonderful* baby."

Jessie went off to the kitchen, wearing a happy smile.

One day, Annie noticed that although the coat that Jessie wore to work each day was made of a heavy tweed, the elbows were very worn.

"Jessie, can I ask you why such a nice coat has worn through at the elbows like that? What were you doing?"

Jessie smiled and showed her sleeves with some pride. Annie saw they were even worse than she had thought. One was ragged and the other had a large hole.

"You know."

"No, I haven't an earthly."

"Aye, ye do."

Annie shook her head.

"It's jist hingin' oot the windaes an' hivin' a blether wi' yer freends. It's the rough windae-sill wears oot yer claes!"

"You mean that's what's worn your sleeves right through? You must do lots of blethering."

"Och aye, we're aye bletherin' in Kelvinhaugh Street!" and Jessie's hearty chuckle rang through the house, as she marched heavily through the hall.

Annie was smiling as she picked up her knitting, she felt relaxed and content.

As Jessie came only in the mornings, Helen did not meet her, but her mother's description of her made her very real. Annie laughed a lot as she spoke of the new cleaner and repeated her daft sayings and her swearing. The baby certainly sounded very much worth seeing.

It was obvious that Jessie Clark was good for her Mummy and Helen was ready to like her too.

"She's a terribly kind person, I think. Mind you, I'm not sure that I'd give her top marks as a house cleaner. If something is taking too much time to clean, she laughs and says,"Och tae hell, it'll dae fine." And leaves it. She's a wee bit of a hasher and I see several chipped plates and cups, but she's awful good company and she would do anything for me. She loves hearing about you too and she wants to meet you soon. She's a very, very nice woman and I think I was terribly lucky to come across her."

Towards the end of January, Bruce was alone with Annie.

"Annie, I hate to say this, but what should our plans be?"

"Well, what do you mean Bruce? Plans about what exactly?"

"Well, your condition. Now that you're a cripple ..."

"Oh please don't use that word about me Bruce. I hate it. I

don't know what a cripple is exactly, maybe they are born disabled. I'm sure I'm not a cripple."

"No, well whatever ... the point is, should we send Helen to boarding school?"

"Boarding school?"

It had never occurred to her that her daughter might be separated from her.

"I certainly don't want that of course, but ..."

"It might be the best thing for her."

"You would need to ask her that herself. I suppose you mean that I should go into some sort of home or other."

"Well, Annie, as things are going ... they're not looking good are they."

Bruce shook his head. He had read of the possible developments of disseminated sclerosis and his mind was full of the horrible possibilities of the disease.

"You see, if your condition continues to deteriorate ..."

"My condition, my condition ..." and she burst into tears.

"Now, now. I didn't mean to upset you. However my father was just saying ..."

"Your father! What the hell is it to do with your father? I've been feeling specially well these last three weeks since Jessie came. We're doing very well. Helen is settling into school and she gives me a hand when she comes home, but ask her! Ask *her* if she wants to go to boarding school! But remember a home for me and boarding school for her, it will all cost money. I don't know where that will come from. Your father perhaps? You'd better think about that side of it too, Bruce."

When Bruce broached the subject of boarding school, Helen was predictably horrified.

What an impossible idea, to think of leaving her mother, just when she needed her so much. They had lived so closely together all her life, with her father and other relatives on the periphery. For the last few years she had been a vital support and partner to her mother, an absolute necessity. Her mother *depended* on her and could not get along without her. Who would look after her mother if she went away? It was a ridiculous suggestion, a heartbreaking suggestion. It hardened her heart against her father even more. She said nothing, she could not put any of these thoughts into words to this insensitive man, she could only weep hysterically and Bruce fervently wished that he had never raised the question of boarding school.

He knew too that Annie was right to question if he could afford such a situation. That had not occurred to him before. Bruce wondered just how his father had thought that he could pay for it, when he was dishing out the advice.

Although Helen was so quick to refute the idea of boarding school, there were times in the next year that she pondered what it might have been like to live like the girls in the Angela Brazil school stories or the Girl's Own Paper. She would never have admitted this, but the disciplined, yet irresponsible and adventurous life of those ideal schoolgirls was certainly appealing and she read about it with avidity and an undercurrent of guilt.

◊

In March there was to be a performance of 'Peter Pan' at the Alhambra Theatre.

"D'ye think the wee one would like to see that?" Bruce asked Annie one night and showed her the advertisement in the evening paper.

Helen was sitting at the table with her algebra homework in front of her. She rather enjoyed algebra. It was like solving puzzles, but she could not concentrate when her father was there, talking and laughing loudly. How could he call her wee one when she was now nearly as tall as he was? When was he going to go? There was a Chopin concert, her favourite composer, on the wireless at nine o'clock. As she had just made her father a coffee as requested, it looked unlikely that he would be gone in time for them to listen to the magical music. Her face bore the typical glower of a dissatisfied teenager.

Annie looked over at her pleadingly. She wished that Helen would just show her beautiful smile to her father occasionally. In order to balance her daughter's scowls, she spoke perhaps over enthusiastically,

"I think that would be a great idea, Bruce. I believe it is quite spectacular with the actors flying around the stage. Would you just go, the two of you? Helen , you would like that wouldn't you? A night out at the theatre?"

Helen had few experiences of the theatre and the thought of people flying around appealed to her. She managed to look polite and interested as she nodded her agreement. She had vague memories of the Peter Pan story, when she was just a kid at Hyndland school. There was that boy that she liked. who played Peter. After a moment, she remembered his name, Raymond Hare. What a name! She wondered where he was now.

Two tickets were bought but as the night approached, Helen was beset by the horror of enjoying something which her mother could not share. It was as though the mature twelve-year-old had regressed to half her age. Each night she became more obsessed with the idea of leaving her mother alone at home, while she was out having this amazing experience. She wept bitterly and declared that it would mean nothing to her, if her mother could not enjoy the people flying through the air too. Annie tried to talk some common sense into her, but failed completely and eventually saw that she must break the news to Bruce.

"I'm afraid you'll need to take some other young lady to see 'Peter Pan', Bruce. Helen's got herself into a ridiculous state about leaving me at home. Says she'd rather miss it than go without me. I know it's crazy. You might manage to get your money back on the tickets, if you go soon enough."

Bruce said very little and left early that night. Annie wondered if he were terribly offended.

However the next night they heard his car park with its usual noisy flourish in the lane.

"Please be a bit nicer to your father tonight." Annie called after Helen, as with a resigned face she stamped off to the kitchen to put on the kettle.

Bruce came in triumphant.

"Got it all fixed for my two honeybuns! Got another two tickets, last ones available! Jessie can come along on Saturday night, she's all set and looking forward to it and she can give me a hand lifting your mother. Now Tuppenny, are ye cheered up a bit now. There's never a problem that can't be solved. What d'ye think of your old man now?"

Helen was absolutely delighted and added a cheese sandwich to the coffee without being asked. She was too happy to say much, but her face made her feelings plain. Bruce was so self-congratulatory and talkative that he stayed till very late that night. Annie thought he might never go away, but she had to admit to herself that sometimes he was very generous and thoughtful.

The night at the Alhambra was a great success, not least because Bruce and Jessie were sitting separately in another part of the stalls. Helen could hear her father's loud laugh, but the faint twinge of embarrassment was not enough to mar her enjoyment. The flying scenes were believable and exciting, the crocodile was delightfully terrifying and Helen found everything twice as enjoyable because she was snuggled close to her mother. Annie was happy to be out in the world again and see her wee girl so pleased. Bruce had managed to get a box of Black Magic chocolates and at the interval the four of them devoured them and discussed what a great show it was. The following week, Annie was thanking Bruce once again and congratulating him sincerely on his superb management and generosity.

"It was an absolutely wonderful night and you made everything run so smoothly. Helen will always remember it and so will I. A really great show, Bruce. You excelled yourself."

"I enjoyed it too. I didn't expect to, but I did. And did the wee yin really enjoy herself d'ye think? Are ye sure?"

"Without a doubt. She loved every minute. But I'll tell you who had the best time of all. It was Jessie. She was *enchanted* and has talked of nothing else for four days!"

An Important Discovery

Helen travelled the two miles to school by tramcar each day. That was a new adventure and quite a pleasant one. The gentle trundling was conducive to thinking and day-dreaming. One morning the tramcar was much more crowded than usual.

"Inside pleeze! Inside only, if you pleeze. Nae seats up the sterr an' nae staunin' upsterrs. INSIDE PLEEZE!"

Helen felt herself pushed into the already over-full interior of the tramcar and grabbed for a hanging leather strap to steady herself. It was March and it was good to leave the cold wind behind at the tramstop. She did not mind standing, as she quite enjoyed the muscle power required to adapt to the unsteady vehicle as it lumbered round sharp corners. It was a bit like being at sea in a storm. She supposed that would be much more difficult, but this was good practice.

Normally she would have gone up the narrow, winding metal stair to the upper deck, where she would try to find a seat in the cabin at the front of the tram, above the driver. The sliding door which cut this little compartment off from the rest of the passengers, appealed to her. Five people could squash into this separate space, but it was best when you had the outer cabin all to yourself although that seldom happened in the morning. Upstairs was always her choice, for even if you were lucky enough to get a seat downstairs, you could never settle. Some old lady was bound to come along and expect you to jump up and offer your seat.

It was unusual to meet any school friends and the journey to school in the morning was a good time for thinking.

She had been in High School now for nearly three months and she was getting used to the labyrinthine building, the exact and demanding teachers in their black gowns and the long day away from home. She had always gone home for lunch in Fife. She did not mind it for herself, in fact it was rather pleasant to eat school meals or take sandwiches, but she felt it must be lonely for her mother at home. How lucky that they had found

Mrs Clark, who would be in the house every morning. She was so kind and jolly, always laughing and her mother really liked her. Helen hardly realised how many deep-seated worries about her mother had been erased by the caring presence of Jessie Clark. She felt very grateful to her. And it was so nice that her father had taken them all to Peter Pan. Jessie had said it was the very best show she had ever seen in her life! Helen supposed she felt grateful to her father, too. Last night he had said he was looking out for a wheel chair for her mother. That would make life easier for them, although it was quite strange to think of her mother sitting in a wheel chair. Helen had never seen one in real life, although the old doctor in the Doctor Kildare films had one.

A more immediate worry was that she still had not acquired the necessary geography text book and there were two geography periods this morning. Text books were in short supply and when a consignment arrived in Mackinlay's, the school book shop, they were quickly sold out. She still had no idea where the ABC second hand book shop was. Besides, the few shillings required to buy a book were not always immediately available at home, although her father would reimburse them, once the book was bought. She had shared a book in school, but had not been very impressed by it. A more interesting book might have motivated her more strongly to hunt it down. As she was supposed to study a chapter at home each week, she was falling badly behind, but somehow this did not worry her as much as it would have done previously. She no longer had any expectation of being top of the class. Even the idea of failing a weekly test did not horrify her as it would once have done. What she really strived for was to make her friends laugh each day.

The tram emptied at Byres Road. Helen took a seat on one of the side benches which faced each other, instead of looking forward in the direction that the tram was going. She had never sat in that seat before and she had an excellent view of all the passengers as they boarded the tram and also the shops and buildings as they slid past. It was interesting to see the expressions on the different faces and she decided to stay downstairs.

The conductress was less agitated now and smiled to her.

Helen glanced down at her small leather attaché case. It had been a present from her mother when she had gone to High School as a little girl. It was glossy leather, with her initials near the handle and she knew that it had been quite expensive. Her mother had been so pleased, when she had brought it out and polished it ready to start school in January. Unfortunately, though it was quite heavy, it was really too small for all the books required in secondary school. It would hardly shut although Helen had other things she would have liked to bring to school that day. Worse than that, it was completely *different*. Helen had thought that being different was something that she would leave behind in Pittenweem, but now there had been glances and whispered comments about her little case. Most girls carried a black zipped bag under their arm. It was made of a plasticised fabric called Rexine and was quite cheap, very light and held a lot. It did not matter if it was rather shabby. How could Helen explain to her mother that she would like to have a cheap, ugly bag rather than the splendid, leather case from Coplands?

Just then the tram passed the Italian ice cream shop. For three months Helen had gone there to buy sweets on the first Sunday of each new rationing month,. It was a pleasant walk and she would buy three quarters of a pound of different sweets. It was fun to choose them. Then she and her mother would be quite greedy and eat them all up that same day. She was sure that she had more fun with her mother than other kids did.

As the tram trundled into Church Street, Helen had a sudden and very vivid experience. Almost a vision, although at the same time she was fully aware that they were passing the Out Patient's entrance to the Western Infirmary.

All the random thoughts which had been passing through her mind disappeared, as though wiped away with a damp rag.

Suddenly her whole being was filled by a great happiness and satisfaction, as the phrase leapt into her head.

"I am me!"

She repeated it to herself and tried to understand. What did she mean exactly? Had she said it out loud?

No, because no one was looking at her. She tried to understand what she wanted to say.

"I ... am." she paused, how could she say exactly what she meant? It seemed terribly important, as if she had suddenly understood something marvellous.

I am ME.

I am me.

What *did* she mean? What words could she use to explain this wonderful fact?

I ... am ... **me**.

She could find no other way of expressing what she meant, but she felt that her whole attitude to herself and to the world was changed forever.

She would never travel down Church Street again without remembering the delight and power of her discovery that day.

"I AM ME."